WITHDRAWN
L. R. COLLEGE LIBRARY

D1129862

N. T. SCHNICK LIBRARY

THE LANGUAGE OF NATURE

THE LANGUAGE
OF NATURE

*An Essay
in the Philosophy
of Science*

BY DAVID HAWKINS

University of Colorado

Drawings by EVAN L. GILLESPIE

W. H. FREEMAN AND COMPANY

SAN FRANCISCO AND LONDON

CARL A. RUDISILL LIBRARY
LENOIR RHYNE COLLEGE

501
H31L
84703
Sept 1973

© Copyright 1964 by W. H. Freeman and Company

The publisher reserves all rights to reproduce this book, in whole or in part, with the exception of the right to use short quotations for review of the book.

Library of Congress catalogue card number: 63-13200

Printed in the United States of America   (*C3*)

In the brief Bibliographical Comment I have tried to suggest the most important works on the philosophy of science.

Acknowledgments are due to Philip Morrison and V. F. Weisskopf for the best part of a modest scientific education and for critical comments on large parts of the manuscript; to Arne Magnus and Burrowes Hunt for helpful criticism of chapters on mathematical topics, and to the latter for pushing me to a more explicit statement, right or wrong, about universals; to John D. Benjamin, T. T. Puck, Aaron Novick, Aubrey Kempner, Frank Oppenheimer, George Zinke, Stanislaw Ulam, Leonard Pockman, Phylis Singer, Malcolm Skolnick, Frances Hawkins, and Emily Morrison for various kinds of help and enlightenment. None of those named should be held responsible for failing to educate me better; they have tried.

From this point on my debts are beyond naming. Very few of the thoughts and arguments in this book are new. But they are newly ordered, and that part is self-education.

October 1963   DAVID HAWKINS

CONTENTS

4. MEASUREMENT

5. LAWS OF MOTION

6. CHANCE AND PROBABILITY

INTRODUCTION

This book has been written in the belief that present-day scientific knowledge has a considerable unexploited relevance to the enterprises traditionally called philosophy. This belief explains both the order and the treatment of the topics in the book. That order and that treatment, as they are not conventional, require a detailed apologia.

Science was once pursued as philosophy or as something not very clearly distinguished from philosophy. Even after the upturn of the scientific revolution and the first branching out of scientific disciplines, some of the great figures could not be classified, without impertinence, either exclusively as scientists or exclusively as philosophers.

Partly through the growth of the scientific disciplines and partly because of shifting intellectual fashions, philosophy has grown away, in the main, from the influence of science. These disciplines have prospered through increasing division of labor and, at times, through separation from one another; but prosperity brings them together again in ways to which the habit of specialization blinds us. What is true among the scientific disciplines is true also in wider spheres of culture. The intellectual fashions that once turned philosophy away from science were characterized by conceptions of the content and spirit of science that are now only historical specimens.

The older conceptions of science, connected with common beliefs about its place in our culture and its relevance to other activities and interests, have become inadequate in ways that this book attempts to describe or suggest. Classical physics—classical physics rather narrowly conceived at that—influenced, for a long time, what workers in other fields did or thought they ought to be doing. Physics, up to the end of the nineteenth century, was the model of exact science, and other kinds of inquiry were called, in a somewhat disparaging way, descriptive science or natural history.

1

This book begins with a discussion of the foundations of arithmetic, geometry, and analysis. The purposes of these early chapters are to define certain ideas that will be used throughout the book and—principally—to consider what is involved in the mathematical description of nature. An old and powerful tradition identifies the ideal of science as the achievement of mathematical description. This ideal has two aspects. One aspect is the coherence and semantic compression achieved by formal deductive systems, and the other is the infinite potential range of discrimination implied by the language of number. But this ideal, in either aspect, is meaningful and realizable only on sufferance of nature. The mathematical style of science is not to be explained as mere human contrivance or convention. Nature has style as well, and the major developments of mathematics are major because they imitate a pervasive style of nature.

Certain philosophical topics are always near the surface in such discussions. Three topics that concern us in these chapters are the sources of mathematical knowledge, the fertility and power of mathematical deduction, and the nature of mathematical truth. These topics are closely linked, and each linkage creates puzzlement. Though the sources of mathematical knowledge are empirical, its assertions are not. Though the truth of derived propositions in mathematics is certified by deduction, its primitive assertions are not. What is this truth, which deduction guards and in a sense expands, but does not generate? There are easy answers, but sometimes these are wrong answers.

Chapter 1 recapitulates certain processes of abstraction in connection, specifically, with arithmetic and thus shows in some detail what it means to say that the sources of mathematical knowledge are empirical. One purpose of this chapter is to explore regions in which the concept of truth itself plays a special role in deduction. One such region is that between logic and arithmetic. The exploration leads to a recognition of two meanings of analytic truth, both distinguished, but in quite different ways, from the kind of truth we assert for contingent descriptive propositions. This distinction makes it possible to say, although still too obliquely for my taste, that mathematical truth, or some components of it, is truth about the world of nature. An easier claim emerges from the discussion of what is widely known, today, as mathematical model-building. Models need not consist of statements alleged to be true but, like the poem that is not to mean but to be, may have another kind of truth, that of verisimilitude or informational richness. Models are discussed here in connection with formalized mathematics and Turing machines. The discussion is expanded in later chapters under the headings "information theory" and "decision theory."

Chapter 2 is concerned partly with the basic ideas of geometry and partly, again, with the meaning of truth in geometry. A famous Kantian thesis is examined here, with some sympathy but also with a final rejection of Kant's most-quoted thesis. A shadow of this thesis is found in more recent doctrines commonly labeled conventionalism. In Chapter 1 the concept of equivalence and equivalence class was introduced; here a related concept, that of geometrical invariance, is discussed. There is a brief account of Klein's Erlangen Program and of its role in the unification and elucidation of geometries. The chapter ends with a discussion of a few arithmetical aspects of geometry and of their relevance to empirical science.

Chapter 3, more expository, treats briefly the main ideas of mathematical analysis. A question raised earlier—whether the sources of mathematics are empirical—recurs here, however, for the sources of the calculus are conspicuously empirical. The history of analysis displays a certain tension between intuition and rigor, and this is connected, it seems, with the polarity of continuity and discreteness. The achievement of rigor has involved a detailed arithmetization of geometry and analysis—a conquest, as it were, of intuition by logic. We know, by the best standards, that this conquest is acceptably complete, but I urge that it be regarded as a well-built bridge between two equally primitive domains of abstraction. The chapter ends with a review of a topic that is implicit throughout the discussion of mathematics and that has its roots in medieval tradition—the problem of universals. The problem, though a fuzzy one, is partially clarified, and the clarification makes possible a reinforcement, again rather oblique, of claims made earlier concerning the nature of abstraction and of mathematical truth.

The descriptive use of mathematics brings to the fore a new set of topics connected with observation and measurement. In Chapter 4 the argument, becoming more polemical, is directed against certain stereotypes of "basic" measurement. I propose that the concept of measurement be widened to include all empirical discrimination, with a wide taxonomy of forms, at best a partial ordering, to replace the present narrow hierarchy. According to this taxonomy, the number system, as exploited in measurement, is an infinite reservoir of relational patterns that can be employed in the description of nature. These patterns may be brought to definition in terms of the invariants of groups of transformations. What is good about a good measurement is then defined by reference to the particular pattern being employed or tested, rather than by the implicitly Pythagorean belief that the best kind of measurement is one that is invariant up to a minimal group of transformations. The mathematical ideal of science does not imply that nature is somehow committed to fitting the specific patterns that have proved fruitful, so far, in this or that part of science. Ambitious programs for making biology or sociology or psychology mathematical—that is, physics-like—leave a painful impression that one is giving orders to nature. But the mathematical ideal is tenable, and not because of any secret knowledge that nature is strait-jacketed by a particular set of cherished patterns. It is not the confinement of nature, but the plenitude of mathematics, that makes the ideal tenable. And only a small part of that plenitude is yet reduced to orderly development.

The linkage of theory and experience involves a need for concepts that function at once reliably in empirical classification and significantly in theory. This dual need cannot be met by any magic: not by theory structures using terms untamed for reliable descriptive use, and not by operational definitions that belong to no theory. But, because there is no magic, a wide range of scientific talent, from the boldest speculation to the most cautious and patient immersion in fact, is sanctioned. We know, of course, that progress occurs through the guidance of observation by theory and the discipline of theory by observed fact; but we do not know a path of discovery that assures this result. Institutional commitments, perhaps especially in the United States, have sometimes elevated mathematicism and quantification to the status of the end-in-itself, humorless and unimaginative.

But polemic should not belittle quantification. In broadening the concept of measurement as much as I think desirable, we must not lose what is crucial. Here is the proper place to introduce a common abstract dimension, with respect to which all measurements, all discriminations, are fully quantitative. This dimension is what has come to be called *quantity of information*. Information is discussed here in a fairly rudimentary way, but it becomes, in the development of the book, a new unifying concept in science. One thing that is crucial to the growth of knowledge, both to its organization and to its extension, is the refinement of discrimination. To be quantitative is to be reliably discriminating in observation, to have high resolving power, up to the point at which further refinement is irrelevant to existing theories and hypotheses and fails to suggest new ones. The ideas of information theory, introduced at this point, will be, in the rest of the book, among the recurring main themes.

Chapters 5–9 have a key that may not be always evident. The key is the contrast between two conceptions of order in nature, the dynamical and the statistical. Chapter 5 deals with dynamical law, first against a historical background—the Aristotelian philosophy of nature and, especially, Aristotle's ideas about purposes in nature—and next in the science of mechanics. Here we consider two characteristics of mechanics as a theory, characteristics that have had a strong impact on philosophy and, indeed, on all modern culture. One of these is the claim of completeness. This has been a great glory and, at the same time, a metaphysical threat, which was already suggested by Newton's subtitle, *The System of the World*. The other characteristic is temporal reversibility, which provoked the poets and the philosophers. The image of nature abstracted by mechanics, taken as official, has been one of the principal sources of metaphysical agony in the modern world. Even as a claim, we shall see, and apart from the qualifications it turns out to need, the claim of completeness is a restricted one, is of completeness *in suo modo*. And the temporal reversibility, likewise, marks the limits of an abstraction rather than the nature of time.

A feature of mechanics involved with the claim of completeness is its deterministic logic. The relation of causality and determinism is discussed here in connection with the classic analysis of David Hume. Necessity is explicated in terms of an emphasis on the assertions of dynamical lawfulness, an emphasis that involves a claim of unconditionality for the generalizations stated. This claim is connected, in turn, with a series of related ideas: isolated system, conservation laws, symmetry principles. These characteristics of dynamics, which have become considerably more explicit since the time of Newton, give to theoretical physics a peculiar and remarkable power and style, which are a shock to those reared with textbook visions of science as naïve empiricism and are a joy to rationalists. Empirical tests are decisive in the end, however, and the history of theory suggests that unconditionality is never more than approximate—a suggestion that leads to the postulation of an infinite, although manageable, complexity. In the social sciences one may even doubt whether any dynamical laws are crucial.

Chapter 6 deals with the other terms of the key, with chance, probability, and statistical order. Even in deterministic theory the qualitative concept of chance and the quantitative concept of probability may be meaningfully defined. An event can be deterministically predictable and can belong, at the same time, to a statistical assembly with fully random characteristics. The sorting out here requires a fairly detailed logical analysis. The meaning of the concept of probability has been highly controversial. The frequency interpretation, which is now popular, is found to be not so much wrong as incomplete. In completing it, we need classificatory criteria, which turn out to be criteria of physical symmetry and not, as is usually maintained, of symmetry with respect to logical form. (The logical side of probability theory is taken up in Chapter 9.)

The classical idea of dynamical order is modified subtly by relativity theory and even more subtly—but more compellingly—by quantum mechanics. These twentieth-century extensions of physics are discussed in Chapter 7. Their development, from the very beginning, has been a great invitation to philosophical discussion. Each, in its own way, requires a recasting of the form in which physical interactions are described, the one because it leads to a fusion of physical and geometrical ideas, the other because it sets a threshold to the occurrence of physical interactions. Controversy over the proper way of interpreting the formalism of quantum mechanics as a scientific theory has been avoided, in the present book, in return for a chance to put greater emphasis on some of the other aspects of it—specifically, on the altered role it gives to identity, form, and structure in nature, and to the idea of atomicity. Quantum mechanics suggests a new formulation of the old idea of levels, of the *scala naturae,* or ladder of nature.

Quantum mechanics, whatever the adequacy of its present formulations, has contributed to the conceptual framework of science both a super-mechanical kind of order and a sub-mechanical kind of disorder, the latter known by the extended term "noise." This contribution gives a certain status to thermodynamics, which, in spite of its early great achievements, had never sat comfortably in the logical seat provided for it by classical physics. The thermodynamic point of view now appears essential to all sciences concerned with the order and history of nature. After reviewing elementary ideas, Chapter 8 treats the theory of statistical processes and the statistical interpretation of thermodynamic ideas. The resolution of the Maxwell Demon problem is a pivotal topic. Here the technical concept of information is reintroduced, with some comments on ideas in the history of philosophy, notably in connection with the *scala naturae.* The chapter concludes with a review of a rather deep topic of great interest to the official critics of science—the nature of time.

The concept of information is next applied to a problem left unfinished in the treatment of probability—the analysis of inductive inference. Human intellectual capacities give rise to a special sort of information-transferring, statistical process. I propose, and partially develop, a way to define the logical notion of credibility in information-theoretic terms. This interpretation, by means of a simple model called the inductive maze, is put in the setting of knowledge as something systematic. The discussion ends with a rather tentative treatment of the role of analogy in inductive reasoning and with some suggestions about the analogical basis of the kind of thing going on in this book—which, risking pejorative associations, is called metaphysics.

The last four chapters are about certain topics in biology, psychology, and the science of society, and it has been necessary, of course, to reject many other topics. Biological studies—and, *a fortiori,* studies of man and society—can be pursued from many points of view. The path chosen here is one required by earlier chapters. I do not claim completeness in synthesizing ideas, but I do claim incisiveness. Recent years have seen a revolution in biology, and it is impossible to emphasize its importance adequately without assertions that require, sooner or later, some sober qualifications. To approach biology, as I do, with the preconceptions of physics—not classical, but contemporary, physics—is inevitably to exhibit a certain narrowness, a certain *esprit simpliste*. This charge I risk. The same statement can be made, with a good deal of justice, about the Young Turks of the seventeenth century, of the Newtonian revolution. It ought to be part of the job of philosophers to probe for the limitations of new viewpoints, but a search for boundaries presupposes a grasp of what is bounded.

An old limitation in biology was imposed by the conceptual gap between mechanistic and teleological descriptions. The revolution in biology has, I think, bridged this gap. Teleological description, in a clearly definable and adequate sense, is a matter, not of postulating new powers or forces unknown to physics, but of learning how to talk correctly about the boundary conditions under which, in living things, physical processes go on. Those who wish to base teleology on an *élan vital* will not accept our explication of what "teleology" means, but they ought to be willing to accept the idea under some other label. Despite the nineteenth-century metaphysical storms, for which some of us are still in posture, there seems no point in letting a good word die from disuse. Biologists are generally more nervous about this kind of thing than physicists, perhaps because they feel more vulnerable.

Chapter 10, on evolution (biological evolution and its sequel of cultural evolution), is more nearly expository than most chapters of the book, and for this the only justification is that the number of such expositions is still very limited. Its central theme, the self-reproducing molecule, is by now familiar, but there has been little appreciation of the extent to which this information-transfer sets the style that distinguishes the animate from the inanimate. In this context the significance of human culture is that of a biologically grounded but *per se* non-biological evolution connected with the capacity, which only in man is developed to a critical point, to externalize acquired information and transmit this information extragenetically. The characteristic time units of cultural evolution are so short compared with those of biological evolution that man, the biological vector of culture, must have a quite peculiar character—or, as some contemporaries would have it, lack of character, or variability.

The approach to some questions about psychology, in Chapter 11, is thus prefigured—as it seems it ought to be—by the specific demands put upon psychological theory by a knowledge of terrestrial history. The shortening of the characteristic times of cultural change brings the fact of novelty into the purview of the individual human life. But that fact argues a certain capacity, and that capacity is an elaboration of animal perception, which we call self-consciousness. The discussion of self-consciousness brings us to some Hegelian distinctions and to the contemporary milieu of existentialism.

In most areas of our lives we operate more or less self-consciously, but we do not have to talk about our operation. Less frequently we have to talk about our self-consciousness, but this talk is not called science. Perhaps, nevertheless, the scientific description of man is incomplete unless the concept of self-consciousness is made part of that description. Some persons believe that such language is excluded, *a priori,* from the discourse of science. My position is that the language of self-consciousness is both legitimate and necessary in psychology, not only because human beings are self-conscious but also because self-observation yields species of discrimination that are not independently accessible. Discussions of the mind-body duality that do not start from these acknowledgments are suspect. The theory of psycho-physical parallelism (either in its old metaphysical form or in the newer but essentially equivalent form of the intertranslatability of mentalistic and physicalistic languages) is implausible, for the corresponding modes of observation entail radically different sorts of coupling between observer and observed.

Whereas the discussion of biology led to an argument legitimating teleological description in certain sorts of contexts, the discussion of human self-consciousness develops an argument against the adequacy of teleological language in the description of human behavior. This leads back to a theme that was introduced in the discussion of biological reproduction—the machine model. Although it is commonly thought that machine models lessen the dignity of living things and of the human psyche, I suggest here that some machines now designable denigrate human capacities less than standard contemporary theories of learning do. This leads us to a discussion of an old topic that has recently been revived: what it is that a machine cannot do.

The discussion of human capacity merges with that of human bondage and freedom—a perennial and very cloudy problem. After some necessary ground-clearing a crucial sense of "freedom" is defined as a learning capacity connected with the modifiability, the metastable character, of human goals.

The inclusion of a chapter on ethics in an essay restricted, as this is, to the philosophy of science may legitimately be questioned. Some aspects of ethics, indeed, have no place here. But the overwhelmingly important fact about man—important for the scientific description of man, not just morally important—is the system of capacities in virtue of which he is a moral agent. Our culture, however, has evolved a curious compromise about ethical topics: one party calls them unscientific, another party calls them non- or supra-scientific, and the two parties agree, in effect, not to talk about them at all in a scientific context. Philosophers generally find weighty reasons, connected with what I call the fundamental theorem of ethics, for respecting the compromise. That these problems are difficult and subtle may justify a tactical scientific restraint but not philosophical avoidance.

The argument is guided here by a parallel and a contrast between two kinds of model-building, the kind that eventuates in a description of the environment and the kind that eventuates in a prescription of conduct. The parallel and the contrast are, more briefly, between Image and Plan.† The constructive process in each case emphasizes the parallel, the product the contrast. The learning that eventuates in choice has both objective and subjective phases, and it is in connection with the latter that the idea of self or agent has meaning. The concept of freedom, developed in the previous chapter, is here brought into relation with its required counterpart, that of responsibility.

In an essay devoted to information theory and model-building, including mythology, a myth may be permitted. It is called the Myth of the Two Gardens. The First Garden is the one that Adam and Eve forsook; the Second is the one that is needed to rescue the exodus from mere pathos. The story of the Second Garden elucidates the concept of man as a *self*-domesticated animal who is, therefore, also wild. What is at stake here is the concept of moral progress.

The final chapter of the book discusses certain conceptual problems of the social sciences—problems that are defined, for the sake of definiteness, in connection with economic theory. Again the bulk of the chapter is expository. The development of economic theory recapitulates, and finds permanent use for, most of the major abstractions discussed in the book. Classical value theory has the logical form of a conservation law. Utility theory is teleological in a restricted sense. Problems about social value, though essential to economic theory, cannot be defined adequately within the framework of either the classical or the utility theory. What is required, instead, is a wider framework,

---

† The labels are taken from *Plans and the Structure of Behavior,* by George A. Miller, Eugene Galanter, and Karl H. Pribram (New York, 1960), which came to my attention only after the text was finished.

defined here by a formal device called a utility functional. Such a device allows for the incommensurability of social aggregate values and, as I think the argument necessitates, of intra-individual comparisons of value as well. Having these indeterminacies built in at one level, economic theory then requires that determinateness come from another level, that of social conflict on a spectrum ranging from overt strife to well-organized debate over ends. The chapter and the book end with a discussion of inadequacies in certain ideal or programmatic formulations of social science in terms of dynamical or statistical law. A question raised earlier about the logical status of propositions concerning the future is here given a kind of answer. There is a sense in which practical competence creates ambiguity of reference to future possibilities. The ideal of complete predictability in human affairs makes itself ridiculous or absurdly ineffectual. There is a point at which we do not wonder, but rather resolve, what will happen. And this obvious fact must, in the end, affect the whole theoretical structure of the social sciences.

1

ON THE NATURE OF NUMBER

It is an old belief, today more vital than ever, that mathematics is the language of nature. The core of mathematics is arithmetic. Here should begin, therefore, the philosophic examination of science. And, if mathematics is not really essential, if it is not the language of nature but only an intellectual tool to be used judiciously (and even sparingly), then, even so, the philosophy of science should begin with it; for the limitations of mathematics are as important as its power.

Science and Mathematics

To those without fluency in mathematics—still the greatest number of educated persons today—the mathematical description of nature is bare, formal, and unrewarding. Nature so rendered is icy and colorless, far from the world that we know, by a more primitive intuition, to be our home. The mathematical intuitions themselves belong to a menial and humdrum region of experience, of household budgets and technology. Mathematical systems may have a certain elegance, but their elevation to high intellectual status merely marks the cultural ascendancy of housekeepers and technologists. Mathematical science is an impressive technique of prediction and control, but it is only that. It is a sort of magic box; it performs a function, but what goes on inside it interests the average consumer as little as the innards of a television receiver.

At the opposite extreme is the Platonic tradition, according to which mathematics is the revelation of an ultimate, and spiritual, reality. Ideas of number and form are exemplified in the world of nature but transcend it; they are in the lower echelon of an ideal order, beyond nature, whose beauty and coherency reside in the Idea of the Good. The mathematical description of nature is admirable; but it is admirable because it leads away from nature to the ideal order beyond. Platonism is only a minor philosophical tendency in the modern world, but it always has its devotees, and a consideration of it is essential to any philosophy of mathematics.

Thus, at the outset, our traditions and our new situation in an age of science and technology present the need of defining the nature and scope of mathematics. To what extent are the content and structure of mathematics a revelation of the nature of things? To what extent, on the contrary, is mathematics a free creation, to be judged on the one hand by its utility in applications, on the other hand by esthetic criteria of elegance and parsimony, but without regard to any supposed standards of truth?

This is the problem, but we shall approach it obliquely. For it is still a question whether philosophy is competent to solve the problem, even whether, in spite of plausible presentations, the problem is a genuine one. Perhaps the relation of mathematics and reality is only an apparent problem, which would disappear if the language in which it is stated were clarified. At any rate, the problem, real or not, is philosophical; and a philosophical problem might be defined as one that could turn out to be purely verbal but never quite does.

In one sense, clearly, the issue over mathematics and reality is a false issue: we cannot get outside knowledge to look at it, to compare it with reality, and thus to find either the presence or the absence of a correspondence between them. The only way to get outside knowledge is to be ignorant. But there is another way of taking the question, and that way will be developed in the following sections.

Number

That our ideas of number are abstractions from experience seems obvious enough to provide a starting-point for the present discussion. The general fact implied by our ideas of number is that things and processes of all sorts can be treated as *discrete,* as separate or separable from one another. The fish that a primitive fisherman catches to feed his clan, the stars in the sky, the letters on this page, the days till the next full moon—all these are examples. The clouds in the sky are less ideally discrete, and counting them might or might not make sense. Words like "time," "aluminum," and "knowledge" function all right as concrete nouns, but in some uses of them the plural form is not exploitable. If one tried to imagine a world in which everything was blurred and overlapping, it might seem that number would not be exemplified in such a world at all.

Discreteness, we see, is one requirement. It is also essential that discrete things form, or be arrangeable in, sets or classes, that they have characteristics by means of which we may determine whether or not they belong to a given set. One might even try to imagine a world in which discrete things were not otherwise well-defined, in which it was not possible to say of a given object—could it then be said to be given?—whether or not it had a given property.

From this point of view numbers may be considered abstractable properties of sets rather than, as some philosophers have maintained, creations of the mind. Numbers are properties of sets, as shapes, let us say, are properties of physical things. But numbers, like shapes, are universals; as different things may have the same shape, so different sets may have the same number. If each object in one set is related uniquely to an object in another set, and vice versa, the sets have the same number. If the primitive fisherman brings home a fish for each member of his household, fish and household are sets identical in number.

To define numbers from this starting-point is to invoke a procedure called definition by abstraction. Since this procedure will be used again, I define here what it involves. To describe the procedure, we first examine the classification of binary relations. Let R be a relation, and let x, y, z, etc. be terms that can be meaningfully said to have, or to stand in, that relation to one another. The shorthand for such a statement is xRy, "x has the relation R to y."

A relation is called *symmetrical* if yRx when xRy.

$$xRy \text{ implies } yRx$$

Applied to persons, "is a fellow countryman of" is a symmetrical relation; applied to lines, "intersects" is symmetrical. Some relations—for example, "is heavier than"—cannot be symmetrical; others—for example, "loves"—are ambiguous as to symmetry.

A relation is called *transitive* if, like "is heavier than" or "is a countryman of,"

$$xRy \text{ and } yRz \text{ implies } xRz$$

Some relations cannot be transitive; others may be or not.

Finally, a relation is called *reflexive* if

$$xRx$$

Examples of such a relation are congruence in geometry and "is a countryman of." Some relations are not fixed in this respect, as "loves"; others cannot be reflexive. Reflexive relations are sometimes puzzling, when expressed in ordinary speech, because we normally use relation words only when the things related are distinct from each other. Still, by any formally correct definition of "congruence," a triangle *is* congruent with itself, and likewise a man belongs to his own country. Such statements sound odd, not because they are wrong, but because they are trivial.

Two kinds of relations of basic importance in mathematics are (1) *order* relations, which are asymmetrical, transitive, and irreflexive, and (2) *equivalence* relations, which are symmetrical, transitive, and reflexive.

Definition by abstraction makes use of equivalence relations, and "matches" or "is equinumerous with" is a case in point. If set x matches set y, then set y matches set x. If x matches y and y matches z, then certainly x matches z. And clearly a set matches itself.

I next define equivalence class. An equivalence class is a class of all those things standing in an equivalence relation to a given thing. A number, in particular, is an equivalence class of sets.

There is a sort of weakness about definition by abstraction: it does not guarantee that the definition is unique. It is logically possible that elements related by an equivalence relation should all have something in common besides their equivalence; and, when we try to exclude anything except the number property, the procedure begins to look circular. This is the point of Plato's doctrine of reminiscence: to know what to abstract is to recognize the abstraction, to have known it before. In addition to all the matching sets, must there not be something else, the universal number itself?

I am talking here, not about number concepts as entities in the mind, but about the meaning of those concepts and about how that meaning is to be defined. To elucidate the meaning, we must refer to the procedure of matching the members of one set against those of another. The view being developed is that the procedure is primary, the number concept derivative. A sorting machine may sort punched cards according to the number of holes in a certain column, and the procedure it employs is essentially the same as that of a human sorter. The machine does not have number *concepts;* the human sorter does. The *description* of the procedure requires number concepts or their near equivalents; but the elucidation of the concepts is in terms of the procedure, not in terms of the concepts we use in describing the procedure.

Instead of talking about concepts, let us talk about number standards, to see if this clarifies the point. What is lacking in the mere procedure of matching is a kind of universality: in addition to all the couples there is the number "two" itself that somehow has to be accounted for. But a standard has a kind of universality, and perhaps this is all that is required. Suppose, for instance, that the primitive fisherman, who has no number words at all, ties knots in a string matching the set of persons he has to feed. He carries the string with him and catches enough fish to match the knots in the string. He then believes, ahead of time, that a fish will go to each member of his household. The string has acquired a new status: things that match it match each other; it has become a standard, like the standard meter or the standard kilogram. It can be transferred from place to place or from person to person. Perhaps, if the Bureau of Standards were on its mettle, it would maintain a standard unit, a standard couple, a standard triple, . . .

This is all very well; a strip of rawhide with knots in it may well serve as a standard, but it is not a number concept, and our account continues to evade the issue. Let the evasion continue, however, a little longer. Our primitive fisherman has other things to worry about besides fishing: the days to the next full moon, the pots he cooks in, etc. At some point he discovers that his knotted strings can be made to match *any* such set: by tying enough knots he gets to the point where *one more* will make his string match any set he is interested in. Every number standard can be constructed by the repeated addition of one. (It is this fact that relieves the Bureau of Standards of an otherwise tedious obligation.) At this higher level of sophistication and abstraction the fisherman makes for himself a set of permanent number standards. I represent his collection in Figure 1.

When this stage has been reached, a new insight comes with it. The number standards have been ordered; each new string matches the previous one, but with one knot extra. The set of *strings* up to and including the last one just matches the *knots* in the last one. The fisherman, replacing the knots in the last string by knots that are dissimilar or by other marks, such as

$$1, \quad 2, \quad 3, \quad 4, \quad 5, \quad 6, \quad 7, \quad 8, \quad 9, \quad \cdots$$

may dispense with all standards but this one. For the mark "4" is uniquely correlated with the set "1, 2, 3, 4" by being its last member; the mark "7" is a sign for the set "1, 2, 3, 4, 5, 6, 7"; etc. The achievement of this single serial

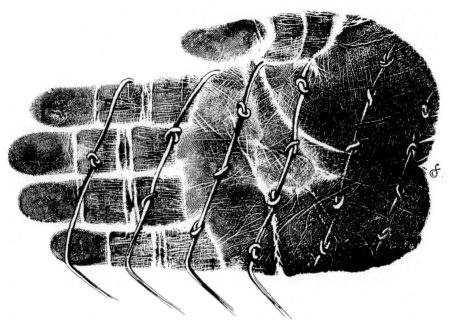

Fig. 1. The Primitive Fisherman's String

standard signifies that number is now employed in its ordinal, as well as in its cardinal, aspect.

In explaining the classification of numbers I remarked that two kinds of relations are of special importance in mathematics. The first of these was the class of equivalence relations, and I used the equivalence relation of matching between sets to define number in its cardinal aspect. I have now used the other fundamental kind of relation, the order relation, and in terms of this I have defined number in its ordinal aspect.

At this point, it is necessary to insist, we are still evading the question about number as such and are only talking about physical standards. The string standards have been replaced by a single string with knots all different from one another or by some sequence of arbitrary, but distinguishable, things or marks. It surely does not alter the case if these are, in turn, replaced by the names "hitch, granny, reef, cat's-paw, ..." or "one, two, three, four, ..." We are still dealing with *exemplifications* of number, not with its essence. But they are standardized exemplifications. "Four" is a name, but as a name it is shorthand for "one, two, three, four"; the last is not *the* number four, but merely a standard quadruple. Has anything been left out?

There is, of course, something mental; for small numbers, at least, we may visualize. Sensory images may exemplify number as well as form, color, etc., and such images may be matched against physical standards. They are just exemplifications, however, and as such they have no privileged status in the explanation of meaning. For this meaning attaches to any exemplification of number, physical or imaged. The conceptual status, the universality, does not lie in any privileged, mental exemplification of number. What is conceptual or universal is that *any* exemplification of number may be used, and be thought of, in the context of its similitude with other exemplifications. The universal "four" is, in the language of Bertrand Russell, the property of all sets that match the set "one, two, three, four." †

At this point the evasion of the nature of number concepts has given rise to a sort of answer to that question. A fuller discussion is given in Chapter 3. But this much can be said now: Number properties are properties of sets. At first sight we want to say that sets match one another because they have the same number property. It is as good to say, however, that they have the same number property because they match. The property *is* the equivalence relation in which a given set stands to others in its equivalence class. What all sets in a given equivalence class have in common (what they have to have in common, at any rate) is simply the equivalence relation. *The* number is the equivalence class itself. The distinctions among numbers are ordinal; so the *naming* of a particular equivalence class depends upon the ordering of elements within some standard set of the class.

Our Platonic impulses lead us to say that, in addition to particular quadruples, the number four exists, and this is quite right. But the word "exist" carries with it an image of our using a name to point to something, and pointing implies isolation and location. So we have the picture of the number four existing (as it were, standing or sitting) *there*. But where? Well, not in any place spatial or temporal, but (we go on to say) in a different realm, Plato's realm of universals.

I mentioned, at the beginning, the Platonic interpretation of mathematics and the uncertainty whether philosophy can settle questions such as these and even the prior question whether such questions are meaningful. I certainly have not settled such questions in any grandly metaphysical sense, but I have defined what numbers are and how they are ordinally related. I have tried to be explicit about what is involved in abstracting the number concepts so

---

† A classic discussion of the foundations of arithmetic will be found in Bertrand Russell, *Introduction to Mathematical Philosophy* (London, 1919; also 1938). For background reading for this section and the remainder of the chapter, nothing is better than Russell's first three chapters.

that they become objects of reference, as it were, over and above the sets of individual things that exemplify them. Any new questions must be answered in a way that is consistent with all these findings. For those who want to discuss the reality of numbers in some ultimate sense—for example, to assert or deny the Platonic interpretation—there is one further, and very important, philosophical distinction. It is a distinction the neglect of which leads to endless philosophical confusion, as the history of philosophy itself will demonstrate. It has to do with two ways in which words may be said to refer to things.

One type of reference has been called *demonstrative, nominative,* or *ostensive.* The context is one in which a thing referred to is literally present to a speaker and a hearer. It is pointed to, is exhibited in some way, is quite literally brought into the discourse. The other kind of reference has been called *propositional* or *descriptive.* For such reference one uses not simply a word, but the form of a statement. Philosophers have worried very much about the nature of our reference, for example, to the bone in Old Mother Hubbard's cupboard, or to unicorns, or to numbers so large that they are not exemplified by any actual set (if any such numbers can be defined).† It is clear, in a general way, that such problems arise only through propositional reference, for we can refer by means of a propositional statement even though there is no thing of which the statement is true. The bone in Old Mother Hubbard's cupboard can be referred to demonstratively only if there is one; but no such requirement limits our discourse when the reference is propositional. Any confusion, however, raises curious problems. If I can refer to the bone in the cupboard at all, it must be somewhere. But where? Well, neither in the cupboard nor outside the cupboard, but somewhere in the realm of things that thought and discourse make us acquainted with.

Our reference to a set of discrete objects can be demonstrative because we can exhibit such a set—for example, the letters of the last word of this sentence, in a particular copy of this book. We thus exhibit a particular quadruple to someone. Our reference to the number four, on the other hand, is propositional. In order to achieve this reference, we must exhibit the form of a statement, such as "x is a set that matches the set exhibited above." The number is not a statement, or a part of a statement; but the defining condition by which reference is achieved is a matter both of pointing and of exhibiting the form of a statement about the thing pointed to, "the x's that match the above set." The quoted expression is not a statement; it is grammatically only a phrase.

† The classic paper on this subject is "On Denoting," by Bertrand Russell, *Mind,* vol. 14 (1905), 479–93.

But it is kept from being a statement only by a trick, which, in English, involves using a blank ("*x*") and a pronominal "that."

It is perhaps this distinction of propositional from demonstrative reference that some anti-Platonists are thinking about when they say that numbers exist only in the mind. Such an assertion, if taken seriously, also makes numbers appear to be objects of demonstrative reference, for it answers the pointing question "where." But at this place, for the time being, my analysis must rest.

The account given above is an attempt to describe, as carefully as may be, the sense in which the number concepts may be called abstractions. A historical account of the genesis of such concepts is a different thing: more roundabout, psychologically more complex, and doubtless more irrational. The abstracting process, considered historically, is not a sort of passive withdrawing of essence from existence. Our number system is an enormously complicated artifact. Its artificial character is in no wise denied: only Art can hold the mirror up to Nature!

The Peano Axioms

So far the discussion has been limited to the number concepts, and nothing has been said about the *propositions* of arithmetic, considered explicitly as a kind of knowledge. It is in this latter area, for the most part, that the great controversies over the nature of arithmetical truth have been waged. Views about that truth have ranged from the rationalistic view that it is a revelation, through intuition, of an ultimate character of things to the conventionalistic view that it expresses only the consequence of arbitrary stipulation of the meaning of number concepts. The latter view, with variations and concessions here and there, is still fashionable today.† Its prevalence is largely a consequence not only of researches in formal logic and in the foundations of mathematics but also of the empiricistic-positivistic tradition following Hume and Kant. The best way to approach it is through the axiomatic treatment of arithmetic invented (1891) by the Italian logician Peano.‡ The axioms make use of three undefined concepts: "one" (or, in some versions, "zero"), "number," and "successor of." The axioms are:

---

† This is exhibited in the examples given by Douglas Gasking in "Mathematics and the World," reprinted in James R. Newman, *The World of Mathematics* (New York, 1956), vol. 3, pp. 1708–22. The thesis here is conventionalism. The whole of Part XI of Newman's collection (pp. 1613–1754) is recommended.

‡ Giuseppe Peano, "Sul concetto di numero," *Rivista di mathematica,* vol. 1 (1891). The axioms were really the invention of J. W. R. Dedekind, in "Was sind und was sollen die Zahlen?" reprinted in his *Gesammelte Werke* (Berlin, 1932), Band 3.

1. *One* is a number.
2. If *n* is a number, there is a number that is its successor.
3. *One* is not the successor of any number.
4. If *m* and *n* are numbers whose successors are identical, *m* and *n* are identical.
5. If for each number *n* the successor of *n* has the property *P* when *n* has that property, and if *One* has the property *P*, then all numbers have the property *P*.

It is the intent of the Peano axioms that the three undefined concepts be used in any way that the axioms permit. The axioms also employ concepts of class membership, negation, implication, etc., but these are all concepts of formal logic. The operative meanings of the undefined concepts are only those bestowed by the axioms; but these are sufficient.

In order to elucidate the role of the axioms, I apply them to the case of a string of plastic snap beads.† The bead called "one" has only a projection, which can be snapped into a second bead; it has no hole into which another bead can be snapped. All other beads have both a hole and a projection. A bead becomes the successor of a bead that is snapped into it. The axioms assert or imply, then, that there is one and only one bead that cannot be a link between two beads, that every other bead is a link between two beads, that no bead has more than one hole or projection, and that therefore no bead can link more than two beads. The fifth axiom, the axiom of mathematical induction, implies that there are not two or more separate strings, one beginning with the unique bead and the others infinite in both directions. This is implied because the beads in a separate string would have a property different from a property of all first-string beads. For example: *One* has the property of being in the first string, and, if *n* has this property, so has its successor; but, if there is a second string, its beads do not have this property, and the axiom is violated.

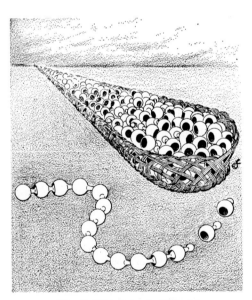

Fig. 2. The Intended Model

† I owe this illustration to Professor Arne Magnus.

No actual string of beads will satisfy these stipulations except potentially; there will always be a last bead, but it will have a projection that *could* be snapped into another bead, and this is rather the way in which infinity is usually conceived.

A further sort of restriction on the axioms appears in the definitions of addition and multiplication. If "the successor of n" is written as n', the definitions say:

$$\text{Addition:} \qquad n + 1 \underset{df}{=} n'$$

$$n + m' \underset{df}{=} (n + m)'$$

$$\text{Multiplication:} \quad n \times 1 \underset{df}{=} n$$

$$n \times m' \underset{df}{=} (n \times m) + n$$

Various sequences of numbers that satisfy the Peano axioms as such will fail to give the customary meaning to these definitions—for example, odd numbers beginning with 7 and prime numbers. But one interpretation—the natural numbers beginning with 1—does give them the usual meaning.

From the axioms and definitions given it is possible to prove the commutative, distributive, and associative laws of arithmetic—restricted, of course, to the natural numbers. By the addition of new definitions, but without new axioms, it is possible to develop the modern number system. The positive and negative integers are defined as equivalence classes of ordered couples of natural numbers, as are the rational numbers. By further definitions, of equivalence classes of unending sequences of natural numbers, one defines the real numbers. Ordered pairs of real numbers, subject to definitions of "+" and "×," are what we call complex numbers. With these the number system is complete.

Having sketched Peano's system, we return to the question of mathematical truth. It is obvious that in an uninterpreted system such as this there can be no question of literal, semantic truth. The only significant thing that can be said about a propositional form involving the undefined concepts is that it is, or is not, deducible from the axioms. If the axioms are interpreted in such a way that they are true propositions involving what are, in some sense, meaningful concepts, the theorems that follow will be true propositions also. But this begs the question as to the meaning of arithmetical truth.†

It is often loosely stated, in support of a conventionalistic interpretation of mathematics, that the theorems in such a system as Peano's are true "by defini-

---

† For a very clear elementary discussion of the axiomatic method, see Alfred Tarski, *Introduction to Logic and to the Methodology of the Deductive Sciences* (Oxford, 1941).

Fig. 3. Forbidden Models

tion," and one may even try to justify such language by calling the axioms "implicit definitions." If we announce that we will not accept any interpretation of "one," "number," and "successor" that does not satisfy the Peano axioms, then clearly the axioms, and the theorems that follow from them, will never be false. The attitude is like that exploited in the prophecies of the famous Nostradamus, which no one can understand unless they are true. Such an account of mathematical truth really begs the question, for it presumes that we know the interpretation to be true before we make it; and, if the interpretation is in terms of ordinary arithmetic, that is just the matter under discussion. Wherein, then, consists the truth of ordinary, intuitive arithmetic?

Logical Truth

It is not possible to prove, within the Peano system, that the relations stipulated by the Peano axioms do, in fact, hold of ordinary arithmetic. The only proof that is possible is the fact that one can develop, within the Peano theory, a set of theorems that are isomorphous with the basic propositions of ordinary arithmetic. Does the fact that ordinary arithmetic starts with statements alleged to be true mean that these truths are empirical—true in a way that depends on contingent facts? Only one philosopher of note, John Stuart Mill, has held this heretical position.†

What everyone admits, of course, is that any empirically testable application of arithmetic depends upon identifications that could, in fact, be incorrect. This is illustrated by a story, cited by Whitehead,‡ about the Council of Nicaea:

> "When the bishops took their places on their thrones, they were 318; when they rose up to be called over, it appeared that they were 319; so that they never could make the number come right, and whenever they approached the last of the series, he immediately turned into the likeness of his next neighbor."

And Whitehead adds, "Whatever be the historical worth of this story, it may safely be said that it cannot be disproved by deductive reasoning from the premises of abstract logic. The most we can do is assert that a universe in which such things are liable to happen on a large scale is unfitted for the practical application of cardinal arithmetic." But the problem is, in fact, deeper than Whitehead indicates. For, if the universe in which such things are likely to happen on a large scale includes the sub-universe of strings and knots and verbal counters, we are going to be committed to a radical divorcement between practical application and pure theory. And such a divorcement, when presented by our imagination, brings troubles of its own: there are no numbers apart from the matching relation, and no arithmetic apart from the ordinal relations among non-matching sets. Arithmetical statements are not true or false in a way that depends on specific contingent facts. But neither are statements of physical law, for example, true or false except through chains of subsidiary interpretative

† John Stuart Mill, *A System of Logic* (New York, 1848), p. 364.

‡ Alfred North Whitehead, "Mathematics," in *Encyclopaedia Britannica,* 11th edition.

statements. There is a radical difference between the two cases, as we shall see; each must be examined in its own right, and premature contrasts will not help. The truth of statements of law will be treated in Chapter 5.

In the present section I shall describe some prevailing beliefs about the nature of arithmetical truth. This description involves the concept of *analyticity*. I shall then review briefly the relation between arithmetic and formal logic, as presently understood, and out of this distinguish two sorts of true statements within logic and arithmetic. The upshot is to maintain, in a more sophisticated way, the insight we have gotten from the case history of the primitive fisherman.

The general view of mathematical truth called conventionalism has been mentioned previously. Conventionalism is a way of claiming, for all kinds of logical or mathematical propositions, that their truth is not truth about any-thing except, in an oblique sense, the conventions of language. We can assert such propositions, that is, because they are true, not by reason of any facts about which we are asserting them, but merely "by convention."

A sharper statement, and one lacking the false implication that logical truth is merely a matter of how we choose to talk, is that propositions of logic and mathematics are *analytically* true. In the older logic an analytic proposition is one whose statement predicates of a subject some property that is already a defining property of that subject. "All white horses are horses" is analytically true, and so is "All squares are rectangles." Since in modern logic we recognize other kinds of propositions than those in subject-predicate form, the idea must be generalized. A broader definition is that analytic propositions are true by virtue of the meanings of the terms they employ. So "Two plus two is four" is analytic, for "two plus two" and "four" are linked by their definitions as differ-ent ways of designating the same number.

One type of analytic statement is the tautology. In the elementary logic of propositions one discusses the ways of combining propositions $p, q, r, \ldots$ by oper-ations of negation, disjunction, and conjunction. Such propositions are called "atomic," their compounds "molecular." The truth or falsity of a molecular proposition depends usually, but not always, upon the truth or falsity of the atomic constituents. Thus "not-p or q" is false if p is true and q is false; otherwise it is true. But this dependence can be weak or strong, and in the extreme case the dependence vanishes. Thus "p or q or not-p" is true regard-less of the truth or falsity of p and of q, while "not-p or q, and p but not q" is similarly false; molecular propositions of the former class are called *tautologies*, and those of the latter class are called *contradictions*. With respect to the atomic propositions of which it is compounded, a tautology is vacuously true.† This is illustrated by a story about a well-known English philosopher, whose wife had just had a child. In reply to a well-wisher's question whether the baby was a boy or a girl, the philosopher is said to have replied, "Yes."

The concept of analyticity is used to explain why deductions are justified. If p represents the conjunction of all necessary premises in a deduction, and q the conclusion, the proposition "p implies q" is an analytic statement. Thus the process of logical proof consists in showing that, though p and q themselves may be analytic or not, the statement that "p implies q" is analytic. From premises that are analytically true, however, only analytically true conclusions follow.

True propositions that are non-analytic are called synthetic. A synthetically true statement is true in a sense that is at the mercy of fact; an analytically true statement is true because of the meanings of terms. The sharpness of the distinction between meaning and fact (thought and reality, language and reality) is therefore crucial. How sharp can it be made?

With this question floating, we turn to the famous contribution of Russell and Whitehead,‡ in which, following the lead of earlier logicians, they showed how to interpret the Peano axioms within the system of formal logic and how thus to prove them, and all of arithmetic with them, as mere parts of logic. The details are elaborate, but the outline is easy to follow. There are three main steps: (1) to exhibit specific numbers; (2) to define "one," "number," and "successor"; (3) to deduce the erstwhile axioms when their terms are so defined.

The exhibition of instances of number is a procedure no different from what we have discussed before except for the fact that the exhibition occurs between the covers of a book on logic. In the earlier chapters of that book a multiplicity of discrete signs, and various relations among signs, have been exhibited and used. It has been taken for granted that some signs have referents that are discrete entities, and that in some cases the relation, between sets of signs and sets of referents, has been a matching relation. Logic has exploited these things, but up to the chapter on number it has not developed the apparatus for talking about them.

A prerequisite has been the definition of identity. To inscribe the identity

---

† For a discussion of tautology and analyticity see W. V. Quine, "Truth by Convention," in *Philosophical Essays for A. N. Whitehead* (New York, 1936), pp. 90–124.

‡ Bertrand Russell and Alfred North Whitehead, *Principia Mathematica* (Cambridge, England, 1910–13), contained the first complete development. The essential ideas had been developed earlier by Gottlob Frege; see his *The Foundations of Arithmetic,* translated by J. L. Austin (New York, 1950).

mark "=" between two demonstrative signs is to tie down the fact that they have the same referent; to negate this is to affirm that the referents, if they exist, are distinct from each other. A matching relation is now affirmed by the conjunction of several statements—for example: an x, and a y, and a z belong to some set S; x is not y, and y is not z, and z is not x; any w in S is either x or y or z. Thus we exhibit a triple.

Having exhibited this paradigm, we define a number (in this case "three") as the set of all sets S for which it holds. The number "one," in particular, is the set of all non-empty sets S of which it can be truly affirmed that, if any x and any y are in S, x is the same as y.

Given a specific number, we can define its successor. The successor is a set of sets for which the defining condition is derived from that of the predecessor in an obvious way. The set of elements in S' and not in S belongs to One. Number in general is then defined as the set that contains One and contains the successor of every number that it contains.

Using such definitions, one can easily see that the first four Peano axioms are true when so interpreted. Proof of the fifth axiom, as a theorem in this interpretation, cannot, of course, make use of this axiom without direct circularity. The fifth axiom excludes the case in which the generic class "number" contains 1, 2, ... and also some quite extraneous sequence, ... $a-1$, a, $a+1$, $a+2$, ... The question is, therefore, whether we can define number in such a way that any extraneous sequence is already excluded by definition. The idea for making such a definition is as follows: Let N be a class that contains 1 and contains the successor of every element that it contains. Clearly, then, N contains everything that we would call a number. But it may be overstuffed: it may contain other entities as well. If we were starting with the Peano fifth as an axiom, we could prove that the set of predecessors of every element in N is finite. But this axiom must now be proved as a theorem. It excludes the possibility of a second string, unconnected with the first string (1, 2, ...). Can we exclude this by definition, and then prove the Peano fifth?† A definition due to Frege does this as follows: If a particular N contains extraneous elements, there is an N' that lacks those elements. The *smallest* set defined as N is defined—namely, as including 1 and the successor of every element that it contains—can then be defined as the intersection of all such sets—that is, as the set, of type N, that is a subset of every set of type N. This is a crucial step, for, if it fails, the fifth axiom fails too: there will be a property that is true of 1, and true of $n+1$ if true of

---

† The specific question goes back, again, to Dedekind, quoted by Hao Wang, "The Axiomatization of Arithmetic," *Journal of Symbolic Logic*, vol. 22, No. 2 (June 1957), 150–51.

n, but not true of all numbers—the property, namely, of belonging to the main sequence.

There is no doubt that Frege's definition is, in some way, adequate; but our assurance that the *greatest* common subset of all sets of type *N* does eliminate all extraneous elements is perhaps itself a covert appeal to the axiom of induction or, in fact, to something stronger. A result known as Skolem's theorem shows that formal systems have "unintended" interpretations or models. To eliminate extraneous entities from the class of numbers is possible only if "property" in axiom 5 is taken in a sufficiently extended sense.†

I mention this problem about the fifth axiom, not out of concern over the niceties of logic, but as a reminder that definition by abstraction is subject to a characteristic difficulty: we find it hard to be sure that a formally defined set contains all those and only those elements that we intuitively want it to contain. And it is at the point where essential definitions by abstraction enter the picture that I want to distinguish two meanings of "analytic." ‡

This distinction is connected with an old problem in the philosophy of mathematics. If a theorem is deducible from a set of premises, to affirm the premises and deny the theorem is to be self-contradictory; the premises must, in some sense, already contain the theorem. Hence, people have been led to say, the sense of novelty, of discovery, in a newly proved theorem is only psychological. The theorem was already somehow there, like the statue in the marble. But this is very misleading. The existence or non-existence of a proof is a quite objective matter, not in any relevant sense psychological.

In some cases in particular—notably in the derivation of arithmetic from logic —it seems positively wrong to say that the conclusions are implicit in the premises in the same sense in which *q* is implicit in the premises "*p*" and "*p* implies *q*." If our emphasis on the abstractive character of concepts of number is right, the statements of arithmetic are implicit, not in the previously developed *statements* of logic, but in the antecedent, pre-formal *practice* of making those statements. Antecedent logic exhibits sets and matchings of sets; these things belong to the apparatus of language and, *a fortiori,* of logical language. But they have in no sense been objects of discourse, explicit or implicit. The apparatus for discoursing about numbers is derived, not solely from earlier logical statements, but also by abstraction from instances of number provided by such statements. Arithmetic is a part of logic; but it is not a mere restatement of

† See Hao Wang, "Eighty Years of Foundational Studies," *Dialectica,* vol. 12, 3/4 (1958), 466–97.

‡ A logical analysis of abstraction is set forth in W. V. Quine, *Mathematical Logic* (Cambridge, Mass., 1947), Chap. 3.

the elementary, pre-arithmetical part of logic. To deny a theorem of arithmetic is not to deny what pre-arithmetical propositions of logic affirm, but to deny a fact about the framework within which pre-arithmetical statements of logic can be made at all.

Thus proof, at this point, is not a tautological restatement of what has been stated before, but rather more like factual statement. The facts stated, however, are not specific, contingent facts of nature, the denial of which might also be consistently stated in language; they are, rather, facts exhibited in the essential schemata of language, facts that would still be exhibited in the very act of denying them. Transitional proofs going from one level of discourse to another, as from logic to arithmetic, are analytic but not tautological; they are analytic of antecedent discourse, not only of what has previously been affirmed but also of the unexplicated form in which the previous affirmations have been made. They close off possibilities left open by antecedent discourse, just as synthetic factual statements would; in that sense Mill was right. But the possibilities have been foreclosed in another way—by the facts exploited in antecedent discourse.

Proof that accomplishes such transitions is proof none the less. But Mill was perhaps right in another sense. The propositions of arithmetic become fully contingent as soon as they are interpreted in terms of empirical groupings and matchings. They are protected from uncertainty only when we interpret them by means of the groupings and matchings essential to discourse; for then we are estopped—as the lawyers say—from denying them: we cannot deny them without exhibiting, in the syntactical constructions that denial involves, the absurdity of that denial.

The point of my argument here is reinforced by reference to the well-known logical paradoxes, which arise from concepts and statements that are, in one way or another, self-referential. One chestnut is the paradox of the barber, defined as one who, in a certain male community, shaves all those, and only those, who do not shave themselves. The definition requires that he do not, and also that he do, shave himself. We must conclude that no such barber exists. There is no trouble with the idea until we notice that the barber himself is one of the set about which the definition generalizes.

A more interesting example is the paradox named after J. Richard. This states what looks like an obvious fact: that there is a number that is the largest that can be defined in less than a hundred English words. One then shows that there is a still larger number—the largest number that can be defined in less than a hundred English words, plus one. What makes the trouble here, clearly, is the inclusion, among "English words," of referential terms that permit us to refer to any number previously defined by calling it "the number previously defined." We have at first a code that defines numbers and in which there is, indeed, a largest number definable in less than a hundred words. But by reference to (rather than repetition of) this code we create a second code, etc. Hence there simply is no largest number of the sort indicated.

A third example of curious results involving the logic of self-reference is the famous theorem of Kurt Gödel. This theorem, which is no paradox, derives from a code for enumerating statements in a formal language that is able to include elementary arithmetic. A proof is a string of statements, in this language, generated by the axioms in successive steps according to specified rules of proof. Numbers can be assigned to such strings and thus to all provable statements within the language. Such theorem numbers belong to a class, C, that can be defined by their arithmetical properties. Gödel's proof shows the existence of a number, n, uniquely characterized by property P, statable in the formal language, such that the number n is the code number of the statement, in the formal language, that says there is a number that has the property P and is not in C.†

From this extraordinarily ingenious construction it follows that the statement numbered n is either true and not provable or provable and not true. In the latter case arithmetic, as formally developed, is self-contradictory. Hence the consistency of arithmetic entails the consequence that there are in the formal system true statements that are not provable by the rules in question. No extension of the system—no addition of new premises or rules of proof—obviates the general conclusion.

Gödel's proposition has a sort of family resemblance to the famous paradox about Epimenides: "Epimenides the Cretan says that Cretans never tell the truth." There is nothing obviously contradictory about what Epimenides says, "Cretans never tell the truth." The trouble arises when this is said by a Cretan, hence with implicit self-reference. The contradiction is not between two parts of what Epimenides says, but between what he says and the fact of his saying it. Suppose he says, "Cretans sometimes tell the truth." Then, even if Cretans always lie (and hence never say that they always lie), there is no inconsistency.

Let us summarize. The barber is all right if he commutes; he just can't live in the community about which we generalize. The largest number definable in a certain way is all right if in defining it we don't expand our resources of defini-

---

† There are numerous expositions of Gödel's theorem. For a semi-popular discussion see Ernest Nagel and James R. Newman, "Gödel's Proof," in Newman's *The World of Mathematics*, vol. 3, pp. 1668–95. For a different approach see J. Findlay, "Gödelian Sentences: A Non-numerical Approach," *Mind*, vol. 51 (1942), 259–66. For a brief account, finally, see W. V. Quine, *Methods of Logic* (New York, 1950), pp. 244–48.

tion. The Gödel theorem is all right in any case, for it shows how to enlarge our resources for saying "true" without, at the same time, enlarging those for saying "deducible in a formal system"; it would not be all right if we equivocated by expanding "deducible *in* a formal system" to "deducible *about* that formal system." The self-reference involved in the paradoxes in one way or another, and in the Gödel theorem by enumerated statements about numbers, calls attention to the sense in which the use of language implies *de facto* conditions that acquire a special logical status when the discourse is directed at them. Such conditions, without involving *formal* deducibility, restrict our freedom to affirm or deny. The concept of logical truth cannot be exhausted by concepts of tautology and formal deducibility; when we have evolved a logical system, we are able to prove *about* it things that we cannot prove *in* it. Gödel's proposition is analytic in the same sense in which we have claimed arithmetic to be analytic: not of what is laid down in the antecedent system—in this case arithmetic itself —on which it is based, but of what is true of that system once it is developed. The Gödel theorem involves new abstractive steps—for example, in formalization of the concept "deducibility."

Surely there is a common pattern here. The truth of what he would say estops Epimenides from saying it. What Mill thought he could say is less contingently inaccessible, for the inhibiting conditions are permanent and generic. In the Richard paradox the reference to a number code gives rise to a new one. In the Gödel theorem, and in the new branch of logic or mathematics to which it belongs, the previously developed arts of formal proof are themselves transformed into mathematical subject matter, leading to arithmetical conclusions beyond the range of arithmetic.

There is, moreover, a hierarchy of Gödelian arguments. Let arithmetic be expanded to include Gödel's unprovable statement as a new axiom. Then in the expanded system there will be a new Gödel theorem, and so *ad infinitum*. This certainly means that "mathematical truth" and "formal deducibility within logic" are permanently dissevered concepts. Mathematical truth is analytic, but it is analytic of conditions implicit in the expansion of mathematics itself, of conditions that are, therefore, inexhaustible. These conditions are not arbitrary, are not conventional.

Is mathematics, then, after all, an exploration of nature, of that aspect of things peculiarly—but not easily!—accessible because of the nature and habit of our language and our knowledge? Is it, in that deeper sense, a language of nature?

By these suggestions I am not returning—at least I do not intend to return—

to the rationalistic philosophy that held that something called pure reason could lay bare the foundations of the universe. We cannot, by thought or discourse, legislate for nature—not even the conditions necessary for the intelligibility of our thought and discourse. These conditions are not legislated by us, nor are they all on the surface, automatically given; we have to find them. We do this first by trying to think and speak well, and then by analyzing what is implicit in the art we have learned. In the process we develop new conceptual tools. Some of these seem relevant only to the furtherance of mathematics itself; but some have relevance, often unexpected relevance, to the scientific description of nature. The relation runs both ways; for, from the time of our primitive fisherman to the present, the attempt to understand how things are and how they go has set new problems for mathematics and given new hints to its development.

My belief about the nature of mathematical truth, stated here tentatively but supported by detailed consideration of arithmetic, is that it is a kind of truth about the aspect of things that becomes accessible to investigation through the self-reference of evolving thought and language. Its claims are limited to this sphere, hence are analytically rather than synthetically true. But their relevance extends beyond, for the evolution of language comes out of man's commerce with nature. To use a word that I shall make much of later, the evolution of thought and language is *informed* by nature—first in man's biological evolution, second in the evolution of culture, and finally in the direct pursuit of enlightenment. If this is a kind of rationalism, it is one that recognizes, at the same time, that reason is the product of experience.†

Models and Turing Machines

The kind of truth we have been discussing is semantic truth, the truth, specifically, of statements or propositions. But there are broader meanings of "truth," both in common language and in traditional philosophy. In interpreting arithmetic and arithmetical truth, I want to say something that gets me into trouble when I try to say it naïvely: namely, that arithmetical truth depends upon the prevalence in nature, and in our discourse, of discreteness, of transitive matchings, and of transitive orderings. It seems reasonable, then, to see what we can do with the broader meanings of "truth." We use such meanings when we talk about poems, novels and plays, maps and models. We attribute truth

---

† One of the nicest discussions of the nature of mathematics and of the mathematician's art is that of John von Neumann, "The Mathematician," in *Works of the Mind* (Chicago, 1947), pp. 180–96, and also in Newman, *op. cit.,* pp. 2053–63.

to them all in one way or another, a truth that may be called verisimilitude. I shall generalize the term "model" for all of these, and I shall use the term again in later chapters.

What, then, is a model? A model is an artifact of some sort, of words or clay or electronic circuitry. To give rise to semantic truth, a model must be accompanied by interpretative statements, as maps usually are. Statements and systems of statements may be thought of as being, sometimes, self-interpreting models. What I have said about abstractive definition is a case in point. The earlier logical discourse says what it has to say in a restricted way, but it also provides a model about which later, arithmetical statements provide explicit interpretation. After the necessary abstractions have been made, we have the materials and the rules of construction for a new sort of theory, number theory, which will be discussed in the last section of this chapter. But number theory, related always to the original model of matching and ordered sets, becomes, in its turn, a model.

A good model, like a good map, is rich: it guides us, under suitable interpretation, to many true statements. Without necessarily consisting of statements at all, or of statements intended as literally true, it facilitates understanding. And in this variable, richness, we can see a meaning for an old and philosophically discredited notion, that of degrees of truth—what I shall later call informational complexity. This does not imply that a model has to be itself complex; it implies that, without the model, what it illuminates would seem complex.

The variable richness does not provide an easy ranking, however, for a very rich model may not allow a simple interpretative framework for translating it into prosaic statement. When the interpretative process itself becomes too complex, the model becomes suspect. Still, some of the most fascinating and compelling models in our lives are essentially inexplicit. The myths of great religions and the great works of art have many guidebooks written about them, but the guidebooks do not replace the models.

Men are model-builders, mythopoets. They work between the poles of explicit prosaic statement and imaginative construction. Philosophers try to be prosaic and say what is literally and semantically true, as do scientists. But even in these fields the tension is felt; mythopoeia has its place and on occasion finds shorter roads to prosaic truth than would otherwise be found.

Stendhal called his novel *The Red and the Black* "a mirror of the nineteenth century." There is no surrounding body of interpretative statement except what critics have to offer. The literal-minded may regret this, but we should have to accept a far more impoverished statement as the price of explicitness. The mirror relation is a complex and interesting one, and we are not done with it. In the present section I wish only to mention a few of its uses in the area of knowledge that is closest to the essence of mirroring itself: the study of matchings and equivalences.

Arithmetic is a theory and not just a model. But it is also a model; indeed, it is a concatenation of models. This elaborate yet elegant system has been constructed by long work and reflection. In so far as nature and our experience exhibit discreteness and multiplicity, arithmetic is a mirror of nature. It abstracts, and exhibits, an essential character of things. I have discussed the literal, semantic truth of arithmetic; certainly it also has the truth of verisimilitude. The test of this truth is the manifold applicability of our number concepts throughout the range of human concerns.

A model does not, *per se,* exist in the semantic dimension. But a system of axioms and theorems, bled of meaning in the sense in which the Peano axioms take the words "one," "number," and "successor" as undefined, remains a model in our sense. Because these words are undefined, the axioms and the theorems that follow from them are not statements but forms of statement. This is one reason why such constructions are called formal. Another reason for the label is that, because the key terms are bled of meaning, proofs that appeal to an intuition of meaning are no longer allowed. Proof must now be based on explicit rules that allow certain manipulations of written signs.

As I stated the Peano axioms, they were incompletely formalized because some words were still used in an ordinary intuitive way. A completely formalized system does not contain meaningful terms at all but only strings of marks, *formulas* (in the literal Latin, "little forms"). Only certain formulas are said to be well formed, while the rest are forbidden. Certain formulas are written down initially and are interpretable as axioms. There are rules, interpretable as rules of logic, that permit the transformation of given formulas into other formulas. The counterpart of a proof is a sequence of such transformations, starting with the initial formulas and terminating in a desired formula. It is this complete formalization that removes any possible ambiguity from the enumeration of statements and proofs in the theorem of Gödel. In calling such a system a model † I have in mind the variety and richness of its interpretations and applications. In its style and mode of precision it contrasts sharply with other things I have called models, with a novel or a myth. But it shares with these the role of a *speculum mundi.* The difference of style is a

---

† Logicians sometimes use the word "model" in a quite opposite sense—namely, for an interpreted axiom system that is, as interpreted, true.

difference in the aspect of things that is to be mirrored, I should say, and not in the function of mirroring.

The style of complete mathematical formalization has other consequences than the Gödel theorem, which was one of its earlier fruits. If the process of proof corresponds to a well-defined repetitive transformation of formulas into new formulas, the entire process is susceptible of mechanization by, for example, a computing machine. If every proof had to be discovered first and then translated into a machine program, the procedure would have little interest. For many classes of theorems, however, algorithms are known, uniform programs of proof by which any theorem of the class can be proved. We can imagine setting a machine so that it would systematically make all permitted transformations or so that it would try them out at random. But the number of steps involved grows at a fantastic rate. The failure to produce a given formula, even after a large number of steps, has no demonstrative value. It can be proved, moreover, that there are classes of problems for which no algorithms can be found. The existence or non-existence of algorithms thus becomes itself an important class of mathematical problems, called *decision problems*. We may quite possibly find algorithms that will permit machine proofs of mathematically important propositions that are now out of range. There is an alternative procedure, still largely unexplored and analogous to procedures of inductive inquiry (Chap. 9) and of biological evolution (Chap. 10), which may introduce explicitly random alternatives into the program of transformations.

Here we restrict ourselves to deterministic machines. Thanks to the work of Turing,† it is possible to describe computing machines rather simply and to show that any machine now built or contemplated can do no more (apart from practical matters of speed and efficiency) than the simple machine described by him. The essence of this machine is that it enters some one of a number of alternative marks, removing any mark that may have been there previously, in any of a sequence of squares on a tape. This tape runs through the machine and extends, as far as need be, on both sides. Initial marks correspond to axioms. After scanning, and entering a new mark, the machine shifts the tape one square leftward or rightward, whereupon the operation is repeated. The machine has to carry something from one operation to the next; it must be capable of entering some one of a set of alternative internal states at the end of each operation, its

---

† A. M. Turing, "On Computable Numbers with Application to the Entscheidungsproblem," *Proc. London Math. Soc.,* ser. 2, vol. 42 (1936–37), 230–65; correction in vol. 43 (1937), 544–46. There is by now a substantial literature on the theory of Turing machines; see Martin Davis, *Computability and Unsolvability* (New York, 1958).

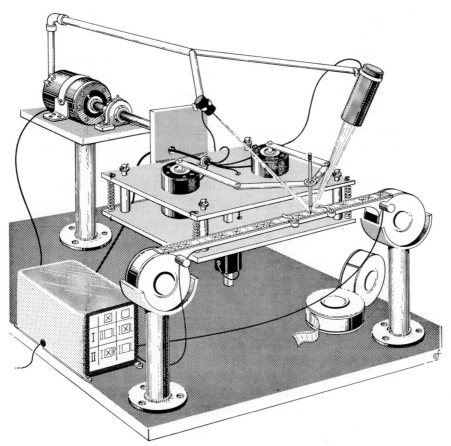

Fig. 4. A Possible Turing Machine

state determining how it responds to the mark it scans at the beginning of the next operation.

The rules of operation of the Turing machine are now defined by circuitry that has the following characteristics: For each mark, a_i, in its alphabet, and for each internal state, s_j, the machine replaces a_i by some specified a_k, goes into some specified state, s_l, and then shifts to the left or shifts to the right.

I shall have more to say about machines and machine behavior later on. I introduce them here because they provide a very extensive class of models, via the technique of complete formalization, for systems of logic and arithmetic and, indeed, for any deductive system that can be formalized. Machines do this through the ideal discreteness of their alternative letters and internal states and the multiplicity of their tape positions. This discreteness and this multiplicity permit us to arithmetize the theory of Turing machines—that is, to show that it corresponds to a part of the theory of arithmetic. This means that, in principle, a Turing machine can be set to define a Turing machine that will perform any type of computation for which there is an algorithm. This hierarchy, of models of theories and theories of models, suggests something essential in the implicit metaphysics of the new age of machine mathematics in which we find ourselves. A way of thought having far wider competence than could have been suspected in advance finds multiplicity and discreteness among its most primitive concepts, fundamental even to its logic. In this metaphysics the language of number is indeed a language of nature; but it is a far more ample kind of language than imagined by those who form their image of it from the rules and routines of school arithmetic.

Number Theory

In the view expressed in the previous pages, the number system is an artifact that both expresses and, in the process, embodies the number aspect of nature. As an artifact, however, it has, in a significant sense, an independent existence. Whenever men develop sufficiently elaborate instruments, these tend to become objects of interest in their own right. The means may outrun the ends, may even suggest new ends, so that invention becomes the mother of necessity. Number theory illustrates these remarks. Some of its lower branches have important applications, but many of its higher branches have so far found little application in the problems of science and engineering.

Since the time of Pythagoras, at least, numbers have been scrutinized from a point of view very different from that of our primitive fisherman. For the natural numbers turn out to have a kind of individuality and a complexity that are not obviously related to their mere ordinal position. If one looks at the Peano axioms, one sees only a sort of machine for producing number after number, in monotonous sequence. Yet, just because of their ordinal properties, the numbers are all unique individuals, and the system of numbers is infinite not only in extent but also in complexity of properties. Each additional number is a novelty, with additive and multiplicative properties that, in principle, no other number can have. It is this logical fact that gives to number theory its particular charm and difficulty.†

---

† There are many popular discussions and several good elementary texts. See the relevant parts of Richard Courant and Herbert Robbins, *What is Mathematics?* (New York, 1941). Among the elementary texts, J. V. Uspensky and M. A. Heazlit, *Elementary Number Theory* (New York, 1939), is very readable. The standard text in English is G. H. Hardy and E. M. Wright, *An Introduction to the Theory of Numbers* (New York, 1938 and later).

One may illustrate almost at random. In how many ways, for example, may a given number be written as a sum? One begins empirically, by counting. Except for the first few cases, however, the sums in question are laborious to enumerate. What, if anything, can be said about the value of this function for any arbitrary number? A little exploration will show that the problem is not completely simple.

The analogous operation, pertaining to factoring rather than partitioning, gives rise to a famous series of problems, some of which have never been solved. Whereas the number of partitions of n increases in a rapid and fairly regular way with increasing n, the number of factors of n is notoriously irregular. For the primes, in particular, it of course drops to two. This gives rise to the famous prime-number problem, that of estimating the number of primes less than any given number.

The common characteristic of all these problems is that they result from various sorts of classification of the numbers and from the attempt to enumerate the classes thus formed. The number system is both the subject matter of investigation and, at the same time, the means of carrying out the investigation.

It is in this connection that we must go beyond the formal, uninterpreted axioms of the number system. For proofs in number theory usually involve the counting of sets that are themselves sets of numbers. The uninterpreted axioms will give us the things to be counted, but not the means of counting them. The claim, sometimes made, that arithmetic can be deduced from the uninterpreted Peano axioms is true only of elementary arithmetic; it breaks down in number theory, in which the number system provides the means of describing its own properties.

This breakdown does not result from any inadequacy of the Peano axioms. Formalistically considered, theorems that enumerate classes of numbers are statements about the formal system in a metalanguage. The point is that the metalanguage must already contain the language of arithmetic as a means of talking about arithmetical properties of the uninterpreted system.

The observation above sharpens our general conclusion that the concepts of arithmetic are abstractions rather than arbitrary, formal inventions. It also, however, raises another question, one that gives point to the remark that the system of arithmetic transcends its origins in experience. The theorems of number theory imply the countability, the denumerability, of infinite classes of numbers, and this means that the techniques of investigation must go beyond the finite counting techniques of applied arithmetic. A simple example is Euclid's famous proof of the infinity of primes. The proof involves the discovery of a procedure by which, from a given prime, a larger one can always be found. If p is the given prime and $p!$ is its factorial (the product of p and all smaller numbers), then $p! + 1$ is either a prime or a product of primes greater than p. For, by definition, $p! + 1$ is not divisible by p or any lesser prime. Thus for every prime a larger prime can be found, and the theorem is proved.

The essential step in such a proof, of course, is the discovery of a recurrence. This does not depend upon the properties of any particular number and therefore supports an infinite chain of deductions, from each prime to the existence of another one. Generalizations derived by mathematical induction are, nevertheless, difficult to describe as reflecting the number aspects of nature. If the physical world is actually infinite, every number is exemplified—for example, by sets of protons. If the physical world is finite, there is a largest number exemplified by such sets. It can still be maintained, however, that every number is exemplified in *some* way. Suppose that only n protons exist. Then there is a larger set—namely, of *partitions* of the set of n protons (larger for $n \geq 5$). By induction it follows that every number is exemplified, even in a finite world.

But we cannot say that every deduction in arithmetic corresponds to some empirical exemplification, to some general fact of nature in *that* sense. The arithmetical infinity is not a given fact of physical reality, yet it is a reality; the rules of counting, abstracted from our dealings with nature, yield more than the experience that went into the abstraction of them. The system of number standards and of procedures for manipulating them has, therefore, the nature of a world that transcends our knowledge of it and even our conjectures about it: complex, surprising, and inexhaustible.

It is even possible—to illustrate the complexity of the system—that some of its properties are indemonstrable. It is plausible, and perhaps demonstrable, that certain traditional problems, or problems resembling traditional problems, are incapable of any solution. One example is the problem of finding the statistical frequency of digits in the decimal expansion of a specific irrational number, such as π or e or $\sqrt{2}$. Another is the problem of proving or disproving that, from a certain number on, the interval between a prime, p, and the next prime is always less than $(\log p)^2$. Such a problem appears to involve, in one's successive approximations to its solution, an amplification of the difficulties that enter into the argument at each step and whose cumulative effect forces one to stop short of the goal.

Such problems arise from the contrast between the necessarily finite character of mathematical proof and the infinity of the natural numbers. Consider, for example, the decimal expansion of $\pi = 3.1415926\ldots$ We know that this sequence is non-terminating and non-periodic. It ought to be possible to prove or disprove the following statement: There is some function, $k(n)$, that approaches 0 with increasing n but that nevertheless bounds the difference between $1/10$ and the proportion of 7's among the first n digits of the expansion above; that is, the proportion of 7's approaches $1/10$ as a limit. If such a function exists, it defines a property of every integer n. Assuming that this property held for n, we could prove that it held for $n + 1$. But it is possible that there might be no general method of proof, and in this case we could never appeal to Peano's fifth axiom to establish the theorem. A proof by mathematical induction allows us to collapse an infinite sequence of steps into a finite sequence because, after some point, the infinite sequence of steps remaining is a sequence of identical steps, and we can make them in one. The Gödel theorem excludes this possibility; it involves, indeed, a property of every integer, but defined in such a way that an inductive argument is impossible. Whether any of the classical unsolved problems exclude it we do not now know.

The situation resembles, formally, the attempt to predict the behavior of deterministic physical mechanisms of the sort used in gambling; we finally abandon such attempts in favor of statistical arguments based on probability.†
The world of number is rich enough to exhibit statistical lawfulness and even a kind of logical indeterminacy. The simplest infinity is not simple.

---

† Compare David Hawkins, "On Mathematical Sieves," *Scientific American,* December, 1958. See also the third section of Chap. 8.

2

GEOMETRY

In the first chapter I tried to set forth something of the nature and origin of arithmetic. My claim was that the arithmetical foundation of mathematics is a genuine, although unique, kind of knowledge about the nature of things. Its uniqueness, which it shares with the growing system of logic into which it has finally been absorbed, is the analytic character of arithmetical truth. Modern philosophy has been increasingly committed to the belief that because of this analytic character, and because of its assimilation within logic, arithmetic is somehow a vast tautology, a body of propositions about nothing at all except some sort of self-created conceptual or linguistic universe. I regard this belief as mistaken, although plausible and rather firmly established.

Geometry, like arithmetic, is a system of ideas the rudiments of which are implicit in common thought and language; the propositions of geometry, like those of arithmetic, are almost equally hard to interpret as statements of external, contingent fact. The older pedagogical tradition of geometry, successfully challenged in the last century or so, held that the propositions of geometry are derived from clear, self-evident truth. The problem here parallels that of Chapter 1, but a discussion of it will throw new light on the nature of mathematical truth.

The Elements

As we turn to the discussion of geometry and the nature of geometrical truth, the issues, although not simple, appear easier to formulate and possibly easier to resolve. One of the great developments in the philosophy of geometry was Kant's analysis of its foundations in the eighteenth century. This analysis was guided by the belief that geometry, as a science, owed nothing essential to the findings of experience but was, instead, an explication of the form in which the mind ordered its experience. Geometrical form was not abstracted, but imposed. A major tendency in later philosophy, partly due to Kant, is one we have already briefly discussed—conventionalism.

This tendency was powerfully assisted by the discovery of the non-Euclidean geometries. If one had to decide, while there were no firm empirical criteria for a decision, which of these geometries was the true one, one was led to the conclusion that the difference among geometries, all equally capable of providing a framework for the description of physical phenomena, was conventional. During the nineteenth century a great variety of geometrical systems was developed. Out of this variety arose a kind of taxonomy, the unifying concept of which was geometrical invariance with respect to groups of transformations.

These purely mathematical developments, though there is no direct connection between them and questions about the nature of geometrical truth, provided very powerful tools by means of which one could classify the properties of a geometrical system into those that remained unaltered under the transformations of a given group and those that altered with such transformations. If, in facing a particular application of geometry, one could define a group of transformations among alternative geometrical descriptions, each of which was correct and among which one had no reason for accepting one and rejecting the others, then the essential content of the descriptions was the same and was defined by the invariants of the group. This identification of invariance with reality is reminiscent of ancient metaphysical doctrine (in the Greek tradition stated by Parmenides and much examined by Plato), according to which the real is what is unchanging. Here, however, the invariant was not necessarily what was unchanging through time but what was unaltered by a change in descriptions from one standpoint or means of description to another.

The concept of invariance is a geometric-algebraic extension of the concept of equivalence class and, like the latter, enables us to make formal definitions by abstraction. I shall discuss the meaning of invariance in some detail below, following the discussions of Kantian philosophy and conventionalism.

At the end of the previous chapter I discussed briefly the characteristics of one branch of mathematics that has grown out of arithmetic—higher arithmetic, or number theory. At the close of the present chapter I mention a few specific applications of arithmetical arguments to problems of spatial organization. In the previous chapter we were concerned with the nature of arithmetical truth *per se;* here we shall examine some of the ways in which the physical properties of things may be shown to depend upon the properties of numbers.

The primary abstraction of arithmetic is that of the set of discrete objects; of geometry, that of spatial form. In place of the primitive fisherman, who must match fish against those who are going to eat them, we consider the primitive builder, who must match the length of a roof beam against the span between the walls to be roofed. The first step, as with number, is the development of standards facilitating comparisons at a distance. When the beam is heavy and has to be cut on the hillside above the village, the builder discovers the advantage of a long "rod, perch, or pole" that can be matched against the span to be covered and then carried uphill to mark the beam to be cut. Again we note the transitivity of the matching relation, but with a new kind of matching, which we call congruence.

To avoid for a moment the introduction of units, we may suppose that the builder acquires a whole set of rods, analogous to the fisherman's string standards; like cardinal number, the attribute of length may be discussed in terms of such standards, independently of any process of ordering or counting. A second step continues the analogy: given lengths may be ordered as may the number properties, although there is no known natural unit analogous to the discrete object in arithmetic. Unless an indivisible quantum of length is someday found, arithmetization will enter geometry only with some process of marking. Marking replicates some given length and thus introduces discreteness into the continuum of lengths. The foot replaces the pile of rods. An economy of standards is achieved, and there is an axiom of completeness analogous to that of ordinal number: every length can be matched—approximately—by some number of replications of a unit length. The elaboration of the adverb here leads to the development, which I postpone, of the real number system.

The ordering of spatial magnitudes is more complex than that of natural numbers because of the three-dimensional character of space; spatial magnitudes have direction as well as measure, and in addition to lengths there are areas and volumes to be considered.

Euclidean geometry is the systematic explication of the relations among spatial magnitudes. It has the distinction, historically, of being the first science cast into axiomatic form and of standing therefore as the model and inspiration of all later attempts at the rational ordering of knowledge, not only in the sciences but even in such fields as law, ethics, and theology. Not only so: more than any other intellectual achievement, geometry has seemed to lead to a most important and surprising conclusion, around which a considerable amount of philosophical controversy has been carried on since the time of the Greeks. The thesis of this conclusion is that, when a rational organization of our knowledge has been achieved, transcending the looseness and vagueness of commonsense belief, its grasp of reality extends far beyond the limitations of sense experience and into the very essence of things. The same thesis has been defended, as I pointed out earlier, in connection with the study of arithmetic; but geometry supports it more vividly. It is the thesis of what has come to be called rationalism: the details of our knowledge we owe, of course, to sense experience, but there is a kind of knowledge, abstract and general, that is prior to experience and that we need even in order to learn from experience.

The modern axiomatization of Euclidean geometry makes explicit a number of axioms that were not stated by Euclid. There are so many axioms, in fact, that they cannot all be listed and elucidated in this chapter. Three classes of elements are assumed: points, lines, and planes. These elements are related in several ways, notably by incidence, order, continuity, and congruence. The geometrical conception of order, both on account of the dimensionality of space and because of continuity, is more complex than the arithmetical. There is nothing in geometry comparable to the simple notion "successor"; the fundamental order relation, instead, is the three-term relation, holding of points, called "betweenness." Incidence is a two-term relation holding between points and lines or between points and planes. It is possible, in terms of the axioms of incidence and order, to define the idea "interval" and to define angles and distinguish them from their complements and supplements. The axioms of congruence for angles and intervals define an equivalence relation and equivalence classes of both. Axioms of continuity, finally, render intervals divisible into arbitrary congruent subintervals, assert the commensurability of all intervals, and give meaning to the idea "neighborhood."

It is also necessary to state the equivalent of Euclid's famous fifth postulate, the postulate of parallels. The sketch I have given is based on Hilbert's formulation of the axioms.† Without the axiom of parallels this geometry is called pan-geometry, and pan-geometry is consistent also with alternatives to the axiom of parallels—alternatives that form the basis of the non-Euclidean geometries. Under a suitably generalized definition of distance these geometries become simply sub-species of projective geometry.

---

† David Hilbert, *The Foundations of Geometry* (La Salle, Illinois, 1902 and 1938); these editions are translations of the sixth and seventh editions of *Grundlagen der Geometrie.*

If the geometrical axioms are regarded as uninterpreted, it may be possible to find new interpretations, quite remote from the intuitive geometric meanings, for the primitive terms. An interesting example, satisfying the incidence axioms of projective geometry and giving rise to still unsolved problems in number theory, is provided by the so-called finite geometries.† If letters represent points and rows represent lines, every two lines determine a point, and every two points determine a line, in the following rectangular array:

$$a \quad b \quad c$$
$$a \quad d \quad e$$
$$a \quad f \quad g$$
$$b \quad d \quad g$$
$$b \quad f \quad e$$
$$c \quad d \quad f$$
$$c \quad e \quad g$$

For every two rows have one letter in common, and every two letters determine one row. Three points not on the same line define a triangle. Thus a, b, and d define the triangle

$$a \quad b \quad c$$
$$b \quad d \quad g$$
$$a \quad d \quad e$$

and we see, also, that the line defined by $c\,e$, which intersects the lines $a\,b\,c$ and $a\,d\,e$, also intersects the other line, $b\,d\,g$. A more familiar representation is seen in Figure 5. This is a theorem, or, more properly, an axiom, of projective geometry (in which Euclidean parallels, if they have to be dealt with, are said to meet in the point of infinity).

We can say, in the terms of physical geometry, that spatial orderings exemplify properties that are also exemplified in non-spatial orderings. But even when points, lines, and planes are given their customary interpretations, a peculiar difficulty about the axiom of parallels remains, a difficulty related both to the development of modern physics and to modern discussions of the theory of knowledge.

So far as Euclidean geometry is concerned, its distinguishing property connected with the axiom of parallels is its scale independence: the features of spatial ordering that it studies are supposed to be independent of size. This

---

† There is an extensive literature on finite geometries. See H. F. MacNeish, "Four Finite Geometries," *Amer. Math. Monthly,* vol. 49 (1942), pp. 15–23.

proposition is, of course, immediately involved in the astronomical uses of geometry, for these extend the concept of length or distance from one obtainable by direct measurement to one that depends upon the proportionality of corresponding parts of similar figures.

Scale independence is equivalent to the axiom of parallels. The non-Euclidean geometries of N. I. Lobachevski and G. F. B. Riemann are based upon postulates alternative to that of parallels and

Fig. 5. Theorem in Projective Geometry

involve the appearance of a parameter called the Gaussian curvature. The significance of this parameter is that it represents a weakening of the concept of scale independence; though certain theorems that do not depend on the postulate of parallels (theorems of pan-geometry) are true independently of scale, theorems on similar figures lose their normal meaning, for in these systems figures are not similar unless they are congruent.

Euclidean geometry retains a special significance in these geometries of curved space; it is included in them as the limiting case of zero curvature, and its theorems remain approximately true in them for sufficiently small figures. The development of these geometries, then, though inaugurating a profound revolution in the whole subject and in its philosophical interpretation, may be thought of as a natural extension and completion of the tradition of Euclid. Historically, the revolution began with renewed attack on an unsolved problem of the Greeks: whether the fifth postulate might not, after all, turn out to be

Fig. 6. Non-Euclidean Spaces

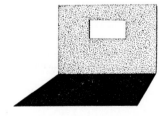

a theorem rather than an independent postulate. It was initiated by Saccheri†
in an attempt to prove the postulate of parallels by *reductio ad absurdum*—
that is, by assuming its falsity and showing that this assumption led to a
contradiction. The desired proof failed, and in the end the non-Euclidean
geometries were shown to be just as self-consistent as Euclidean geometry.

The question of geometrical truth is different from that of arithmetical truth
in that the propositions of geometry are no part of formal logic. The obvious
alternative is that geometry is a kind of physical science, no less empirical in
its foundations than mechanics or the theory of elasticity, although more abstract and general. The geometrical concepts of point and line, plane and
solid, and of the various measures related to these, are idealizations of the
familiar features of objects and their spatial orderings, and the propositions
involving them are empirically verifiable to a high order of approximation.

This view has not, however, been universally accepted. Kant,‡ in the eighteenth century, proposed an interpretation that repudiated the then conventional
notion of self-evident truth without adopting the alternative view of geometry
as empirical science.

Kant and the Forms of Intuition

The main problem in Kant's analysis of knowledge was the existence, as
he believed, of a body of general knowledge that was inextricably involved
with the description of our experience but did not, in any obvious way, owe
its validity to the findings of experience. In his own terminology such knowledge was *a priori*—that is, known to be true independently of empirical fact—
yet synthetic, making assertions beyond the bare elucidation of the meanings

---

† In *Euclides ab omni naevo vindicatus*, Girolamo Saccheri (1667–1733) investigated a quadrilateral formed by two equal line segments, *AC* and *BD*, perpendicular to the given base *AB*. From
the assumption that the angles *ACD* and *BDC* are unequal to right angles he tried to arrive at a
contradiction. In the nineteenth century K. F. Gauss, János Bolyai, and N. I. Lobachevski formulated
the geometry called hyperbolic, in which through a point not on a line there is more than one
line parallel to the line. In this geometry the sum of the angles of a triangle is less than a straight
angle, and the angles in Saccheri's quadrilateral are acute. Riemann developed the first elliptic
geometry in mid-century and Felix Klein, later in the century, a second. In these two geometries
there are no parallels to a line, and every line is endless but finite, like the circle. In Riemann's
geometry every pair of lines in the plane intersect in two points, like the great circles on a sphere;
in Klein's geometry they intersect in one point. In both these geometries the sum of the interior
angles of a triangle is greater than a straight angle, and the angles of the Saccheri quadrilateral
are obtuse. See Fig. 6.

‡ Immanuel Kant, *Critique of Pure Reason,* especially "Introduction," V; "The Transcendental
Esthetic," Section I; and "The Transcendental Analytic," Book II, Chap. II.

of our concepts. Our experience of the physical world, in particular, involves, in our perceptions, an orderliness and a reproducibility without which such experience could not be distinguished from fantasy or hallucination. The concepts of space and time were related to the ways in which we order our perceptions of the physical world; they were required by, rather than learned from, such perceptions.

For Kant, therefore, geometry was not an empirical science; it was, rather, an elucidation of the ways in which the mind synthesized information provided by the senses into a systematic and organized perception of nature. The truth of geometry was not a grasp of the ultimate order of reality (in Kant's language, was not transcendent of experience) but was, rather, its faithfulness to the mind's ways of ordering sense impressions. Kant called such truth transcendental, lying beyond the scope and relevance of specific experience. To use a suggestive if somewhat vulgar analogy, Kant conceived the mind as a kind of decoding machine, which received the messages (themselves no more than dots and dashes)† taken from the incoming channels of the senses and translated them into the orderly patterns of intuition and conception that constituted our perception of the source, of nature. Our knowledge of the truth of geometry was, so to speak, an internal affair of the mind, a replication at the conceptual level of its own intuitive way of organizing experience. It was not *a priori* certain, however, that our experience could be successfully organized in the patterns of Euclidean three-dimensional space plus time, and beliefs about the orderings of specific objects and events were, at most, empirically verifiable. But for Kant the alternative to failure would not have been the ordering of physical phenomena according to some different set of principles, for this would have implied that we first perceived things and events as physical and only then investigated their spatial relations. Kant would have said, rather, that the ordering of our sensations according to spatio-temporal patterns was what constituted them, in the first place, as perceptions rather than as mere sensation. What perception presupposed in any local situation of experience, moreover, conception required on a global scale. We linked together our various perceptual spaces, whose contents varied from person to person and from time to time, as parts of one public spatio-temporal order, singular and infinite. This order was empirically real so far as we did success-

---

† In spite of the vulgarity the analogy is not bad. Kant said very little to clarify what he meant by "sense manifold"; but it was what perception organized. It lacked organization, and it lacked the unity that *con*sciousness bestows. Like chaos in the myths, it was defined privatively.

fully synthesize our experience by means of it; but as ultimate, metaphysical reality it was illusory.

Kant's attempt to establish the *a priori* necessity and universality of our spatial intuition and of the geometry abstracted from it was part of a general theory of knowledge. In opposition to certain empiricistic accounts of knowledge, Kant wanted to maintain the rationalistic emphasis upon the role of reason; and, in opposition to the rationalistic accounts of knowledge, he wanted to maintain the necessity of sense experience as the only final test of belief. Knowledge was an artifact: sensation provided the raw material, and reason shaped it. Given the artificer and his style of operation, knowledge was determined by sense experience. Given the sense experience, knowledge was determined by the artificer in patterns of his own origination. In the necessity and universality of mathematics Kant thought he saw the telltale mark of its mind-dependent origin.

But there is no absolute separation of matter and form, of material and style. If we take this statement seriously, we cannot accept Kant's distinctions without softening or relativizing them, without thereby raising again the very doubts that Kant thought he had settled. Style must be appropriate to its material; style evolves through work. A particular work of art is the product of the artist, but on a longer time scale the artist himself is a product of his work. If we concede so much, it is no longer clear either that geometry owes nothing to sense experience or that the geometrical truths that seem self-evident at one stage cannot be questioned and reshaped in response to the demands of further experience.

The contrast of form and matter is misleading if it implies that sensory information can be molded in perfectly arbitrary patterns. It is notorious that our way of perceiving and of describing what we perceive is highly selective and is affected by many sorts of conditions. It becomes possible to say, with some plausibility, that we fashion our perceptions in a way that conforms to wish and preconception. Kant did not say this, for he was not concerned with idiosyncrasy; the transcendental character of the *a priori* forms of spatial intuition was, for him, characteristic of the human mind. But a wing of Kantianism could and did go that way. Once the principle was established that the forms of perception—and by extension the forms of belief—were mind-dependent and not determined by the intrinsic character of things perceived, it was only necessary to add that these forms were themselves functions of psycho- and socio-dynamic development, and one went from Kantianism to all the varieties of subjectivism, relativism, and cultural determinism that have at once plagued and enriched modern philosophical thought.†

And yet the point of departure for all this, the form-matter dichotomy, is radically suspect. We can just as well say—indeed, we can much more intelligibly say—that the matter of perception—sensation in its *de facto* qualitative variety—is mind-dependent and that the form is transferred from without. In a language that I shall elaborate later, our perception is *informed* by what we call its object. But this *information* is not instantaneous. A single perception occurs within a context, and only in that context does it have meaning as perception. The context is itself historically determined; it is a function of psychodynamic, sociodynamic, and biodynamic development, and its beginnings are ancient. In its most variable elements, this context is a precipitate of antecedent perceptual experience; in its least variable, of biological evolution.

Involved in all this is a principle that makes radical subjectivism and radical relativism unintelligible. Processes of information require what communications engineers call the matching of information source with information receptor. Without going into technical meanings at this point, I give a simple illustrative analogy. A message is first encoded for transmission, then transmitted, and finally decoded. The decoding operation is the inverse of the encoding operation. Radical relativism is the belief, I suppose, that one mind's codebook has no necessary resemblance to nature's or to that of another mind. The messages it constructs, the patterns it purportedly discovers, are shaped to suit its own needs or wishes rather than to fit the nature of things. Error and distortion are, of course, real enough. But these do not support the radical relativist's contentions, for they can be defined only as exceptions to a rule, which says that judgment does not err and perception is not distorted. A closer look at the communication analogy supports common sense and undermines the relativist's account. Two important facts emerge.

The first fact is that the set of possible messages from nature is much larger than the set that nature actually uses. This is demonstrated by the ease with which, in artificial laboratory situations, perception can be disoriented and judgment misguided. Such situations transmit to the subject message com-

---

† For the most persuasive non-Spenglerian statement of cultural determinism in mathematics see Leslie A. White, "The Locus of Mathematical Reality: An Anthropological Footnote," *Philosophy of Science,* October 1947, or in James R. Newman, *The World of Mathematics* (New York, 1956), pp. 2348–64. I agree with much that White says but not with the main point: that human culture is the locus of mathematical reality. Culture is likewise, and likewise is not, the locus of astronomical reality. No culture has ever been uninformed by the nature of the world.

binations that we describe as abnormal, contradictory, or confusing. Illusion and error result when the abnormalities of the stimulus are not great; when the degree of abnormality increases, however, the result is confusion and disorientation. The codebook does not translate all possible messages; it translates only a small but important subset—those that it is nature's habit, in our milieu, to provide.

The second important fact about the analogy of communication, which relativists overlook, is that the channels of communication are always noisy and that the noise has to be filtered out in one way or another. A single original message is received as any one of a variety. Perception and judgment must manage to ignore the accidental differences among this variety, to abstract the common pattern, the *Gestalt*. Error is avoided when the variety, the cluster of messages that may be received instead of the single transmitted message, is readily distinguished from any other such cluster, coming from a different initial message. In perception and judgment this means that the mind's way of grouping the incoming signals must be such that it mainly ignores the differences originating in the noisy channels, but not those originating in the stable variety of the environment. If the groupings were arbitrary rather than adaptive, nothing, literally, would be received—except noise.

For these reasons there are quantitative as well as qualitative conditions affecting the flow of information. Variety and uncertainty cannot be eliminated; but, the more arbitrary the decoding operation becomes, the less information is received. The raw incoming signals must be grouped and analyzed and interpreted, for they do not bring the codebook with them, and there are different ways of carrying out those operations; but it is wrong to say that the different ways are equally valid. One transfers a greater quantity of information than another. Human beings can, indeed, be dominated by rigid patterns of perception and categories of thought, can be shaped by psychogenic causes beyond the control of experience. But as these fail to match the patterns and categories of reality, they prevent discrimination and thus reduce the gain of information. A completely arbitrary framework of perception and knowledge may, indeed, appear possible; but its existence is inconsistent with either perception or knowledge. A mind so constituted would be the mind of a catatonic.

The analogy of communication fails, of course, in the end. We cannot directly compare notes with nature in the matter of codebooks. The codebooks that we possess (or that we are) are products of the long history referred to above. It is good that the analogy fails at this point, for the failure prevents a dilemma. We imagine someone looking at a transmitted message and at the received message and independently comparing them. When we carry the analogy over, we have to imagine a Perceiver who perceives things as they really are and compares them with things as humanly perceived. Kant called this fictitious capacity "intellectual intuition" and its object "the thing in itself." Such intuition might be imputed to God, but not to man. Men perceived through the pulsed code of the senses, and then only by means of their own mind-dependent codebooks.

Kant was no relativist; but his analysis is an open invitation to relativism in a different age and intellectual climate. My criticism of the way of thought that is common to Kant and the relativist is that it arises from a broken-down analogy. Perception is not perception of a received—mental—object problematically related to a real object that we do *not* perceive. The proper counterpart to the received message in communication is not the *object* of perception, but the perception itself, the psychological act—whose object is, precisely, the physical object of perception! The decoding operation involves, to be sure, the apparatus that Kant designated as synthesis in intuition within spatio-temporal forms of perception. But nature *has* given us the codebook—not once and for all, but through a long evolutionary history. And the codebook *must* give, at least in a first approximation, the inverse of nature's encoding operations. Distortion and error are real, but they are real only as deviations and perturbations of the process of perception, a process that would not occur at all if there were a total mismatch between nature's encoding and our decoding.

This remark applies with particular force to Kant's original problem about the nature of our spatial perceptions. Our three-dimensional and more or less Euclidean ordering of perceptions is, indeed, a kind of stereotyping; but it would be disastrously uninformative except in the perception of a world that was stably three-dimensional and more or less Euclidean in its intrinsic spatial order. By clever manipulation of the sensory input one can provide stimulus patterns that are highly unlikely to originate spontaneously in such a world. As I said above, the typical result is disorientation and confusion. The sensory channels are too well matched to the normal message source to allow any consistent decoding of message sequences that violate the basic customs of nature.

Kant was right, then, in asserting that *particular* perceptions do not carry with them the full scheme of spatial and temporal order by means of which we credit them as veridical perceptions of physical reality. There is, indeed, a very elaborate kind of synthesis that I have compared to decoding. But Kant was wrong in supposing that perceptual reality is therefore a constructed reality having only a problematic relation to things in themselves. The relation between matter and form in perception is not one between two completely independent components somehow magically fused. It is, rather, the relation between a statistical sample and the universe of which it is a sample, or, more properly, the relation between a small sample currently being collected and a much larger—but in principle incomplete—sample accumulated and summarized from past history. The general forms of perception are independent of the particular sensory input, and it is only through them that input is transformed into acts of perception; but these forms have been abstracted from antecedent sensory input. Only so are mind and nature matched, and only through that matching is there any perception at all.

It is thus true that our forms of perception are bio- and socio- and psychodynamically determined; but the development is not arbitrary, may not go this way or that. Variation of the patterns may be biological or social or psychological in origin. We cannot have wide variety and claim, at the same time, that all varieties are equally good. Aberrant forms of perception are aberrant in that they reduce discrimination and render an increasing part of the potential information indistinguishable from mere noise.

Conventionalism

A rather easy line of descent goes from Kant to conventionalism, which can make a somewhat more plausible case in geometry than in arithmetic. The case is more plausible because, even within the usual interpretation of the geometrical elements and relations, alternative geometries are possible. This possibility is connected with the way in which the congruence axioms are interpreted, and that, in turn, affects the truth or falsity of the axiom of parallels. The simplest way to demonstrate this possibility is to map a Euclidean three-dimensional space into a non-Euclidean space and then to assume that congruence is defined in the latter by measuring rods that *change* under displacements and rotations exactly as they would change if they were images of rigid rods in the original Euclidean space. There is then a perfect isomorphism between the two systems.

It is sometimes forgotten that, in making such transformations, one must transform everything, including the statement of the laws of physics and the facts of cosmography, and that there is, therefore, in a strict sense, no difference between the two systems. According to a famous principle enunciated by Leibniz, God himself would not have to say which of these two worlds exists, for there is no difference between them by which they could be distinguished; they are identical, and only the labels are different.†

Leibniz's principle states that two alternatives, if they are not distinguishable, are identical. But "distinguishable" here does not mean distinguishable in practice or in the present state of knowledge; it means ultimately, in principle, distinguishable. In this sense we can, ultimately and in principle, determine whether the sum of the interior angles of an optical triangle is 180° or not. If it turned out that this sum was less than 180°, we should still have the option of changing the laws of optics in such a way that the sides of such a triangle were not straight but had just the right curvature to restore the Euclidean theorem. "Straight" lines could no longer be identified with optical rays. In the general theory of relativity Einstein adopted the opposite compensation, a non-Euclidean geometry that would maintain the constancy of length of a rigid rod despite changes in the gravitational field.

We see that two questions are involved here: (1) whether Euclidean geometry, applied under *given* conventions of measurement, describes the metrical relations of space correctly; (2) whether it is possible to shift from one geometry to another with *compensating* changes in the conventions of measurement. One may doubt whether this distinction is as simple and clear-cut as it appears. The projections of one space into another may be trouble-free for small regions of space, but there *are* differences between them. We may say that these differences are merely apparent, are due to inessential differences in the manner of description; but they could always acquire physical meaning through new laws or new cosmographic facts, and then the spaces would no longer be indistinguishable. In a spherical geometry, for example, parallel lines meet in two points at a finite distance, and light rays emitted from one point converge at another, antipodal, point. By a suitable reformulation of physical laws and metrical rules we can regard space as spherical, but it then becomes a real possibility that every galaxy can be seen twice, in opposite directions.

---

† The best discussion in Leibniz's fragmentary writings is "Zur Analyse der Lage," in *Leibnizens mathematische Schriften* (Berlin, 1948–63), vol. 5, p. 178, translated by Leroy E. Loemker, in *Gottfried Wilhelm von Leibniz: Philosophical Papers and Letters* (Chicago, 1956), vol. 1, pp. 390–96, as "On Analysis Situs." This is the mathematical basis. For the applications see Leibniz's correspondence with Samuel Clarke in H. G. Alexander, *The Leibniz-Clarke Correspondence* (Manchester, 1956) (also in Loemker, *op. cit.,* vol. 2, pp. 1095–1169): Letter III, 2–6; Letter IV, 3–6; Letter V, 21–29, 47, 52, 55–60. The story of Princess Sophia (IV, 4) has an extraordinary flavor of philosophic insight and arithmetical innocence.

Fig. 7. "Circle Limit I": A Poincaré World? [*From* The Graphic Work of M.C.E. (*Oldbourne Press, London*) *with the permission of the artist, M. C. Escher*]

Poincaré, in one of his famous models,† postulated the existence of a finite spherical world in which rigid bodies shrink as they move toward the periphery. With suitable specifications of detail this universe, which we describe as finite and Euclidean, would appear to its inhabitants to be infinite and to have non-Euclidean geometry. But, although we may stipulate that the inhabitants can never, because of shrinkage, reach the boundaries of their world, we can *only* stipulate that the existence of a boundary in the one model and its non-existence in the other should be inessential. If we are describing a real world (and not just a stipulated one) and can give *some* meaning, physically, to the

---

† The classic discussion is to be found in Henri Poincaré, *The Foundations of Science* (Lancaster, Penn., 1946). See also his article "Geometry and Space," newly translated and appearing in *Philosophy of Science,* edited by Arthur Danto and Sidney Morgenbesser (Cleveland and New York, 1960); this contains a brief account of the model in question.

existence of a boundary to it, how can we, at the same time, be sure that its inhabitants are not smart enough to find that boundary? Our model is more inclusive than theirs, and at some point our ability to give meaning to spatial relations outside their sphere may become involved in the formulation of the laws of their sphere. If this happens, the isomorphism between our description and theirs breaks down, and the two no longer satisfy the condition of Leibniz's principle.

Conventions in geometry may be changed for reasons of convenience, but with the growth of knowledge a choice at one time conventional may be found, at a later time, to involve differences that can no longer be regarded as inessential. As we shall see later in connection with the idea of invariance, a judgment to the effect that two descriptions of phenomena differ in no significant way is always, itself, a judgment subject to the test of experience. Leibniz's principle is an elegant and important one, but its application in any particular case rests upon a hypothesis. For we may say that two alternatives that we *do* distinguish are *not* distinguishable only if we also say that the distinguishing terms we use are irrelevant, in their differences, to the character of the things we are describing.

The virtue of conventionalism is that it reminds us, at any particular stage of knowledge, that alternative ways of describing things are all adequate to what we know at that stage. When this view becomes a dogma of indifference, when it asserts that qualitative differences between one geometry and another cannot have empirical significance, it becomes a kind of mindless Kantianism.†

The view set forth here is that physical geometry is neither a system of self-evident truths legislating for the universe, as some philosophers may have thought, nor an explication of mind-dependent forms of perception, independent, as such, of any empirical tests. It is, rather, a part of our empirically tested and testable knowledge of nature; but it has, in the description of nature, a special role and a special kind of priority. Spatial properties are involved in any demonstrative reference to physical realities, and Kant was right in saying that we do not identify phenomena as physical except in consequence of their spatial ordering. We do not first identify things as physical and only afterward find that they have spatial location. But metric geometry cannot be derived, as Kant supposed, from our "*a priori* forms of intuition." Its theorems can be

---

† An excellent review of the long controversy over the conventionalistic interpretation of the axiom of parallels is to be found in a paper by Adolf Grünbaum, "Conventionalism in Geometry," in *The Axiomatic Method*, a symposium (Amsterdam, 1959). An extensive work that may be consulted is Hans Reichenbach, *The Philosophy of Space and Time* (New York, 1957); selections from it are found in Danto and Morgenbesser, *op cit*

tested with high precision under the given conventions of measurement, and these conventions themselves rest upon judgments that the growth of knowledge may confirm or cast into doubt.

Geometry is involved in the description of natural phenomena of all kinds, from the minutest to the grandest, and in the formulation of physical laws at all levels, from the lowest to the highest. It is indifferent—as the more physical abstractions, such as the facts of charge or mass, never are—to mere change of scale. (I shall have to qualify this statement, in the end, in view of relativity theory, but at some levels it is still correct.) The geometrical abstractions have a blandness, an indifference, a lack of coupling with the qualitative and decisive physical characteristics of things—characteristics that are always strongly size-dependent. Lilliputians and Brobdingnagians are geometrically possible but not physically possible. In this respect, indeed, the abstractions of geometry resemble those of arithmetic—as generically involved in all our more particular knowledge of nature, and therefore as removed from the *kind* of empirical status of, let us say, paleobotany or biochemistry. Epistemologically, the essential difference between the status of arithmetic and that of geometry is the connection of arithmetic with the structure and function of language, and the consequent inclusion of its axioms within the formal system of logic.

Analytic Geometry

One of the great modern innovations in geometry is the algebraic representation of it, invented by Pierre de Fermat and René Descartes. It is worth mentioning, at the outset, that the terms "analytic" and "synthetic," applied to this topic, give a somewhat misleading sense of the contrast between the classical and the Cartesian approach to geometry. Analysis is the process of constructing a chain of argument backward from conclusion to premises, whereas synthesis is the process of working forward from premises to conclusion. The usual expository, textbook order is synthetic; the process of discovery is usually analytic. Greek geometry, no less than modern, was both analytic and synthetic. Algebra, however, is analytic in a special sense: it characterizes the unknown as if it were known and works backward by routine manipulations. Descartes' geometry was analytic in this sense, for it provided a dictionary by which geometrical problems could be translated into algebraic ones.

We shall explore two of the consequences of this innovation, which have led far beyond the province of geometry. The first and more important is the discipline of mathematical analysis, the subject matter of the next chapter.

The second is the profoundly important concept of geometrical invariance, which will be discussed in the next section. The innovation also throws light upon the nature of geometrical truth. The axioms of Euclidean geometry may be interpreted in terms of algebraic relations holding among ordered triples of real numbers, and they then become true propositions of a branch of arithmetic dealing with vectors defined as ordered sets of real numbers.

Geometry, then, as far as its purely mathematical side is concerned, may be thought of simply as a branch of modern mathematics, beginning with arithmetic and having no independent status. But this judgment does not affect the status of geometrical axioms interpreted physically. Not only may the physical geometry we use be interpreted algebraically (it is true in this sense), but so may all sorts of radically incompatible geometries, and in this sense they are equally true. And, even if our geometry were physically false, this would not affect its isomorphism with a part of arithmetic. What such isomorphism signifies is, to speak of it once more, the vast richness of the number system, which may mirror within itself not only the actual geometrical order of things but alternative geometries, other worlds, as well.

The Erlangen Program

Essential to the Cartesian representation of geometrical form is the use of a coordinate system to which measurements of position are referred. This has the effect, in physical applications, of introducing, in place of the points and lines of synthetic geometry, numbers specifying these by their relations to other, standard points and lines in the coordinate system. The association of points with number triples is possible only for a given frame of reference, yet the choice of such a frame is arbitrary. Hence any property of the system under consideration must be described by means of coordinates but must depend on them only in an inessential way. In the language of Leibniz, two representations that are different are nevertheless indistinguishable. In Euclidean geometry, for example, linear transformations that represent parallel displacements, rotations, or reflections will leave unaltered all the expressions that correspond to properties of spatial figures. Thus the distance between two points whose coordinates are (x_1, y_1, z_1) and (x_2, y_2, z_2), given by the expression

$$\sqrt{(x_1 - x_2)^2 + (y_1 - y_2)^2 + (z_1 - z_2)^2}$$

remains unchanged under the linear transformations mentioned above. The same is true for the analytic expression of the angle between two lines, for the classification of quadratic equations into different types of conic sections, for axes and foci of such sections, etc. The congruence of two geometrical figures is expressed by the equivalence of their defining equations under these same transformations.

Each linear transformation is said to transform space into itself. The set of all such transformations is a *group*. A set of transformations is a group if the successive performance of any two transformations in the set is a transformation in the set, and if the inverse of any transformation in the set is also in the set.

The importance of the group property (which the set of translations, rotations, and reflections in the plane, or in three-dimensional space, possesses) is that it guarantees, for the transformations under consideration, that they constitute a closed logical universe. The invariants with respect to transformations of a given group may then be held to characterize, not the individual transformations alone, but their group.

Felix Klein, in his dissertation of 1872, proposed for geometry a thoroughgoing re-examination based on these ideas, a re-examination that he called the Erlangen Program after the name of his university.† Its purpose was to find the invariants corresponding to a given group of geometrical transformations. He was able, within a single taxonomic scheme, to unify metric geometry, affine geometry, projective geometry, and what we now call point-set topology, which investigate the respective invariants of successively wider groups of transformations. I shall utilize this terminology later in discussions of measurement and of physical theory.

The concept of invariance with respect to a group of transformations has proved to be of great importance in modern physics. From a purely technical point of view its prominence is a result of the widespread geometrization of physics; from a more general point of view it is a result of the way the concept is related to certain basic concepts that appear in physical theories: isolated system, conservation (as of energy or charge), symmetry.

Pythagorean Geometry

Rationalism is the belief that some things are known by reason, independently of experience. Modern scientific thought has, in the end, rejected rationalism,

---

† The best accessible source is Klein's own *Elementary Geometry from an Advanced Standpoint* (New York, 1932). The original is entitled *Vergleichende Betrachtungen über neuere geometrische Forschungen* (Erlangen, 1872).

even in its attenuated, Kantian form, in which what is thus known is only the mind's mode of organizing experience. But there is an extreme form of rationalism that, like all perennial philosophical alternatives, enjoys occasional rebirth. This is the belief that first principles, known through reason, determine not only the general outline of nature and experience but the details as well. Such is the belief that the phenomena of nature may be predicted, ultimately, in terms of the arithmetic of the natural numbers.

The early Greeks, particularly the followers of the half-legendary Pythagoras, developed a mode of geometrical analysis that identified geometrical magnitude with number; a line, for example, might be conceived as a row of pebbles, or a triangle as a two-dimensional array. An implicit belief in atomism, lacking the Platonic distinction between geometrical form and matter (between the abstract consideration of geometrical relations and the exemplification of those relations by material bodies), gave rise to a special kind of analytic geometry, which we call Pythagorean. The relation is not between geometrical points and real numbers, as in Cartesian geometry, but between geometrical "atoms" and the integers. The famous Pythagorean discovery of the incommensurability of the side and the diagonal of the square took place in this context; it presumably motivated the later sharp distinction between number and magnitude, and the consequent separation of geometry from number theory. From this early development came a good deal of elementary number theory, such as the classification of numbers as triangular, square, pentagonal, etc.

The rigid quantization of space via the assumption of discrete, identical building blocks establishes a relation between geometry and arithmetic in one direction; the concept of invariance under arbitrary, continuous, and uniquely reversible transformations illuminates certain relations between number properties and geometry. Here belongs a theorem of Leonhard Euler's, which requires, in a familiar special case, that the number of edges of a polyhedron be two less than the sum of the number of vertices and the number of faces. Involving ideas both of group theory and of topology is the Greek discovery of the five regular polyhedra, which Johannes Kepler later tried to use in explaining the radii of the five then known planetary orbits.

In the nineteenth and twentieth centuries there has been a vast expansion of these disciplines that relate geometry to the arithmetic of integers, and there is a varied and impressive list of physical applications. One simple and famous example is the law of rational indices in crystallography, which prescribes, *a priori,* the number of possible crystal classes, of crystal forms that can be built from a uniform lattice of atomic or molecular units.

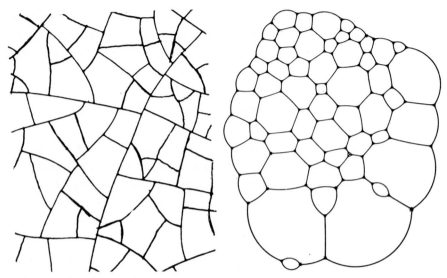

Fig. 8. Cracks in Ceramic Glaze   Fig. 9. Soap-bubble Raft

[*From "The Shape of Metal Grains," by Cyril S. Smith, in* Symposium on Interfaces (*American Society for Metals, Metals Park, Ohio, 1951*)]

There are many examples of the physical importance of Pythagorean geometry. It is well known that a floor can be covered with regular tiles of only three kinds, triangular, square, and hexagonal. For an irregular network such as glaze cracks (Fig. 8) or that formed by a layer of bubbles (Fig. 9), the number of edges per face may vary; but Euler's theorem still holds (for the plane count the outside as a face). A sphere, by the same theorem, cannot be covered with a hexagonal network. If one examines Hooke's seventeenth-century drawings of the poppy seed† or, from the nineteenth century, Haeckel's drawings of the Radiolaria,‡ one finds, on the surface network of cell boundaries, the proper exceptions to hexagonal coverage.

More complex examples of the relevance of topology are found in the geometrical properties of granular structures such as multicellular organisms and metal grains.§ The logical interplay of topological and physical arguments is sufficiently complex, in such studies, so that one cannot readily discriminate the

---

† Robert Hooke, *Micrographia* (London, 1665; reprinted by Dover, New York, 1961).

‡ Ernst Haeckel, *Allgemeine Naturgeschichte der Radiolarien* (Berlin, 1887), and *Natürliche Schöpfungs-Geschichte* (Berlin, 1898).

§ The classic paper is Lord Kelvin's "On the Division of Space with Minimum Partitional Area," *Philosophical Magazine,* 24 (1887), pp. 504–14. See also Cyril Stanley Smith, "The Shape of Metal Grains with Some Other Metallurgical Applications of Topology," *Symposium on Interfaces,* American Society for Metals, October 1951.

contribution of each. The Platonic regular solids occur in isolated crystals—except, it has seemed, the last on the list, the twenty-sided icosahedron. Recently, however, it has been found that certain virus particles, examined under the electron microscope, have icosahedral symmetry. The greatest of the Platonic solids is, evidently, the mystic signature of life!

A final reference will emphasize the importance of Pythagorean concepts in contemporary science. The quantum principle, which I shall discuss in detail later, implies its own kind of Pythagorean geometry. Atomic structures and atomic spectra are determined, in essence, by the quantum conditions, which, together with the exclusion principle, determine the distribution of electrons in the electron clouds and thus the chemical and spectral properties of the atoms. The so-called magic numbers that explain the periodic table recur in the theory of the internal structure of atomic nuclei.

Now the common characteristic of all physical applications of the arithmetic of integers is that empirical properties of physical systems turn out to be connected with, and modeled by, purely formal relations among the natural numbers. This fact is often not at all obvious *prima facie*. Connections that we explore by empirical means turn out to be the expression of arithmetical truths that are not at all contingent. On learning to understand things in this way, we are filled with the glow of the Pythagorean sentiment: patterns and connections in nature that appear to be contingent matters of brute fact are, in reality, the expression of an underlying order—the order of mathematics, the order, especially, of number.

There is, however, one overriding qualification: heat the crystal, and its elegant structure is lost in the molecular chaos of liquid or gas; and this is true of atoms and nuclei as well. Nature is Pythagorean only when cold. Heat and noise have to be part of the picture of nature for us, as Chaos was for the Greeks.

Apart from such scientific qualifications, however, there remains the implied rationalism of the viewpoint I have been discussing. From such a viewpoint empiricism is only a poor substitute for the higher and more austere verities of arithmetic and of the logic out of which arithmetic springs. The number theorist may proceed—empirically—to count primes or suchlike; but in the end he tries to construct a proof, to establish a theorem from which the results of his counting could have been predicted and by means of which he can subsequently dispense with mere counting. In the same spirit one may denigrate empiricism in general as a poor substitute for what a mind more subtly prepared could somehow establish as necessary.

The late Arthur S. Eddington went further in this direction than most, both in his cosmological speculations and in philosophical principle. On one occasion he was moved to assert: "An intelligence unacquainted with our universe but acquainted with the system of thought by which the human mind interprets to itself the content of its sensory experience, should be able to attain all the knowledge of physics that we have attained by experiment." † Such views are likely to be ignored simply because of the widely prevalent "dogmas of empiricism."

There is a sense in which such views may indeed be dismissed. Theories that postulate the existence of entities and conditions bringing the arithmetic of integers to bear on the description of specific natural phenomena are open to acceptance or rejection only on the basis of experience. But the implications of this remark are two-sided; it implies also that such theories cannot be rejected except upon the basis of experience. What may, for emphasis, be called epistemological rationalism rests upon a fallacy of suppression, a failure to notice that even the simplest deductions from logical truths to empirical matters of fact depend also upon empirical hypotheses, which, when examined carefully, must support the weight of any detailed factual import that such deductions may have. In the case of analytic Riemannian geometry I pointed out that its isomorphism with a certain part of algebra—a vector algebra over the real numbers—does not justify or explain its truth as physically interpreted, but illustrates, rather, the richness of such algebras, others of which would also be isomorphous with all sorts of *untrue* physical geometries. The same sort of comment can be made in the present instance. The applicability of the law of rational indices to the determination of crystallographic classes, for example, depends upon the *empirical* statement that atoms in a crystal are arranged in a regular geometrical lattice. The truth of these statements is an empirical matter and does not in any sense follow from number theory; their effect, on the contrary, is to establish an isomorphism between a certain theoretical description of crystal forms and a certain vector algebra over the natural numbers. It is only in this sense that any empirical statements follow from the properties of the concatenated models of arithmetic. The empirical identifying statements that establish isomorphisms in these cases may be simple, yet the consequences are enormously rich. The elaboration of such disciplines as geometry and arithmetic gives us the means to an extraordinary semantic compression. In the language of our discussion of models and their verisimilitude, arithmetic and geometry are marvelous mirrors, which have facilitated many discoveries far from the original sources of our

---

† Arthur S. Eddington, *Relativity Theory of Protons and Electrons* (Cambridge, England, 1936), p. 327.

arithmetical and geometrical knowledge. Kantians like Eddington want our picture of nature to be a mirror of the mind; and so it is. But the mind is also a mirror of nature; and not always, or *a priori*, a flat and unclouded one.

In the perspective of the present book what is remarkable is that systems of concepts abstracted from our dealings with certain aspects of nature should prove widely applicable in dealings with other aspects. The sense of metaphysical surprise that this should be so is lessened by two considerations. The first, from the evolutionary viewpoint, is to the effect that other systems of concepts, equally abstracted from common experience, have not proved so fruitful in science and have therefore become subordinated or eclipsed. In science, as in biological evolution, there is a process of natural selection. The second consideration is that some aspects of nature do not readily yield to description by these abstractions of number and form. Of this fact I shall speak more fully in the following chapters.

3

MOTION AND ANALYSIS

Arithmetic and geometry raise the problems of mathematical reality in the simplest and most classical form. But the mathematics of modern science is still a far development from those subjects. Here I shall present a historical sketch of some of the most important mathematical ideas underlying the physical sciences: the fusion of algebraic and geometrical ideas that is essential to the analysis of motion. This will include the extensions of number ideas and the definitions of continuous functions and analytic functions. The subject matter of analysis is the domain of encounter between two initially rather unrelated systems of abstraction, the arithmetical and the geometrical, the discrete and the continuous. In the older geometry the use of spatial figures was an indispensable means—in one sense, indeed, a literal part—of the mathematical language. Spatial construction, in sand or on paper, was exhibited; when suitably exhibited as the objects of demonstrative reference, and when talked about with suitable safeguards of logic, spatial constructions gave rise to abstractive definitions. Lines, circles, and the like became objects of propositional reference. The ruler and the compass, material objects under the control of the mathematician, defined in this way the essential *logical* tools of investigation and proof.

With the algebraic translation of geometrical form, on the other hand, these old tools were put aside or put in an ancillary position. The class of ruler-and-compass constructions was itself defined algebraically—namely, by its isomorphism with a restricted class of algebraic manipulations. But there were grave difficulties in the fully algebraic transcription of geometrical abstractions. These difficulties, successfully overcome only in the nineteenth century, have determined much of the content and style of modern mathematics and much of its emphasis on logical rigor. These developments occurred in intimate relation to the growth of physics after the seventeenth century and to what we here call the geometry of motion. This geometry freed physics from the limitations of static pictorial representation, and physics set before it the problems out of which it grew. These are the subjects that I shall review in what follows, and I shall thereby conclude our discussion of mathematics *per se*.

The final section is not illustrative, as the concluding sections of the previous chapters have been. It is a summary of a philosophical question that we have been concerned with throughout: the nature of mathematical reality.

The Geometry of Motion

In the previous chapter it was suggested that the development of non-Euclidean geometry, in spite of its great importance, was a less radical innovation in the traditions of the subject than is nowadays conventionally believed. Other and earlier developments in modern geometry are at least as important.

In Greek geometry attention was always concentrated upon the rigid body and its boundaries. In modern geometry, starting in the seventeenth century, there is increasing attention to the dynamical rather than the corporeal. A line or a curve may be viewed as a boundary or as the locus of a moving point, just as a surface may be conceived as the locus of a moving line or as separating adjacent volumes. The distinction is analogous to that between the ordinal and the cardinal aspects of number, the one suggesting process and the other static coexistence.

The Greeks were, inevitably, concerned with loci, but in the style of their mathematical art that idea tended to get eliminated from their final, formal proofs. Certain dynamical concepts have, on the other hand, played a crucial part in modern geometry, and perhaps our most characteristic style has been dynamical. Such a thesis was propounded by the culture-historian Oswald Spengler, who for his own purposes regarded mathematics as one of the fine arts, and who saw deep affinities between modern music, painting, and mathematics as expressions of the dynamical, "Faustian" spirit of West European culture.† To us, for example, it seems most natural to define the conic sections as loci of moving points. Apollonius of Perga regarded them as sections (in

---

† Oswald Spengler, *The Decline of the West* (New York, 1926), Chap. 2.

the original sense) of the cone. As Neugebauer† has shown, however, the origin of this subject among the Greeks was probably connected with the investigation of the sundial and was therefore a problem of loci, of moving points rather than of static sections.

One of the earliest innovations in post-classical geometry was its use in connection with the scholastic problem of the "forms of motion." Such investigations were part of the intellectual background of Galileo,‡ the founder of modern dynamics. The decisive step was the mapping of time into distance via the concept of uniform motion. Galileo did not use graphs of motion, but his language is geometrical—for example: "If a moving body, carried uniformly at a constant speed, traverses two distances, the time intervals are to each other in the ratio of these distances." § In his work on uniformly accelerated motion, likewise, he speaks of velocity as proportional to time, and he concludes that distances traversed in such cases will be proportional to time squared. Without resorting to any new mathematical ideas, Galileo and his immediate predecessors set the stage for the greatest of modern mathematical innovations, the differential and integral calculus developed by Leibniz and Newton. Geometrical loci were no longer necessarily to be thought of as spatial traces, shadows, of moving points, but might directly represent the form of the motion itself. Geometry was applied to the study of abstract spatio-temporal relations, not merely to relations that are spatial alone. The four-dimensional space-time continuum of the theory of relativity, though a distinctive development of the nineteenth and twentieth centuries, is unthinkable except as the completion of a process initiated by Galileo. The equivalence relation of congruence among rigid bodies was extended by Einstein to the time dimension, reverting to Galileo's innovation, as the idea of spatial congruence itself reverted to that of the primitive builder:

> Not only the practical geometry of Euclid, but also its nearest generalization, the practical geometry of Riemann, and therewith the general theory of relativity, rests upon this assumption, i.e., that rigid bodies congruent at one time and place remain so at any other time and place. Of the experimental reasons which warrant this assumption I will mention only one. The phenomenon of

---

† Otto Neugebauer, *The Exact Sciences in Antiquity* (Princeton, 1952), is required reading for understanding the exact sciences in antiquity.

‡ For the scientific background of Galileo one should read Herbert Butterfield, *The Origins of Modern Science* (London, 1949); A. C. Crombie, *Augustine to Galileo: The History of Science, A.D. 400–1650* (London, 1952); A. R. Hall, *The Scientific Revolution, 1500–1800* (Boston, 1956); Alexandre Koyré, *From the Closed World to the Infinite Universe* (New York, 1954). Above all, one should read Galileo Galilei, *Two New Sciences,* translated by H. Crew and A. de Salvio (New York, 1914), reprinted by Dover.

§ Galileo Galilei, *op. cit.,* Third Day.

the propagation of light in empty space assigns a tract, namely the appropriate path of light, to each interval of local time and conversely. Thence it follows that the above assumption for tracts must also hold good for intervals of clock-time in the theory of relativity. Consequently it may be formulated as follows: —If two ideal clocks are going at the same rate at any time and at any place (being then in immediate proximity to each other), they will always go at the same rate, no matter where and when they are again compared with each other at one place.†

The Calculus

As a result of the Galilean geometry of motion and the Cartesian algebra of geometry, there came to definition a whole new series of problems, out of which developed the differential and integral calculus of Newton and Leibniz. Under the sway of the principles of dynamics, the geometry of motion concentrated attention upon wide new classes of geometrical loci. The constraints that defined the loci studied by the Greeks had been, for the most part, due to mechanical linkages—for example, in the case of the conchoid, the spiral, the trisectrix. In the period when the calculus was invented the essential constraints belonged, rather, to the geometry of motion and were the very laws of motion. It was a curious and helpful coincidence that these led again to the conic sections, which had been elucidated by the Greeks from an entirely different starting point.

The matrix of ideas in which the calculus developed was, however, one that related the new subject to the whole preceding tradition of mathematics, and it would be a historical error to say that the subject arose simply out of the geometry of motion. A mere list of the relevant developments of the sixteenth and early seventeenth centuries is extensive. Problems of arithmetical calculation, which were especially serious in astronomy, led to the invention of decimal notation, of tables of logarithms, of the theory of the logarithmic and exponential function, and of infinite series. From the side of geometry, Greek methods of finding areas enclosed by given curved boundaries were re-examined (or re-invented)—methods depending upon dissection of area or volume into very thin strips or layers. In 1615 Kepler published a treatise in which he developed such laminar representations for calculating the volumes of wine barrels.

Both Newton and Leibniz, nevertheless, took the crucial intuitive concept of the calculus from the geometry of motion—that is, from the relation of distance

---

† Albert Einstein, *Geometrie und Erfahrung* (Berlin, 1921), translated by G. B. Jeffery and W. Perrett in *Sidelights on Relativity* (Methuen & Co., London; E. P. Dutton & Co., New York, 1923).

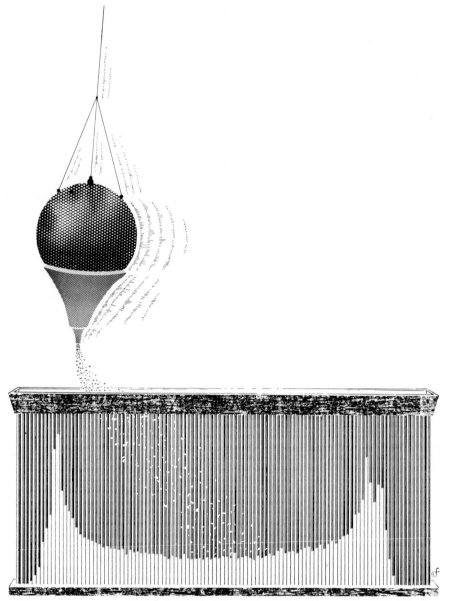

Fig. 10. A Motion and Its Graph

and velocity, an extension of the Galilean concept to the general case of non-uniform motion. Newton's fluxion is such a velocity, a rate of change of some variable with time, defined at an instant by the limit process. Leibniz, never at a loss for metaphysical insights, saw in the concept a key to the relation of being and becoming.

In this connection arose a special problem, connected with infinitesimals. In the passage to the limit one considers a ratio, $\Delta y/\Delta x$, and the limit is the value that this ratio approaches as Δx and Δy become arbitrarily small. One might—and one did—try to think of the limit itself as a ratio of infinitesimals, magnitudes that are not zero but are smaller than any finite quantity. The logical difficulty was not—as is sometimes asserted—with the infini-

Fig. 11. Tangents and Cusps

tesimals *per se*, but in defining their precise relation to the finite increment of a function—an increment corresponding to the finite increment of time or, more generally, of the independent variable. There are, indeed, quite rigorous axiomatic systems for infinitesimals, but they do not resolve the problem above, which was finally solved, in terms of the limit concept, by what is now known as the mean-value theorem. Intuitive geometrical representation makes this theorem seem obvious: it says that between two nearby points on a curve there is a tangent parallel to the line connecting the two points. But to express this in a rigorous fashion, while excluding such things as are shown in Figure 11, presupposes an explicit analysis of the concepts of continuity, differentiability, etc.—in short, of the concepts of modern analysis.

The logical difficulties in the foundations of the calculus arise from the need to bridge the gap between the abstractions of geometry and those of arithmetic— namely, between the concept of a set of discrete entities, which is involved in the concept of natural number, and the concept of continuity, which, intuitively at least, is the very antithesis of discreteness.

The sense of a contradiction latent in the concept of motion was expressed, classically, in Zeno's paradoxes, which depend upon the fact that a finite interval may be resolved into an infinite series of sub-intervals. The problem of a rigorous foundation for the calculus is therefore related to the resolution of these paradoxes.† The sense that location and motion are complementary, the sense that an object *is* somewhere only if it is at rest there, resides there, is at the source of these paradoxes. For a moving object a "where" has to be qualified by a "when," and the precision of location involves the definition of a time by an

---

† The paradoxes of Zeno are to be found in Aristotle, *Physics,* Book 6, 233ª and 239ᵇ.

event; but events are not instantaneous, and the sharpest definition of an instant depends upon something like the location of a moving object.

The long history of debate over Zeno's paradoxes suggests that they are not so much puzzlements to be cleared up as permanent signposts marking the approaches to the bridge over the gap referred to above, between the domains of the discrete and the continuous. Considered as modes of abstraction, the domains antedate the bridge. This is a bridge cantilevered out from one side, the discrete; and where it ends it still gives us a little jolt, however careful the engineering. The mean-value theorem seems obvious, intuitively, but only because the intuitive meaning of "curve" excludes the counter-examples in fact without conceptualizing them in the process. But, in order to conceptualize them and state the conditions of the theorem, we have to develop, for that purpose, a language that talks about "points"; and points are, in a common sense, discrete objects, logically correlative with intervals. But "interval" brings us back to the primary intuition of continuity, and so the discussion seems to run in circles. To define intervals as sets of points, after points have been defined as termini of intervals, seems like a vicious circle. Aristotle said that to try it would be a philosophical blunder. It can, however, be done. But that it can be done, and how, depends upon the arithmetization of geometry. Within the domain of number we build a system that meets our intuitive requirements and sharpens them, and we call this "the continuum." The intuitive notion is or seems simple, and we do not have to learn it in school; the arithmetical notion is not. There is an inherent bias here, one that is necessary if logical clarity is called for. Logic exploits the discreteness of symbols and their matchings. Number is built into logic, and number concepts are made rigorous by means of logical structures that exhibit them. The analogous procedure for the physical continuum is to exemplify it in communication—by motions of the hand or by glides in song. In that case concepts of continuity might acquire a certain *a priori* status, as indeed they did in Euclid's geometry.

The Dedekind Cut

The apparent one-sidedness in the relation between arithmetic and geometry as mathematical disciplines is somewhat mitigated by the observation that arithmetic, in order to be the basis for an arithmetization of the concepts of geometry, must itself be developed far beyond the abstraction of the natural numbers. The first step is the development of the rational numbers. The arbitrariness of measuring units—the fact that a length or any other such measure may be expressed as n units of which each is one mth of a given unit—is the principal inspiration for this development, which provides in a practical way for the continuity of such magnitudes, making it possible to determine a measure to the limits of the possible or desired accuracy. But the necessity of regarding this procedure as only approximate is easily demonstrated. The hypothesis that 2 is the square of a rational number leads to a contradiction; if we wish to say that the square root of 2 exists and is a number, it is, at any rate, not a rational number.

The simplest and most elegant demonstration that such entities exist and are qualified to be called numbers is that of J. W. R. Dedekind. A *cut*—later to be identified as a real number—is a *set* of rational numbers that, if it contains a given rational number, contains all smaller ones, does not contain all rational numbers, and contains no largest one. A specific cut could thus be defined as the set of all negative rationals and all non-negative rationals, r, such that $r^2 < 2$. Clearly there is no largest rational number having this property; for, if p is a rational number in the cut, its square is less than 2, and we can find another rational number, q, whose square is between p^2 and 2 and which therefore also belongs to the cut.

The sum of two cuts is defined as the set of all sums of rationals, one from each cut. The zero cut is defined as the set of all negative rationals. One cut is greater than another if it includes a rational not included in the other. The definition of the product of two cuts, except for minor complications due to sign, is analogous to that of the sum. The arithmetic of cuts satisfies all the laws of arithmetic, and the cuts therefore deserve to be called numbers. Included among the cuts are special cuts, one for each rational number, defined as all rationals less than the given rational, and these we may identify with the rationals. To distinguish them, cuts are called real numbers.

The important property of cuts is that they fill in the gaps between rational numbers. If the set of cuts is divided into two mutually exclusive and exhaustive sets, with all the members of one smaller than any member of the other, then there is a unique cut not less than any member of the one set, and not greater than any member of the other. More imprecisely but picturesquely, the upper and the lower set of cuts trap a given irrational or rational: either the upper set contains a least cut while the lower contains no greatest, or the lower contains a greatest while the upper contains no least.

This definition contains a feature that is essential to the cut's gap-filling function: that the cuts are infinite in membership. Using only a finite set of rationals, one could define only further rationals. This feature corresponds to the fact that the expression of an irrational number as a sum of rationals is possible only if the series in question is infinite. Irrationals expressed by infinite series may therefore be located, among the rationals, with only a finite degree of accuracy. In the language of a later chapter, the exact location of an arbitrary irrational requires an infinite amount of information.†

Even in the Dedekind theory we may find, if we wish to, the shadow of a sort of Zeno paradox. For suppose now that we define a new system of cuts, using, for this purpose, the real numbers rather than the rational. We discover that nothing new is added by this process, for every cut in the set of real numbers will correspond to a particular real number, and the arithmetic of cuts of cuts will be identical with that of cuts of rationals. There are, however, *two* possible ways of defining a cut: the one I have given and the one that interchanges algebraic signs. By the latter way a cut becomes a set of numbers having no least member and, if it contains a given number, contains any greater number. If the second definition is used, we get exactly the same results as above. The square root of 2 is, under the one definition, the set of negative rationals, 0, and positive rationals with squares less than 2; under the other it is the set of positive rationals with squares greater than 2. These sets are strict complements; every rational belongs to the one set or the other, and, if one of them defines the square root of 2, the other does so equally well. But now consider the cut as a cut in the set of *real* numbers. If we apply the first definition, the cut is the set of all negative real numbers, 0, and positive real numbers with squares less than 2; the complementary set then contains a least member, which is precisely $\sqrt{2}$. The second definition defines the cut as all real numbers whose squares are greater than 2, and its complement contains a greatest member, $\sqrt{2}$. Thus we get two logically distinct partitions of the set of real numbers, each of which defines the same irrational number. No contradictions arise, for no rules are provided for combining the Dedekind cuts with the anti-Dedekind cuts; still one may notice that, although they partition the real numbers at the same place, they are not the same partition. What ought not to happen to the bishops at Nicaea can happen to a cut.

Complex Numbers and Vectors

An integer (positive, zero, or negative) is defined as an equivalence class of ordered pairs of natural numbers; that is, the pair (a, b) is equivalent to the pair

---

† The language here is troublesome. We can often define irrationals quite briefly; but to locate one means to give two rationals, one greater and one less than the irrational. The inaccuracy of location is the interval between the rationals.

(c, d) if, and only if, $a + d = b + c$; and any pair in an equivalence class defined by this relation can be the name of the class, just as any discrete set can be the name of a natural number. We use $(a, 0)$ as a name for the positives (it is also written $+a$), $(0, a)$ for the negatives (or $-a$), and $(0, 0)$ for the integer that we usually fail to distinguish from the natural number 0. The naturals are isomorphous with a part of the integers: there is a one-one correspondence between the naturals and the non-negative integers, between the operations in the first domain and those in the second, and in the results of these operations performed on corresponding elements.

A rational number is defined almost identically, but with a dot replacing the plus sign in the equivalence relation between (a, b) and (c, d): $a \cdot d = b \cdot c$. The elements a and b are already defined as integers. All couples such as $(a, 0)$ are outlawed ("dividing by 0"). There are various conventions of naming, the commonest being to select that pair of an equivalence class whose elements are relatively prime.

The real numbers are defined in terms of cuts among the rationals. By a development alternative to the one we have used, the reals may be defined as equivalence classes of sequences (Cauchy sequences) of rationals. Thus, from beginning to end, the filling in of the continuum of real numbers may be represented as a process of abstraction in which ordered pairs (for integers and rationals) or endless sequences (for the reals) are first defined and then grouped into equivalence classes. By this grouping we declare all differences among pairs or sequences in a group inessential to what is being defined.

When we review this development, we may well have a sense of protest. The natural numbers are already equivalence classes of sets, the integers are equivalence classes of ordered pairs of equivalence classes of sets, and so on up the ladder of abstractness and complexity of statement. Though the development I have sketched has come to be the standard one, one mathematician† has written to me:

> "I am used to taking sets, e.g. sets of division problems, defining operations and relations in the collection of these sets (e.g. the rational number system), proving, by working with the elements, that certain properties hold. Then I would like absolutely and permanently (until next time I teach the course) to forget that 2/3 is a set of ordered pairs of integers, and think of it as an object with properties of its own."

Clearly we ought not to, and will not, surrender the clarity and rigor that have come with the modern development of the number system. But clearly

---

† Professor Burrowes Hunt.

also there is about it a sense of artificiality, which dies hard and which might repay examination. The suggestion may be made that this sense of artificiality is connected with two different meanings of "abstract." One of these relates the number concepts to their mathematical elucidation in relation to the basis of the natural numbers, the other to their applications in the description of nature.

Before we discuss this matter, however, it will be useful to examine one more development: that of the system of complex numbers and of the genus, vectors, of which complex numbers are a species.

The complex numbers constitute a further extension of the number system. They are defined as ordered pairs of real numbers, but no equivalence classes are needed here. The two complex numbers (a, b) and (c, d) are equal if, and only if, $a = c$ and $b = d$. The decisive characteristic lies in the rules for addition and multiplication:

$$(a, b) + (c, d) = (a + c, b + d)$$
$$(a, b) \cdot (c, d) = (ac - bd, ad + bc)$$

These are just the rules one gets if one writes (a, b) in the more conventional notation $a + ib$, in which i is such that -1 may be substituted for i^2.

The complex numbers originated, of course, in the attempt to represent the roots of an arbitrary quadratic equation. The symbol $i = \sqrt{-1}$ has no meaning in the field of real numbers. Early in the nineteenth century J. R. Argand and Caspar Wessel first represented complex numbers by points in the plane (and thus by their coordinates, ordered pairs of real numbers) and showed that multiplication by i corresponds to the rotation of coordinates through a right angle. In contrast to the rationals and reals, complex numbers were introduced into modern mathematics more because one kept bumping into them than because of any initial intuitive meaning. They were required to give algebraic closure to the real-number system (that is, every polynomial equation has a root). They form the basis of the theory of functions of a complex variable, within which many of the unifying viewpoints of modern analysis have originated. In physical applications their intuitive meaning has become clear enough, notably in the phenomena of wave motion, whose periodicity may be represented by the geometrical concept of rotation.

A vector is an ordered set of numbers. Integers and rationals are, therefore, equivalence classes of vectors. Complex numbers are vectors, of a species whose rules of combination also qualify them as numbers. Since real numbers are isomorphic with the set of complex numbers of the form $(a, 0)$, the complex numbers include the reals.

Other sets of rules for the combination of vectors, other vector algebras, are important in physics. The addition of vectors represents successive displacements, the composition of forces, etc. The absolute value of a vector is the square root of the sum of the squares of its components, in graphical representation its distance from the origin, in physical meaning its magnitude. We obtain the product of a vector and a real number (a scalar) by multiplying each vector component by the number; it therefore signifies a change of absolute value, of scale. The scalar product of two vectors, a scalar, is illustrated by the concept of work, which may be represented in vector algebra as the product of a force vector and a displacement vector. The scalar product is the product of the magnitudes of two vectors and the cosine of the angle between them.

Other rules for the combination of vectors, which will not be discussed here, have the same formal character. They give a condensed algebraic expression of important physical relations and permit us to think of the terms entering into these relations in a simple way when a more elementary description would involve us in distracting geometrical detail. We introduce the concept of work for the case in which force and displacement are parallel, and in that case the use of real numbers is sufficient. But, if a displacement is not parallel to the force, a geometrical element enters the problem, the solution of which carries us back to the Pythagorean theorem. In vector algebra this geometrical element is put into a merely implicit form through the definition, in this case, of the scalar product. The statement of the general concept of work (for non-parallel vectors) is then isomorphous with that of the special case. The example is rather elementary, but it suggests something of the long evolution that has gone into the elaboration of the precise language of physics.

Another example of the utility of vector concepts, in appearance merely a matter of notation but in the end of great importance, is the idea of a vector field, in which directed magnitudes are functions of position. Electric and magnetic fields, and flux density in the description of fluid motion, are examples. Ordered sets of numbers may represent directed magnitudes, but they have other obvious uses. In economics, for example, a bill of goods is a vector, and businessmen have been speaking this sort of vector prose all their lives.

There are other examples of this sort of development, but even the listing grows tiresome. One can generalize and say that the formal elaboration of the different number species involves at each step the formation of an *ordered set* of numbers and the formulation of rules of combination for such sets. The complex-number field is the most general that satisfies all the laws of number. Beyond this are other vector algebras as well as algebras for tensors and matrices.

This elaboration of languages grows more complex and, in a sense, more abstract—but more abstract in relation to the natural numbers, not necessarily in relation to the description of nature. A point in three-dimensional space is not more abstract than a point on a line, even though one is *represented* by a number-triple and the other by a number. A stick 2/3 foot long is not more abstract than a couple of apples. The apples exemplify natural number; the stick exemplifies, in relation to a foot rule, the same number that (2, 3) exemplifies in the field of rationals.

Continuity

In mathematical analysis the concept of continuity refers not to the continuum of real or complex numbers but to the continuity of functions. The functions that are the analytic analogues of the classical geometrical curves or of trajectories in the geometry of motion provided the subject matter of analysis in its early history. The lack—from a more modern point of view—of rigor in that early period was quite unavoidable, since rigor depends upon precision in the articulation of concepts, and such precision was not achieved until the nineteenth century. Beyond a certain point mathematics can neither advance securely, nor be applied securely to the description of nature, without this concern for rigor. Yet analysis developed vigorously over the greater part of two centuries on what would now be regarded as the shakiest of foundations, and this of itself shows that the essential subject matter of this branch of mathematics is not an arbitrary creation of the mathematical imagination, but a more or less orderly system of abstractions derived, in the first place, from experience. The modern postulational treatment of the subject is disciplined, from start to finish, by the need to produce a formally adequate statement of something with which the mathematician is antecedently well acquainted.

A function, f, is continuous at a point, x, if for every $\epsilon > 0$ there exists a $\delta > 0$ such that

$$|f(y) - f(x)| < \epsilon$$

for all points, y, for which $|y - x| < \delta$. One might render this defining condition as "values of the function are arbitrarily close together for arguments that are close enough together." The definition defines continuity at a point; for continuity in an interval we must assert continuity at every point in the interval.

Lest our previous remarks on the care-free development of analysis in its earlier stages be interpreted as a belittling of the importance of rigor, it should be observed here that we have a very good instance to the contrary: the belief that prevailed until the nineteenth century that continuous functions were *ipso facto* differentiable. It seemed obvious that a continuous function had a definite slope at almost every point. K. T. Weierstrass provided a famous counter-example: a function continuous throughout its domain but nowhere possessing a derivative. Although this function was for long regarded as a mathematician's curiosity, it is the type of function that does, in fact, describe, in idealized form, the Brownian motion of a particle, subject at every moment to random changes in its trajectory and thus nowhere having a trajectory that can be regarded as well defined. Such an example as this seems to illustrate the power of analysis to transcend the limits of our intuitive concepts and of the ranges of experience from which those concepts are abstracted. In transcending these limits, analysis—using the word now in its broadest sense—opens to view possibilities excluded by the framework of our customary unselfconscious ways of thought.

Analytic Functions and Fourier Series

The class of analytic functions is defined by a property that is of basic importance in the classical development of mathematical physics. An analytic function is one that can be expressed by a series, finite or infinite, of powers of the argument:

$$f(x) = \sum_{n=0}^{\infty} c_n x^n$$

Such functions not only are differentiable, possessing, in fact, derivatives of all orders, but have a further, and quite remarkable, property, which fits them to the standard uses of geometry and physics: the characteristics of the function in the neighborhood of a single point—its value, its slope, the rate of change of its slope, and all higher derivatives—are necessary and sufficient to determine all the coefficients of the power series itself and thus, within its domain of convergence, the entire function. As a practical description this is meaningless, but in the ideal limit of infinite information concerning either aspect of the function (the local or the global), the other aspect is thereby determined. When a function represents the changes in the state of a system through time, it is this feature of analyticity that gives meaning to the concept of determinism, which I shall discuss in Chapter 5. Conversely, however, we can approximate the coefficients of an analytic function, or its derivatives of higher order, in observational practice only by examining its values over wider and wider intervals.† The transformation from the integral to the differential viewpoint, and from the differential to the integral viewpoint, is important because the spatio-temporal aspect of natural processes is linked to the dynamical aspects, to momentum and energy, via relations that can be expressed by means of differential equations that define analytic functions.

Among the many mathematical developments that have their roots in elementary geometry and their applications in physics, one of the most important is the theory of Fourier series, which is a natural extension of the theory of analytic functions. Certain power series occur commonly in the solution of the equations of physics that define the exponential function $f(x) = e^{ax}$. When a is a real number, it represents geometric increase or decrease. When a is purely imaginary, the function—a complex function whose real part is the sine function and whose imaginary part is the cosine—is periodic and represents simple harmonic motion.

When it becomes necessary to deal with the motions of a continuous medium rather than those of individual particles, the equations of motion take the form of partial differential equations, and Fourier analysis becomes an important tool. We may approach the physical meaning of these equations by first assuming that the medium is discontinuous, consisting of a large number of particles (such as the atoms in a vibrating string). This requires a separate equation for each particle; but, if the behavior of the particles varies continuously with their spatial location, the whole system may be described by a single equation involving derivatives with respect to space variables as well as time variables. This equa-

---

† This is not strictly correct; for, if we have only some number of points on a curve, we cannot, without further assumptions, find out anything about its derivatives. By some method of curve-fitting we find a smooth curve through the points or nearly through them. A widely fluctuating slope of a curve is consistent with very smooth *average* behavior and would be overlooked by curve-fitting. In an example by Professor Arne Magnus, a falling body might be displaced from its starting point by distance

$$s = t^2 - 10^{-10} \sin (10^{20}t)$$

while the velocity would be

$$v = 2t + 10^{10} \cos (10^{20}t)$$

Such an object, vibrating in the direction of its displacement, would be moving in a way indistinguishable by ordinary sorts of measurement from Galileo's ideal falling body, but its instantaneous velocity would range over an enormous interval in imperceptible periods of time. Such a "jitter motion" (*Zitterbewegung*), considered as a *physical* possibility, is fraught with consequences and is not just a logical curiosity. In quantum mechanics, as we shall see, nature declares our impotence to make these discriminations of displacement and velocity below the quantum threshold. We can come to terms with Zeno's paradoxes, but they describe the nature of things—paradoxically—better than he knew.

tion represents the limiting behavior of the system as the number of particles in a given region approaches infinity; its exact significance is, therefore, that it describes the behavior of matter in the continuous state.

The Fourier series is essentially a power series in powers of the complex exponential $e^{\alpha i t}$. In the description of wave motion within a confined space the separate terms have physical significance as distinct modes of vibration, the series itself representing the superposition of these distinct states. It is a remarkable property of the Fourier series that any arbitrary function (subject to rather mild restrictions) can be represented by a proper choice of coefficients.

A descendant, like vector algebra, of the elementary geometry of the triangle, the theory of Fourier series and related series has become a standard part of the language of physics. Its appropriateness in quantum physics, in particular to the description of particles, is what gives detailed content to the idea of the wave nature of corpuscles.

The Fourier representation of a physical system is a theoretically adequate one to the extent that the system exhibits only *linear* kinds of internal interactions. For each of a set of specifiable states or modes, a linear system behaves in a way that can be represented by a single term in the Fourier expansion; and its behavior in any state can be represented by an appropriate linear combination of such terms. Departures from linearity characteristically give rise to complexities of a less tractable kind. The mathematics of non-linear systems is of a higher order of difficulty and as yet only partly developed. Nature was kind to Newton in giving him planets not much troubled by multiple gravitational interactions. She has been kind also in presenting subsequent physics with many problems that involve only linear, or nearly linear, interactions. But these are not universal, and in some of the fundamental problems non-linearity prevails. To anticipate a dogma expounded in Chapter 5, nature is infinitely complex, and this implies that no interaction is ever quite linear. Toward the extremes of any physical variables, non-linear connections, surprises of scale, always appear.

The Nature of Mathematics: Universals

In these chapters we have examined enough of the foundations of mathematics to return better informed, if not wiser, to the questions posed at the beginning of Chapter 1 concerning the nature of mathematics itself and of its relation to the sciences. Answers, or at least some elements that go into these answers, have been developed along the way. The concepts of number and form are abstractions derived from man's dealings, his practical-cognitive relations, with nature.

Without denying or even, it is hoped, minimizing the creative aspects of mathematical invention, I have set forth the thesis that the material studied by mathematics is material *de rerum natura*.

But mathematics is not a study of nature, is not a science in that sense, for what it examines is neither the contemporary world of nature nor the record in that world of its past nor its pointings toward the future. The subject matter of mathematics, so far as it has one, is, rather, a part of human culture, the precipitate of our experience with the nature of things. So is the subject matter of anthropology and psychology, and in that sense mathematics does not even have a subject matter. Mathematics does not describe certain aspects of culture; rather, it exemplifies them, explicates and reworks them. It has a subject matter only in the sense in which a novel or a play has a subject matter. Like the work of art, it is, in this sense, presentative rather than representative, a model rather than a description.

With respect to literal, semantic truth, the question has two sides. The pure mathematician takes certain primitive statements as given; their truth is simply stipulated. But these statements are subject to interpretation in terms of meanings otherwise given; and, when they are so interpreted, their truth or falsity is determined independently. This interpretation can be in terms of other, purely formal systems, as when geometry is mapped into a part of arithmetic, or arithmetic into the formalism of logic. Or the interpretation can be in terms of the concepts by which we describe empirical subject matter, and then it is a matter of fact, logically contingent, whether the primitive statements of the mathematician are true or false. This is so of arithmetic, geometry, or analysis: very often such applications run beyond the possibility of any complete verification or disproof, even in so elementary a procedure as counting a set by two different procedures and comparing the results, for there is always the possibility that the sets counted are not identical. It is so *a fortiori* in the applications of geometry and analysis, where our assumptions can sometimes be exactly tested only in the ideal limit of infinite information.

The concepts of mathematics are, then, abstractions, elucidated by the primitive statements that the mathematician makes about them or by means of them. But the term "abstraction" has implications that need, at this point, to be spelled out. I shall spell them out by referring to a classical philosophic problem, the problem of universals.

In a third-century commentary on Aristotle's logic, Porphyry asked whether the genera and species of Aristotle's logic are substances, or whether they exist only in the human understanding; and, if they are substances, whether they are corporeal or incorporeal, and whether they exist separately or only in individual things. The problem became an important one in the eleventh century and remained so in later medieval philosophy. The attempts to solve it fell into three main classes.

Realism was the belief that universals exist in reality, outside the mind. Aristotelian realism held that universals exist so, but only as qualifying individual things. Platonic realism held that universals exist in their own right, apart from the individuals that participate in them. *Conceptualism,* on the other hand, held that universals exist only in the mind but are derived or abstracted from individual things. It is not easy to distinguish conceptualism from Aristotelian realism; the point at issue is whether, apart from their entertainment by the mind, and as exemplified in nature, universals may properly be so called. *Nominalism,* finally, was the doctrine that universals are only names, but names used equivocally to refer to many individual things.

The vitality of the problem of universals in the Middle Ages was due to the fact that it epitomized, under one heading, a number of issues that modern philosophy has tended to distinguish. Not all of these are relevant to our purposes here; but, as Quine† especially has pointed out, there is a resemblance between the medieval problem and recent discussions of the logical foundations of mathematics.

A crucial philosophical question in modern logic is whether, and in what sense, classes may or must be said to *exist;* and this is, in essence, the question of Porphyry. For a substance, in the Aristotelian sense, is something that has attributes. If species and genera are substances, they have attributes in the same sense in which individuals have attributes. Certain individuals have attributes in virtue of which we call them men. If the species man is a substance, it has attributes and exists in the same sense—logically—as the individual men. Quine has argued that the analogous problem in modern logic comes up with the need to use such expressions as "there is an x such that . . . ," in which x refers to classes and not just to individuals. An "ontological commitment" is involved, *prima facie,* a commitment to the existence of classes in a sense over and above the existence of their individual members (if any). From our point of view, which is not necessarily that of the technical logician, the substance-attribute formulation seems just as clear and closer to the tradition. If attributes are correctly predicated of classes, there is a *prima facie* ontological commitment to the reality of those classes. And this commitment will be somehow more than *prima facie* if these predications are not completely reducible, in meaning, to

† See W. V. Quine, *From a Logical Point of View* (Cambridge, Mass., 1953).

statements about the properties and relations of the *members* of those classes.

It is necessary to look first at certain ambiguities in the class concept that has come down from the tradition of logic. We must first distinguish class membership from class inclusion. Both relations may be rendered in English by "*x* is *y*." In the first case, that of class membership, *x* refers to an object and *y* to a class, as, for example, in "this pen is black" or "that crystal is rhombic." In the second case, that of class inclusion, both *x* and *y* refer to classes, and the statement means "whatever is a member of *x* is a member of *y*" or "the members of *x* are members of *y*." The sense of "is" in "Socrates is mortal" is different from the sense of "is" in "to be human is to be mortal." In one of our ancient traditions these two relations were thought of as identical, so that somehow "Socrates" stood in the same relation to "man" as "man" stood to some higher category, like "rational being." The neo-Platonic background of early medieval thought gave point to the exploitation of this confusion. The neo-Platonic philosophers thought of the world of particular things as emanating by stages from the Divine, and they identified these stages with a sequence of genera down to individual species and, finally, individuals. This is the neo-Platonic *scala naturae,* or, as it is also called, the "ladder of perfection," and we shall meet it again. In the Middle Ages extreme realists were people who thought that the reality of individuals came only from their species, the reality of the species only from its genus, etc., and thus were exposed to the charge that they identified the natural world with God, the *Summum genus*—which is the heresy of pantheism.

The concept of class membership and the concept of class inclusion must both be distinguished from that of another relation of "belonging to"—namely, that of membership of a part in a whole, or system. If these are confused, the denial of the reality of a universal may carry with it the denial of the reality of a whole, hence the denial of any unifying relation among the parts, and the system "falls apart." Thus the nominalism of Roscellinus contradicted, it was thought, the dogma of the Trinity. His view implied, it was said, that "One Divine Being" is no more than a name for the three separate persons of the Trinity—a heresy condemned by the Council of Soissons. Nominalism might also make difficulties for an ecclesiastical nationalist, since on such principles he might appear to be implying that "One Church" is but a name for the separate local churches.

Of course the existence of specific material relations among the parts of a system is not of itself a matter of logic. But there is a logical schema involved: a class or set, defined in terms of some common trait of its members, becomes a system or a whole in virtue of some multi-term relation among its members. Since the concept of relation is a logical concept, it is possible to define the concept "whole" within formal logic: the members of a class of things may be called a whole or a system whenever a multi-term relation is specified as holding among them. The relation in question has, of course, to be other than the relation of belonging to the same class. Such a whole may be treated as a single entity, and it has certain properties of the same kinds as its members. Thus arises the ambiguity of such a concept as "man," which may mean either the abstract class defined by common properties or the system of human life defined by biological and social relations among the members of the class. Associated with the window pane I look through is a class of atoms, those that compose the pane. But the pane is not a class; it is an individual thing of the same logical type or order as the atoms in it, and it has attributes of the same kind: shape, mass, etc.

Consider now the statement "The window pane is rectangular." If the pane were to be construed as a class of atoms, the class would have an attribute—rectangularity—not reducible to attributes of its members, and we should have to admit an ontological commitment to the reality of classes in the sense explained above. The thing that is rectangular, however, is not the class, but the system of its members.

From this point of view it may be observed that a class seems to be hypostatized, referred to as an entity, when the properties ascribed to it are extensional properties—properties that the class has in virtue of its membership. The outstanding example, considered in Chapter 1, is number. The entity that has the number property is not the set considered as an abstraction, but the totality of its members—in fact, a whole of parts. Needless to say, the concept of whole in this case need signify no organic unity; the membership of a class constitutes a whole in the minimum logical sense that the members coexist and sustain such relations to each other as permit them to be correlated with members of other classes. Thus number properties of classes are properties of the wholes, the collectivities, whose parts are elements of the class. Number characterizes concrete particular physical realities in the same way that mass or color or shape does. Newton thought—in essence correctly—that the mass of a body could be measured by the number of elementary particles in it.

Classes can, of course, themselves be enumerated: there are five prime numbers less than twelve. The "five" here is a property, not of a physical system, but of a collectivity whose elements are themselves classes of classes. Such collectivities do not have color or mass or shape. But again there is no neo-

Platonic ladder. Primality is, in the first instance, a characteristic of concrete particular wholes. It distinguishes

$$(.\,.), \ (.\,.\,.), \ (.\,.\,.\,.\,.), \ (.\,.\,.\,.\,.\,.\,.), \ (.\,.\,.\,.\,.\,.\,.\,.\,.\,.\,.)$$

from

$$(.\,.\,.\,.), \ (.\,.\,.\,.\,.\,.), \ (.\,.\,.\,.\,.\,.\,.\,.), \ (.\,.\,.\,.\,.\,.\,.\,.\,.),$$
$$(.\,.\,.\,.\,.\,.\,.\,.\,.\,.), \ (.\,.\,.\,.\,.\,.\,.\,.\,.\,.\,.\,.)$$

having to do with the internal matchings among subsets that are possible in the second group and not in the first. And the "five" that characterizes the first group is on the same *logical* level as the "five" that belongs to it—a property of a physical set, in the one case of dots and in the other of brackets.

But what shall one say about infinite collections—about the statement, for example, that there are infinitely many prime numbers? Or that there is no even number >2 that is not the sum of two primes, a statement not known to be true, false, or even provable? What we abstract from finite sets is the successor relation; we do not *exhibit* an infinite collection of discrete objects except privatively; we exhibit the monotony of the successor relation. Here we come to the point of the ontological commitment involved in generalizing about a class of classes. But, since every natural number is exemplified, either in an actually infinite universe of particles or in the groupings of a finite universe, there is no reason not to accept the ontological commitment involved. It is not a commitment to higher levels of reality in a neo-Platonic hierarchy, but a commitment to a description of nature in which every whole may be matched with a part of a larger whole.

For what historical labels are worth, this is Aristotelian realism, not Platonic. The system of mathematics builds up through a long sequence of abstractive steps; propositional reference to higher-order abstractions is always grounded in demonstrative reference to the concrete and the particular. Platonic realism derives its plausibility, I believe, from the confusion of these kinds of reference. In any literal Platonism or neo-Platonism, it seems, classes *qua* substances would have properties not grounded in the lowly particulars of nature; they would be, literally, otherworldly. But we find, instead, that the attributes of classes *qua* substances are found, not by inspection of a higher world, but by analysis. It seems to me that any true Platonist would have to affirm the synthetic, and deny the analytic, character of mathematical truth.

Nominalism is unacceptable to me because it seems committed to denying the significance of class attributes altogether and thereby to denying the significance of the greater part of mathematics. Abstractive definition is an analysis of ideas developed at a lower level of abstraction, but not a mere restatement of what has already been *said* at the lower level. Reference to universals is, as I have argued in Chapter 1, propositional rather than demonstrative; but propositional reference is not logically reducible to demonstrative reference even though it depends upon it. When one discourses about the number 2 or the number 6×10^{23}, one is discoursing, not about a couple, or about a batch of gas, but about a universal.

Finally, we are committed to a rejection of conceptualism by the same kind of argument that weighs against Platonism. If the higher-order abstractions are not objects of demonstrative reference, we must reject the attempt to say that they have a kind of local, ostensible existence in places called "minds." It is no help to argue *where* universals exist, for the primary confusion is in the notion that they exist any*where,* and the primary insight is the insight that they are just the kinds of entities that do exist, but exist no*where.*

For those who know Plato it should be confessed that Plato himself is, and is not, a Platonist. Among all the great philosophers Plato is the one who least asserts and most suggests. Most great philosophers are famous for their answers, but Plato is famous for his questions. Platonism is not a flat-footed system of philosophical assertions but a challenge to the complacent or the skeptical; Plato is light on his feet. Plato is one of those extraordinary individuals against whose challenges the subsequent history of thought proves its instability. The Socrates whom we know through Plato's writing is the daimon, the clan deity, of the philosophic enterprise, and because of him philosophers know that beyond the next answer they propose lies an ironic question.

4

MEASUREMENT

Mathematical abstractions are derived from experience, but the propositions linking them, the truths of mathematics, are analytic, are independent of particular fact and of experience as the acquaintance with particular fact. In the first part of this statement "experience" is a term without a usable plural form; in the second part the term has a meaningful plural. If we bear in mind the distinction between the member-class and the part-whole relations, "experience" in this sense is a generic, abstract concept referring to particular experiences not as "cat" refers to particular cats but rather as "space" or "time" refers to particular spaces or times, as the name of a more or less unified whole.

When we turn from the discussion of mathematics to its uses in the detailed description of nature, however, the particularistic meaning of "experience" is the essential one. Every measurement involves a particular finding or set of findings, certified by perception and independent of wish or bias. The effort to make science turn upon the findings of measurement, to force nature, as Kant put it, to answer questions deliberately and carefully posed, is the essential discipline of science. It has not always been so. For experience in the largest sense, including perception and also memory, thought, and belief, contains other resources for settling questions about nature, especially reasoned argument from accepted premises. It is not obvious, it is not always even true, that resort to particular empirical fact is the best method of testing old beliefs or getting new ones. But it is right much oftener and in a much deeper sense than the generality of mankind has been willing to believe, and this rightness has been ineradicably impressed upon us by the growth of science.

The conjunction of this empiricist belief with the older belief in the ultimately mathematical character of the language of nature has focused attention upon measurement as the bridge between nature and knowledge. The analysis of the procedures of measurement goes, therefore, to the heart of scientific methodology. It provides what Kant called the "schematism" that must accompany abstract, universal concepts if they are to be linked significantly with the immediacy of act and perception.†

Observation and Measurement

According to general belief, science—or, at any rate, good science—is necessarily quantitative. A dubious corollary states that by being quantitative one will, inevitably, develop good science. When a science, or some part of a science, has failed to develop rapidly and surely, it is often said that what is needed is the introduction of quantitative methods. The argument is familiar in the literature of biology, geology, economics, sociology, etc. It has even been heard, from time to time, in political science, history, and ethics. So strong is the belief in the efficacy of measurement as the gateway to science that it becomes a kind of badge of office. In American universities at the present time one finds a sort of academic pecking order based upon the prevailing accuracies and austerities of measurement. In the entrance hall of one university's physics building are displayed the "really basic" standards of measurement: the meter stick, the kilogram, and the pendulum. Physics pecks first.

In the present chapter I shall discuss various aspects of measurement, my primary aim being to oppose the view of science suggested above. I shall try to replace that view by one that is more generous to certain areas of knowledge that, by invidious standards of quantitative precision, rank low on the scale. I shall do this by a deliberate and perhaps unconventional enlargement of the concept of measurement, to the point where it becomes synonymous with what is ordinarily in science called *observation*. Any act of classifying a thing by its observable properties or relations is, in this sense, a measurement; and in *this* all good science is metrical, but not necessarily in the narrower sense ordinarily associated with the word.‡ Thus, quite generally, measurement is

---

† *Critique of Pure Reason,* "Transcendental Analytic," Book II, Chap. I.

‡ Cf. Ernest Nagel, "Measurement," *Erkenntnis,* Band II, Heft 5, pp. 313–33; reprinted in *Philosophy of Science,* edited by Arthur Danto and Sidney Morgenbesser (Cleveland and New York, 1960). Nagel states this view but finds reason for abandoning it in favor of the narrower and more conventional interpretation.

some procedure of observation the outcome of which reduces the extension of a set of alternatives.

To the charge that such a widening of the concept involves a tendency to ignore or suppress important differences between observation and measurement (as those terms are usually employed) I reply that there is, in fact, a wide variety of types of measurement, which may be distinguished as sharply as ever, and that all types of measurement exist in a common, abstract, quantitative dimension, that of *quantity of information* (as that term is understood in contemporary information theory). To eulogize "measurement" above "observation" is justified in some fields of science at some stages of their development—in sixteenth-century astronomy, for example, or in nineteenth-century chemistry or spectroscopy; that such an emphasis, by some inherent requirement, is always justified for all of science I simply deny.

On Basic Measurements

In the logical as well as in the academic hierarchy, measurements of time, distance, and mass have often been regarded as basic to all others, and thus as somehow occupying a fundamental position, also, in the epistemology of science, it being held that all other measurements can, in one way or another, be reduced to these.† Before we consider such measurements and the claim that they are basic, it is useful to question the gravitational metaphors involved in the claim. These metaphors are often involved in philosophical thinking, and they tend to prejudice it by implying among things a kind of relation that need not, in fact, obtain. The axioms of a formal theory are "basic," and the theorems "rest" on them. Sometimes the metaphor is inverted, and the theorems "depend." In both cases the metaphor implies a further question, which we have learned not to ask: On what do the axioms rest or depend? One is reminded of the Hindu story, in which the earth rests on the back of an elephant, which stands on the back of a turtle, which swims in an infinite sea—and don't ask any more foolish questions. So great is the tyranny of the gravitational metaphor that it was a painful experience for the learned (as it still may be for the child of today) to conceive of the earth as a sphere freely poised in space. The essential logical value of the metaphor is that it will stand for an implicative or causal relation that is asymmetrical and transitive. Its disvalue is that it implies such relations where they do not exist.

----

† See N. R. Campbell, *An Account of the Principles of Measurement and Calculation* (New York, 1928) and *What is Science?* (London, 1921).

Philosophers have often—more often than not—discussed knowledge in terms of the gravitational metaphor. Knowledge must have some "foundation" upon which it "rests": axioms of reason, sense data, the scientific method, the pragmatic test, etc. A contemporary, C. W. Churchman, has aptly described this tendency in the theory of knowledge as fundamentalism.† Now there is a sense in which any discourse, especially a philosophical one, is analogous to the description of a physically isolated system. The delineation of its subject matter rests upon some set of concepts and distinctions and upon beliefs involving them—beliefs that provide for the discourse its boundary conditions, which, though the discourse depends upon them, remain unexamined in it. Such conditions are the "foundations" of the discourse; they define its universe without being in that universe; there is upon them a one-way dependence. But another discourse may partition things differently, so that what was before fundamental becomes derivative and what was derivative becomes the foundation or part of it. Although in this sense *any* philosophy of science will appear fundamentalist to its critics, it does not follow that science itself is correctly described by the fundamentalist metaphor. To say that sense perception or reason or any other operative component of the scientific process is fundamental to the others is to single out their dependence upon it for special examination while ignoring or suppressing the converse dependency.

Thus, in the case of "fundamental measurements," there is a sense in which certain classes of measurements are fundamental in physics, and in which physics, built on these foundations, is fundamental to other sciences, etc. But an examination of these measurements shows that from a different point of view they are not at all ultimate, being, in a variety of ways, dependent on things other than measurement.

According to the usual account, some measurements can be made directly, but others must be made indirectly—that is, through further, direct measurements of other magnitudes. Length, for example, can be measured directly, by a direct comparison of lengths, but viscosity, for example, must be measured indirectly. Churchman quite properly objects to this distinction, pointing out that the problem of precision in measurement always involves us in a widening circle of other problems: in the measurement of length, for instance, we have to be concerned about temperature coefficients, plastic deformation, the straightness of the line of measurement, the psychological state of the person making the measurement, etc. The ability to define accurate methods of measurement

---

† "A Materialist Theory of Measurement," in *Philosophy for the Future,* edited by R. W. Sellars, V. J. McGill, and Marvin Farber (New York, 1949).

depends, in the last analysis, upon the whole state of science and technology at the time.

Although Churchman's criticism of the fundamentalist position is fair enough as such, the distinction between direct and indirect measurement still has a certain validity. One may notice the fact that there is a kind of upper limit to the accuracy of any single numerical measurement, such that to measure anything with an accuracy of more than, say, one part in 10^{20} is virtually impossible.† The amount of involvement in producing apparatus, in making theoretical calculations and side measurements, is a very steeply increasing function of the desired accuracy, so that the over-all cost of measurement becomes virtually infinite for very high accuracies. Conversely, however, this means that inaccurate measurements are relatively cheap, and that the need of theoretical analysis and side measurement is practically missing—not missing in principle, but taken care of by casual and even unconscious precautions. If this were not true in at least some cases, there would be no measurement at all.

As Churchman points out, the general defense of a fundamentalist position involves a smokescreen; to try to take an anti-fundamentalist position, to question the fundamentals, is to put oneself in the dilemma, it is said, of being involved either in a logical circle or in an infinite ocean, in which, in the words of a contemporary author, there is "no foundation, all the way down." There is, however, nothing wrong with a circle or an infinite regress. A map that maps only itself is an indeterminate absurdity; but a map that maps any larger region containing itself is perfectly all right, for the changes in the thing mapped, which result from the mapping, are convergent; the map is perfectly determinate and can be drawn to any degree of accuracy; it involves an infinite regress but one that makes no trouble. Even though any measurement may involve, in principle, side measurements, so that side measurements may also involve their own side measurements, etc., the *whole* process can involve only a finite amount of measuring. If every measurement involved a side measurement, the infinite regress would indeed be a vicious one, and there would, as stated, be no measurement at all.

---

† The statement is not deep, and it depends on the definition of accuracy: a method that will discriminate *any* one of N alternatives has an accuracy of "one part in N." A piano-tuner can discriminate pitch to a fraction of a cycle in the neighborhood of the given standard, but he cannot determine an *arbitrary* pitch with this accuracy. The subject belongs to information theory, to be discussed later. See Léon Brillouin, *Science and Information Theory* (New York, 1956), Chaps. 14, 15, 16. The Mössbauer effect is a recent example of high accuracy and an almost ideal case of highly quantitative science at its best; here a metric art rather akin to the piano-tuner's permits a test of the general theory of relativity. The accuracy involved at this writing is about one in 10^{12}, comparable to a second in 30,000 years.

On this account, whether or not a measurement is "fundamental" is a matter of degree, and the most "fundamental" measurements are those that require us to take the least necessary precautions in making them because the means of measurement are the least dependent upon extraneous variable conditions requiring special control; to put it another way, the magnitudes being measured are the most easily isolated types of order relation—abstracted and idealized, for that reason, as separate dimensions of experience. Indirect measurements, on the same account, approach the opposite end of the scale, where the amount of side measurement is such that, if all measurements were as indirect as these, there would be no measurement at all.

The Measurement of Time

A detailed account of any of the problems of quantitative measurement will illustrate these observations. The measurement of time is a particularly interesting example, and its problems are related to a number of issues I have already discussed.†

The common-sense conception of time intervals is connected with the prevalence of periodicity in our experience, a periodicity that forms the practical basis of human planning. With the development of urban existence the natural periodicities, biological and astronomical, were supplemented by artificial ones, and the various astronomical periods, diurnal, lunar, and solar, were correlated with one another. Until the seventeenth century artificial clocks were very poor affairs compared with the astronomical ones. In that period the practical needs of mercantile technology and the intellectual interests provided by the new science of mechanics combined to produce the pendulum clock and the balance-wheel chronometer, and the clock became a favorite image for the mechanistic cosmology. Much of the impetus of this development came from the discovery (usually ascribed to Galileo) that the period of a simple pendulum is practically independent of the amplitude of its motion. Christian Huygens later designed a pendulum for which, in theory, this property held absolutely. The modern mechanical clock illustrates perfectly the logical circularity to which the fundamentalist creed is opposed. To establish the isochrony of the pendulum, Galileo used his pulse rate, and the laws of mechanics, established by experiments equally crude, gave it theoretical sanction. The same laws, applied by Newton to the description of the solar system, justified the

---

† See Adolf Grünbaum, "Geometry, Chronometry, and Empiricism," in *Minnesota Studies in the Philosophy of Science*, vol. 3, edited by Herbert Feigl (Minneapolis, 1962), pp. 405–526.

belief, which had been held all along, in the isochrony of the motions of the heavens.

The laws of mechanics define, in principle, a perfect clock, a clock that can be used as a standard against which to criticize the very clocks by which the laws themselves have been experimentally established. Philosophers, by profession suspicious of the reasoning processes of others, have often regarded this as a vicious circle; but it is not. A bad clock used as a standard not only will fail to confirm dynamical laws but will lead to all sorts of other consequences as well. The king's heartbeat is a bad clock because, if it were taken to be a good one, it would imply all sorts of causal relations between the king's physiology or state of mind and the rest of things, which slow down when he is angry and speed up when he sleeps. The most convinced royalist might doubt this evidence of the king's power and resort to mechanical devices (not, of course, called clocks) of wheel and pendulum for the conduct of daily life. A good clock is an isolated system, isolated in the sense that it fails to display what may be called the king's-heartbeat effect. In recent years the diurnal motion of the earth has been shown to display this effect: its use as a basic time standard "causes" slight *simultaneous* accelerations and retardations of the orbital motions of the other plants. It is concluded, properly, that the earth's rate of rotation changes slightly. The theoretical concept of an ideal clock is meaningful because there is, in nature, a practically infinite collection of independent or nearly independent periodic processes. Any of these is, more or less, a good clock; but that is best which, when taken as a standard, induces the least concomitant variation among the others.

The notion of a dynamically ideal clock had meaning for the age of Galileo and Newton. For the age of Einstein and Heisenberg the ideal itself has to be recast, on both the cosmological scale and the atomic. In the extremes of the great and small worlds of physics today, discrepancies, which in mid-range are counted as accidental, grow to dominate the account of things and so prove to be of the essence. The general discussion belongs to Chapter 5.

Measurement and Invariance

Such magnitudes as distance, area, volume, time interval, mass, and force have obvious physically defined characteristics corresponding to arithmetical addition, and they have a natural zero. All that is lacking is a natural unit. We may thus transform any set of numbers representing distances, time, etc., by multiplying them by an arbitrary constant, which alters none of the relations among them but merely represents the same magnitudes by a different unit. We express this limited element of arbitrariness in the numerical representation of such magnitudes by saying that they are invariant up to the group of scale transformations, or up to multiplication by an arbitrary constant. In geometry, as we saw in Chapter 2, distance is invariant up to the group of translations, rotations, and reflections of the coordinate system. The physical concept of energy is invariant up to an arbitrary linear transformation, since there is no natural zero of energy. The relations between saturated colors may be represented geometrically or algebraically by the color triangle, and the numbers assigned to them are invariant up to a wider class of transformations, the projective—such as transform the circle into an ellipse. Certain magnitudes, such as utility in the usual account of it in modern economic theory, are well ordered in the sense that they permit the comparisons "greater than" and "equal to" but nothing further. Numbers assigned to such magnitudes are invariant up to a monotone, or order-preserving, transformation.

As I observed earlier, in connection with analytic geometry, such isomorphisms as these are to be thought of, not as demonstrating a magical and special quality in things that permits their representation by numbers, but rather as demonstrating the flexibility and richness of the number system, which may be thought of as a vast storehouse of relational patterns, of analogies or isomorphisms available for use whenever or wherever they may prove valuable. The concept of invariance up to a given group of transformations makes possible a special but very important technique for defining relational patterns that exhibit some, but not all, of the specific features of the number system.

Because of the prestige associated with physical measurements and the general nebulous sense of virtue associated with mathematicism in science, invariance up to a more restricted group of transformations is felt, in general, to be better than invariance up to a less restricted group of transformations. I can, however, give illustrations that point both ways. In the first place, there is nothing final about a particular way of defining this or that quantity; for, when a field is investigated more deeply, the conception of relational patterns found in it may change. A classical example is temperature, which, to prescientific common sense, permits ordering with respect to hotter and colder, but not much more. The assignment of numbers in such cases would be quite arbitrary—that is, invariant up to the group of monotone transformations. With the development of the theory of the gas thermometer this was changed, and temperatures could be assigned numbers up to an arbitrary linear transformation. The further development of thermodynamics fixed for temperature an absolute zero, so that temperature turned out, in fine, to be as good and re-spectable a measure as mass or length. In this case the restriction of the range of arbitrariness in measurement is concomitant with the growth of fundamental knowledge, and the gain is a real one. One has, however, only to look at a case of really unfinished business to see that there is no guarantee of progress in such restrictions.

When the concept of utility was first introduced into economics at the end of the nineteenth century, it was assumed, rather uncritically, that utility was measurable at least up to an arbitrary linear transformation. In the course of time, however, it became fairly clear that no way of assigning numbers to utilities or preferences would enable one to say, for example, that the preference for C over A was twice that for B over A. As a result of these criticisms, it became customary to treat utilities as mere orderings—that is, as numbers up to an arbitrary monotone transformation. More recently, however, Neumann and Morgenstern[†] have proposed a new method of measuring utility, based on the assumption that comparisons of the more and the less preferable can be made not only for specific items but also for mixtures of items based on probabilities or relative frequencies. Thus, if A is preferable to B and C is preferable to A, and if A is equal in desirability to C 20 percent of the time and to B 80 percent of the time, we may take the number 8/10 as a reasonable measure of the ratio of preferability of A to C compared with that of B to C. The suggestion illustrates the fact that in utilities no *inherent* limitation makes it impossible to measure them in the usual sense. There will be further dis-cussion of the concept of utility in Chapter 13. Even here, however, it is rather obvious that such a proposal as that of Neumann and Morgenstern has merit not because, of itself, it makes utility a more quantitative concept, but rather to the degree to which the added precision plays a role *within the framework of economic knowledge*. There is nothing inherently or automatically good about such an innovation. We may find, indeed, that for some purposes in economics even the concept of ordinal utilities, with its implication that human beings and groups make decisions by reference to independently given psy-chological impulses that somehow render all alternatives comparable, may be unduly restrictive; the concept of ordinal utility might for some purposes be replaced by other, still more abstract types of relational patterns.[‡]

[†] John von Neumann and Oskar Morgenstern, *The Theory of Games and Economic Behavior* (Princeton, 1944).

[‡] See K. J. Arrow, *Social Choice and Individual Value* (New York, 1951); K. O. May, "A Set of Independent Necessary and Sufficient Conditions for Simple Majority Decision," *Econometrica*, 20, 4 (October 1952), pp. 681–84.

Relational Patterns

Invariance up to a group of transformations permits a classification of relational patterns that could be expressed, equally well, in terms of equivalence relations and equivalence classes. The possibility of transforming one representation into another and vice versa means that the group of representations is an equivalence class, and a relational pattern, an invariant, may be identified with the equivalence class. Thus integers, rational numbers, real numbers, and complex numbers may be regarded as invariants.

In the discussion† of measurements one particular sequence is usually picked out, that of numbers up to (*a*) no transformation, (*b*) multiplication by a constant, (*c*) a linear transformation, (*d*) a monotone transformation. In view of the possibility of renaming equivalence classes as invariants, we could have started even higher in the scale, since real numbers are already mere invariants. Then at the absolute top we should have the natural numbers. The arbitrary and invidious character of the hierarchy above may lead one to suspect that it represents a residue of Pythagorean metaphysics, with the top layers decently hidden from view. The scientific value of this particular hierarchy, in many fields, is beyond the need of any metaphysical justification. Nevertheless, we must seriously ask whether it is not wrong and misleading to view it as a hierarchy. There are, first of all, many other kinds of transformations and invariants than these, and of relational patterns that can be abstracted from the number system. The set of all such patterns does not form a hierarchy, a well-ordered sequence. There are, for example, topological trees, partial orderings, that may still be subject to various sorts of quantification beyond mere ordering (Fig. 12).

But let us return to the standard list. One of the distinctions that have been connected with the differences between *b*, *c*, and *d* is that between extensive and intensive magnitude. In *d*, mere ordering, we can assign numbers to the items ranked, but we cannot thereby rank differences, or intervals. In *b* and *c* we can rank differences; of three boards, *A*, *B*, and *C*, it is possible to say that the difference $A - B$ is greater than or less than the difference $B - C$. Lengths are additive, and this implies invariance of order among first (and also second, third, etc.) differences.

The additive property has been held to be characteristic of *extensive* mag-

---

† A very good presentation is that of S. S. Stevens, "On the Theory of Scales of Measurement," *Science*, vol. 103 (1946), 2684, reprinted in *Philosophy of Science*, edited by Arthur Danto and Sidney Morgenbesser (Cleveland and New York, 1960).

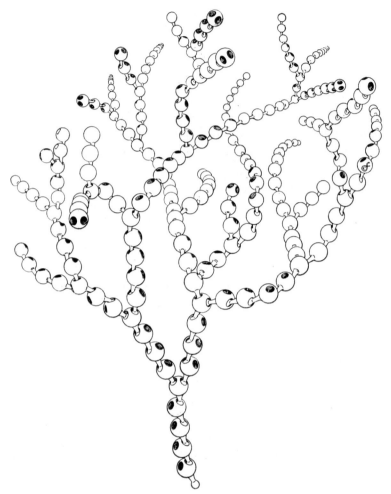

Fig. 12. A Model of Partial Order

nitudes (weight, length, etc.) and to distinguish them sharply from mere *inten-sive* magnitudes (density, viscosity, etc.) on the ground that no *physical* operation with the latter is isomorphous with arithmetical addition. But we *can* measure intensive magnitudes in the sense of *b* or *c*; we can do so, it is explained, because such measurements are not fundamental but derived. This classification is objectionable: it reduces to two alternatives a much more com-plex variety of metrical techniques, and the distinction between fundamental and derived, as I have previously urged, is a relative and pragmatic distinction, which can change with the state of knowledge and technique. Electrical re-sistances can be added but are not ordinarily regarded as fundamental; in the context of relativity theory mass is not additive under conditions such that the physical addition involves a change of positional energies; in the same context lengths may be variable too.

The whole question is whether we can specify a procedure of such a kind that meaning can be given to the idea of equal intervals (or other possible invariants) within the framework of our knowledge. We always *can* find a procedure for defining equal intervals, by arbitrary fiat if necessary. Does the procedure employed give us something significantly related to other variables within the system of knowledge? If it does, the relevance of that relational pattern is thereby established; if not, then not.

Measurement and Its Validation: Operationalism

Implicit in the discussion of measurement so far is the assumption that the results of any particular measurement are not ends in themselves but play a role of some kind. In the present section I shall discuss more explicitly the relation between measurement and theory in science, and in the process I shall generalize the concept of measurement itself in line with the purposes set forth at the beginning of the chapter.

Descriptive concepts, including those ordinarily called quantitative or metrical, have as function in the economy of knowledge the linkage of two universes of discourse, the concrete perceptual and the abstract conceptual. In being classified under this or that conceptual heading, any empirical object or state of affairs is not merely brought into relation with the particular abstraction that is the basis for classifying it; it is classified with some things and apart from others, and it is involved in all the consequences resulting from the linkages, logical and factual, of this class concept with others.

In his description of the psychology of thought, William James† distinguishes two generic aspects of the thought process, which he calls "sagacity" and "learning." Sagacity is the ability to categorize, to see in the concrete particular situation an exemplification of some abstractible characteristic, some universal; learning is the capacity, derived from past experience and education, to link the universal thus discerned with other universals, to the end that the particular be characterized in some non-obvious way that is useful for the purposes at hand. In an amusing story for which James does not vouch, a dog goes each day to fetch the pail with which his master bails out the boat in which they subsequently take a ride. One day the pail is missing, and, after some

† William James, *The Principles of Psychology* (New York, 1890), vol. 2, Chap. 22, *passim*.

delay, the dog comes to the lake carrying in his mouth a large sponge. The point of the story, to which its truth is inessential, is the dog's ability to abstract, from among the characteristics of the pail, the one that is relevant to his immediate purpose, and then to find another object that can be classed with it in this respect, however different this object's other and now inessential characteristics. By learning the dog is able to define the characteristic of the pail that is essential to the purpose; by sagacity he is able to discern just that characteristic in an otherwise quite dissimilar object.

A descriptive concept must be usable as a basis for classifying things, and it must be linked with other concepts in a way that supports reliable inferences about the things thus classified. It must have, as it were, two kinds of reliability: that of being reliably related to other concepts in the system of knowledge, and that of reliably guiding the classification of particulars.

But we do not, in general, possess concepts that satisfy both these requirements in high degree. What is characteristic of common-sense concepts is that they are linked together in a rather loose, implicit system of beliefs; and, since such concepts are not sharply defined in an empirical sense, it is a considerable problem to say just how they apply in particular cases. Nor is it easy to improve the situation. We see the vagueness and indeterminateness of the dynamical concepts in the physics of Aristotle and his medieval followers in a particularly striking way because a new system of dynamical concepts, possessing both kinds of reliability in high degree, has subsequently been elaborated. But this achievement is coextensive with the whole history of experimental and theoretical inquiry; there is no magic in it.

What *is* always easy is to increase one kind of reliability at the expense of the other. We may construct coherent theories at the expense of the empirical reliability of the concepts employed, or we may give concepts reliable empirical reference at the expense of significant generalizations about them. Either procedure may be a useful tactic in scientific research, but neither is more than that. Using the labels as names for intellectual tendencies rather than for philosophical theories, we may refer to the former procedure as rationalistic and to the latter as empiricistic. Empiricism, the tendency to specify descriptive concepts primarily with reference to means and methods of observation and measurement, may lead to revised concepts, among which new theoretical relations can be conjectured and, in the end, demonstrated experimentally. Rationalism, the tendency to elaborate theoretical systems without much reference to the empirical meaning of concepts, may lead to new sorts of observation and measurement. Galileo's concern for the techniques of measuring time and velocity was necessary to his formulation of the law of falling bodies; his law of inertia was necessary to a perception of the significance of forces and their measurement in problems of accelerated motion. Both tendencies, interacting, are involved in successful scientific inquiry. The amount and kind of emphasis to be placed on each sort of tactic will vary with the situation in which research is going on.

If, in our distinction between tendencies, we replace the term "empiricism" by "operationalism," we come into an area in which there has been extensive debate in the last quarter of a century in America. The new term comes from a very influential essay by the physicist-philosopher P. W. Bridgman, in which he elaborated the thesis that the meaning of metrical concepts is, or is defined by, the method of measurement.† Bridgman's thesis was elaborated with special reference to certain problems of modern physics, resulting from the discovery of important ambiguities in basic physical concepts. The special theory of relativity, for example, implies that no precise operational meaning can be given to the concept of simultaneity applied to events spatially distant from each other. A complete description of the means used for determining simultaneity will include the fact that physical signals must be transmitted from the vicinity of both events to an observer, and that the relative times of arrival will depend upon the velocity of the observer. In the framework of classical physics there was no reason to believe that the transmission time of signals was essentially involved in the definition of simultaneity at a distance. The transmission of signals is, nevertheless, a part of the operation of determining the time interval between events at a distance; and, if this fact had been clearly understood all along, there would have been less shock in the discovery that simultaneity at a distance has only a relative, not an absolute, meaning.

Bridgman also pointed out that the relativistic proposition that there is a limiting velocity beyond which no body can be accelerated depends upon the operational definition of velocity as displacement per unit time and would not hold of velocity defined—that is, measured—by some other means. Bridgman's emphasis arose out of the crisis of physics in the first part of the century and was an expression, in philosophical terms, of the self-consciousness about basic concepts that the theory of relativity had evoked. It was realized, for the first time, that concepts that have a perfectly precise empirical reference under the ordinary conditions of human experience exhibit ambiguities when extrapolated far beyond that range, and that therefore one must pay attention in measurement to operational features that are ordinarily ignored, on pain of mistaking the theoretical import of the results of the measurement. Bridgman's thesis thus had a

† P. W. Bridgman, *The Logic of Modern Physics* (New York, 1927).

very important point, but the point was made in an erroneous way. For it ignored the fact that the *relevant* features of an operational procedure are those that have *theoretical* import. In the case of simultaneity at a distance the process of signal-transmission was important because in the theory of relativity such signals could not be transmitted with more than the speed of light and because the speed of light is the same for all observers. Instead of taking operations as basic and the concepts as defined by them, we could take the concepts as basic and the operations as prescribed by them. An operation is in the nature of a universal; it has to be repeated on different occasions and by different persons. This means that we have to specify what features two or more performances of an operation must have in common to qualify those performances as the *same* operation. Such specifications are not arbitrary; they stem from some system of general beliefs, however hazy and implicit. In relativity theory, and in physics quite generally, the theoretical criteria are sharp and explicit. Hence the especial one-sidedness of Bridgman's thesis.

Operationalism has been influential in fields of investigation quite remote from the original sorts of problems with which Bridgman was concerned, especially in psychology and in some areas of the social sciences. In these fields the state of scientific development was very remote from that of the physical sciences, and in the United States the influence of operationalism was to reinforce tendencies, already conspicuous, away from theories involving concepts that did not prescribe well-defined techniques of measurement. In particular, operationalism reinforced opposition to the type of psychological theory represented by the Freudian tradition, in which the means of observation could not be sharply distinguished from the perhaps arbitrary subjective judgment of clinicians. Some recent American discussions of psychological methodology have been more generous to the rationalistic tendency† defined above and have recognized that the guidance of theory in the design of measurements and ex-

---

† L. J. Cronbach and P. E. Meehl, "Construct Validity in Psychological Tests," *Psychological Bulletin,* 52 (1955), 281–302; J. A. Taylor, "Drive Theory and Manifest Anxiety," *ibid.,* 53 (1956), 303–20; R. Jessor and K. R. Hammond, "Construct Validity and the Taylor Anxiety Scale," *ibid.,* 54 (1957), 161–70; W. F. Hill, "Comments on Taylor's 'Drive Theory and Manifest Anxiety,' " *ibid.,* 54 (1957), 490–93; D. C. McClelland, "Methods of Measuring Human Motivation," in *Motives in Fantasy, Action, and Society,* edited by John W. Atkinson (Princeton, 1958), Chap. 1. If one works through this sequence, one may see, first, the formulation of a need for tests bearing some relation to theory. In the irreverend language of applied mathematics, "construct validity" translates as some theory into which measurements can be plugged. American psychological testers have not always been quick to make "theory" a nice word; hence, perhaps, the euphemism. The following papers discuss the problem of motivation theory in relation to a particular test. The final paper is concerned with the fact that different measures aimed at the same variable give only weakly correlated results.

periments may be of substantial importance even when the theory in question is sketchy and speculative.

In order to emphasize still further the equal importance of theoretical and empirical reliability in the descriptive concepts of science, I shall mention two cases in which the theoretically significant descriptive concepts correspond to what are, on the empirical side, very complex constellations of observables.

In biological taxonomy, for example, the "measurements" that determine the boundary lines between species are complex enough and sufficiently ill defined to bother a determined operationalist. Yet taxonomic science has achieved a high degree of empirical reliability. Among the indefinitely large numbers of traits by which one organism may be distinguished from another, the taxonomist singles out certain traits that are, when taken together, more or less reliable indicators of many others. If one wished to represent this type of observation geometrically, one would have to visualize the species as a closed region, an ellipsoid, in a many-dimensional space. In some dimensions the representative ellipsoid may be greatly elongated, indicating that precision of measurement is not critical; in others it may be foreshortened. From the present point of view the taxonomists' procedures for determining the place of an organism in the kinship map of living things should be regarded as a type of measurement just as quantitative, just as much to be eulogized for the services it performs, as any other type.

Another case of measurement that provides the same sort of multidimensional comparison is presented by descriptive concepts pertaining to social institutions —for example, the concept of monopoly in economics. This concept may be elucidated in terms of highly simplified theories by reference to the ability of an individual firm to gain some measure of control over the prices at which its products are sold. What is called for in such theories is, in consequence, some single measure of the "degree of monopoly" achieved by a firm or in an industry or in an economy as a whole. When we turn, however, from abstract formal models to a historical-descriptive account of the evolution of the European or American economies in the last fifty or a hundred years, we find that the phenomenon of monopoly exhibits a qualitative richness and a variety that defy any simple, one-dimensional description. How is the degree of monopoly going to be determined, empirically? Measures of "concentration" have generally been used—such, for example, as the share of business done in an industry by its five largest firms. But there are other measures of obvious importance: barriers to the entry of new capital into the industry, the diffusion of ownership into adjacent industries in vertical integration, the control of patents, the ma-

CARL A. RUDISILL LIBRARY
LENOIR RHYNE COLLEGE

nipulation of demand through advertising, product-differentiation, etc. One might despair of finding any simple measure of the degree of monopoly, or one might construct such a measure by brute force, as it were, taking it to be some simple average of several measurable features of the actual situation. But this problem, unsatisfactory from the point of view that calls it forth, is, in reality, no cause for despair of being scientific; the trouble lies, not in the difficulty of measuring monopoly, but in the type of theory that requires such a linear, one-dimensional measure. A better theory will be concerned with the effects of monopoly not only on prices and profits but also on the growth and structure of the economy: on technology and technological innovation, on investment, on patterns of employment. For these purposes the theory of monopoly requires just such a multidimensional description as the historian has, in the meantime, been elaborating.† *The difficulty of measuring the degree of monopoly is an indication of the crudeness of the theory that requires such a measure.* The crude theory, on the other hand, does single out something that is essential to a kind of first approximation, something that implies an interconnectedness among all the facets of monopolistic organization, that implies that they are facets of one thing—namely, of an institutional evolution in the direction of increased control over variables affecting the economic power of the firm. For the purposes of this crude theory, crude measurements suffice.

Measurement and Information

The unifying framework of ideas into which the endless varieties of measurement may be fitted is provided by what has come to be called, in recent years, information theory. We may start with a phrase that was introduced a quarter of a century ago by the physicist-philosopher A. S. Eddington. In a classic description of the nature of physics, Eddington referred to an examination problem about an elephant sliding down a grassy bank. For the elephant the knowing student substitutes a mass of two tons, the reading of a pointer when the elephant is placed on the scales. For the grassy bank he substitutes the reading of a plumb-line against a protractor: 60°. The grassy turf is replaced by a coefficient of friction, the reading of another line against another protractor. In summary, Eddington concluded: "The whole subject-matter of exact science consists of pointer-readings and similar indications." ‡ But what, then, of all the

---

† An excellent summary account of these and related theoretical problems is Frederik Zeuthen, *Economic Theory and Method* (Cambridge, Mass., 1955), Part IV. For a descriptive account of American industrial organization see Joe S. Bain, *Industrial Organization* (New York, 1959).

‡ A. S. Eddington, *The Nature of the Physical World* (Cambridge, England, 1928), pp. 251–53.

qualitative features of the situation? The scientist (at least, in Eddington's account, the "exact" scientist) has nothing to do with them, and he summarily removes them from his picture of reality; they are left over to the poet, the mystic, or the philosopher. Without fully realizing it at the time, Eddington in this thinking recapitulated much of the historical-philosophical struggle over the issue of primary and secondary qualities.

But there is a difference between Eddington's analysis and the classical one. The division, for Eddington, was not between primary and secondary qualities, but between the qualities of things and their numerical representation. Hence the significance of pointer readings, which were, for Eddington, the primary and only necessary data of "exact science." Nor did he mean by the phrase the coincidence of a physical pointer with marks on a physical scale. He meant, rather, the pointer reading observed in the perceptual field of some observer, for the measuring instrument was regarded, not as a means of knowing something else, but as a part of the thing to be known, of the physical world, and just as problematic in its nature as atoms or the electromagnetic field. In Eddington's mode of thinking there is, so to speak, only one isolated system, the universe; and its boundaries are not physical boundaries, but the boundaries of direct perceptual awareness—of pointer readings. One may say that it is not the physical system that is isolated from the rest of nature, including the observer; instead, it is the observer who is isolated, at the periphery of his own consciousness. Eddington embraced the subjectivistic side of a dilemma that will be discussed later, but—as befitted the preoccupations of an astrophysicist—with pointer readings rather than the colors, sounds, etc.

The virtue of Eddington's shift of attention away from the qualitative profusion and richness of sense qualities toward the logical austerity of pointer readings is that it puts attention on the *informational* aspect of perception. Eddington's restriction was an absurd one, but it was absurd precisely because *every* sense quality or configuration of sense qualities is, or may be regarded as, a pointer reading. For the quality might have been absent, or the constellation might have been different, and in all cases what is significant cognitively is that *one,* rather than *another,* of a range of alternatives is realized. From this point of view all perception is measurement. Nor need perception be limited, in this account of its function, to sense qualities. The physical pointer, if we assume that it can be read correctly, is just as much a measurement as the appearance of such a pointer in the visual field; and so is the shape of a spider's web or of a spiral galaxy. The capacity of an observed fact to convey information is not dependent upon its status as an entity, whether subjective or objective, physical or psychical. The significance of the red spot on my hand as an indication of infection does not depend upon the outcome of philosophical debate about the status of secondary qualities. It is not the quality itself but the fact of its presence or absence that is significant. From this point of view the character of empirical knowledge would not be affected if the existing manifold of sense qualities were replaced by something like a teletype code of psychical impulses.

In my criticism of the Kantian philosophy of spatial perception I made use of an analogy between perception and communication. The analogy requires, in perception, some process analogous to decoding. That process is generally considered under information theory, to which we now turn.†

In that theory a message is considered, apart from any question of meaning, simply as one of a set of alternative messages. The receiver has both to receive the message and to identify or define it correctly. A unit message, the shortest kind, is the presence or absence of a single pulse in a given time interval, or, in general, one of *two* alternatives. The simplest definition of the quantity of information conveyed by a message is the minimum number of unit messages, or bits (binary digits) of information, sufficient for its certain identification by the receiver. If the possible messages in the set are N in number, the best possible code (or strategy of identification) is one in which each unit message dichotomizes the alternatives still remaining, dividing them as nearly as possible in half, and indicates which half the correct message is in. Thus, if there are 1,024 possible messages, transmission will require 10 unit messages, or bits, since each object out of that number may be represented by a sequence of 10 binary digits. In general, the quantity of information is that value of the natural number r for which

$$2^{r-1} < N \leq 2^r$$

Since measurement is likewise a process of defining or identifying some existing alternative out of a set of possible alternatives, we may say that the quantity of information conveyed by a measurement is the minimum number of binary discriminations that is sufficient to determine the correct alternative.

So defined, the quantity of information is a natural number. But there are theoretical reasons for preferring a slightly different measure, the real number r' such that

---

† C. E. Shannon and Warren Weaver, *The Mathematical Theory of Communication* (Urbana, Ill., 1949). A good survey and discussion are in Colin Cherry, *On Human Communication* (Cambridge, Mass., 1957). The earliest paper was that of R. V. L. Hartley, "Transmission of Information," *Bell System Technical Journal*, 7 (1928), 535–63.

$$2^{r'} = N$$

or

$$r' = \log_2 N$$

The theoretical reason in question is that, if a sequence of messages were going to be transmitted, or measurements taken, each identifying one out of N alternatives, the real number r' would prove to be the minimum number of bits sufficient, *on the average,* to achieve correct identification. To discriminate 1 object out of 5 requires 3 bits: we first split the set into 2 and 3; if the object is one of the 3, we must split into 2 and 1; and, if it is one of the 2, another split is necessary. But, if we waited until we had three such five-fold discriminations to make, we should have altogether $5^3 = 125$ alternatives, and this would require 7 bits, since $2^7 = 128$. But this is an average, per discrimination, of $7/3 = 2.33$. In the limit of still larger numbers this could be reduced to an average of $\log_2 5$ ($= 2.32$, nearly).

I shall return to the subject of information theory and measurement in a later context (Chap. 8) and discuss a somewhat more general definition that takes account of complications connected with probability and what is now known, metaphorically, as noise. None of this will affect either our present definition or the isomorphism of communication and measurement.[†] The amount of information gained in a measurement is simply the number of binary choices, or bits, needed to determine the result. From this point of view, Eddington's pointer readings are not simple; each contains many bits of information. If the weight of the elephant is given as 2.03 tons, the maximum information conveyed is about ten bits, apart from the location of the decimal point. Finding the shape of the spider's web or the galaxy, in some system of description, is a measurement of a higher order (and hence "more precise"?). Every measurement, every observation, may be made, or may in any case be represented as if made, by a sequence of binary choices and thus as containing or conveying information. What matters, from this point of view, is not this or that special sense, whether visual, auditory, etc.; not this or that kind of determination, whether quantitative or qualitative; all that matters is a complex of choices whose simplest instance is a single binary "yes" or "no."

The analogy of communication seems to fit easily the classical dualism of a world of subjective sense impressions and a conjectured external reality, the former connected with the latter by open channels, the special senses. But, as I

---

† Cf. Jerome Rothstein, *Communication, Organization, and Science* (Indian Hills, Colorado, 1958), especially Chap. 2.

suggested in the discussion of Kant, the analogy is a bad one at this point. In perception the received message is not *what* we perceive, but the perceiving of a *what,* a what that is the analogue of the transmitted message. Measurement, as I have defined it, is the use of perception to discriminate among conceptually defined alternatives in order to reduce their number. Perception is a non-deliberate sort of decoding, over which we have no conscious control. Measurement is a way of taking what we perceive as signifying the elimination of conceptually formulated, alternative possibilities. In this case the analogy of decoding is the answering of a question, the question that requires the simplest answer being the binary, yes-no, 1-0 type. Conception proposes in order that perception may dispose.

In social communication the literal concept of a code may be analyzed as a *standardized* sequence of questions: the sender imputes them to the receiver, and the receiver, knowing this imputation, imputes to the sender the intent to answer them. In measurement the receiver has, again, no literal conversation with the sender, and the analogy breaks down. Instead, there is an attempt, in terms of previous knowledge, to control the situation by standardization of technique, so that nature's response to a prod will be the answer to a question posed by the measurer. But the problems of knowledge are deep, and I shall not solve them here.

What I have attempted in the present chapter is to attack the claim, commonly made both in the name of science and in opposition to it, that its genius, its mark of distinction, is the preferential use of the kind of information that is represented by the clock, the meter stick, and the weighing machine, and that its real world is therefore a world of number and geometric form, all else being discarded. To the extent that in one field of knowledge or another such kinds of measurement do become fundamental, their definition and their role are matters of antecedent knowledge that was gained through cruder means of observation. In other fields it is equally a matter of knowledge that such methods are not appropriate. The number system is, as we have illustrated in many ways, an abundant source of isomorphisms, of analogies for descriptive concepts of order and form, many of them not quantitative in any ordinary sense. What matters in all cases, whether we resort to these analogies or not, is that a discrimination of the actual from the possible is involved, and that in that sense (the sense of information theory) all such discrimination is measurement. Accurate physical measurements may convey a large quantity of information, but so may a Darwin's repeated observations of the facial expressions of animals. Which sort of discrimination is best—most scientific—depends upon the nature of the subject matter and of the theoretical framework within which observation is going to have scientific utility.

Physics has taught us to speak *a* language of nature, the language of mass, distance, and time. But this language, which I shall discuss in the following chapter, appears as *the* language of nature only while we remain, so to speak, in the primary grades. Beyond those there is a larger literature, for which the grammar and rhetoric of that language are essential but not adequate.

5

LAWS OF MOTION

Having examined the claim of narrow mathematicism in science and found it wanting, we should now give credit where and in what measure credit is due. The stronghold of mathematicism is the system of the laws of physics. Here the questions to be raised are not so much about the appropriateness of the differential equations of physics as about the adequacy of the philosophical beliefs that accompany the elaboration and substantiation of those laws. These beliefs have been extremely influential, not only in directing the course of scientific work, but also in other areas of human interest.

Law and Modern Science

The conception of scientific law has been one of the major foci of philosophical interest and debate since the seventeenth century. Before that time it was not a prevalent concept, and its function in the economy of ideas was taken care of, in some measure, by various other concepts. The "laws of nature" have been, for three and a half centuries, more or less, crossroads connecting the important areas of intellectual ferment: the physical sciences, economics and politics, ethics, epistemology, and metaphysics. The historical setting for the development of those laws was the sixteenth- and seventeenth-century development of astronomy and mechanics intruding into an intellectual environment of medieval Aristotelianism. The development was closely tied, moreover, to the emergence of the geometry of motion and thus, in turn, to the mathematical traditions of arithmetic and geometry.

I shall speak first of the intellectual environment, of the framework or network of concepts into which the new science intruded. Developments in the history of science—or, for that matter, anywhere in the history of thought—do not appear in a manner that contemporaries can afford to regard as merely filling a gap, an intellectual vacuum. The very formulation of what we do *not* know is, inevitably, a function of prevailing belief. What appears from an external point of view as the development of positive knowledge is a process by which new ways of marshaling information are organized, partly by means of, and partly in conflict with, established connections of ideas. John Locke's famous metaphor of the mind as a *tabula rasa* is, from this point of view, the very reverse of truth. New knowledge has to make room for itself within the system of previously stabilized belief, distort that system if need be, and finally force a reorganization.†

Aristotle on Motion

The immediate background of Galileo's studies of motion was the late medieval discussion of Aristotle's physics. The latter is not, primarily, physics as we understand the term, but philosophy. The Latin synonym of the Greek *physis* is *natura;* Aristotle's *Physics* is a philosophy of nature. Since it was philosophy and not science, Aristotelian physics was not, in any simple sense, contradicted by Galilean physics. If it were true that the philosophy of nature could be pursued independently of science, one could argue—as some modern Thomists have argued—that the traditional antagonism between Aristotelianism and modern science, dramatized in the work and life of Galileo, was all a mistake.

Such an argument seems wrong. Philosophic interpretation and scientific description are not so radically irrelevant to each other, and this should be especially clear to a modern Aristotelian, for of all the classical philosophers Aristotle was the least inclined to carve up the realm of inquiry in such a separatist fashion. The new science of Galileo and his age was both a product of the medieval development of Aristotelian thought and a challenge to it of major proportions.

---

† The fact here briefly alluded to is explored in depth in Thomas S. Kuhn, *The Structure of Scientific Revolutions* (Chicago, 1962), published also as Vol. II, No. 2, of the *International Encyclopedia of Unified Science* (Chicago, 1962).

The modern concern with studying things in isolation rather than in uncontrolled interaction has its counterpart in Aristotle's conception of *natural* changes as distinguished from those that are artificial or accidental. Every kind of thing behaves in a way that is natural to it, in a way that expresses its nature, except as artifice or accident may intervene.† Our knowledge of the nature of things is gained by abstraction from our experience of their characteristic modes of behavior. Although gained in this way, our concepts refer, not to the behavior as such, but to the things themselves, as the originative source of their behavior. Our understanding of things is attributive: the nature of anything is not merely a summary, but an explanation, of its normal behavior; the thing behaves as it does *because* it has such and such a nature rather than some other.

This substance-attribute pattern of explanation is often called empty and formal: a magnet attracts iron because it is the nature of magnets to attract iron (and of iron to be attracted by magnets). But every pattern of explanation is capable of being empty and formal. The Aristotelian framework of ideas applies to individual things, to substances. Attributed to an individual thing, its attributes, among them dispositional properties, will help us to predict its behavior. Bringing two objects together in various orientations, we may conclude that *this* one is a magnet, *that* one unmagnetized iron, and thus predict further differences in their behavior.

When Aristotle turns to the specific topic of motion as a kind of change, he brings with him the idea that motions, like other forms of change, express the nature of the thing that moves. He finds two basic kinds of motion, circular and rectilinear, and all complex motions are a compound of these two. Corresponding to the two simple kinds of motion are two simple kinds of body, celestial and terrestrial; the celestial motions are naturally circumferential and the terrestrial motions naturally radial. Celestial body is thus of a different kind from terrestrial; Aristotle calls it *ether*. Terrestrial body is of four kinds: fire and air move naturally upward, fire in greater degree; earth and water move naturally downward, earth in greater degree.

This conception of elementary motions corresponding to simple elementary kinds of body is made very much more meaningful by Aristotle's cosmology, adapted from one of the great triumphs of Greek astronomy, the homocentric system of Eudoxus of Cnidus, so called because the motions of fixed stars and planets, sun and moon, were all on spheres concentric with the earth. This system was an elaboration of earlier homocentric models, and by it Eudoxus reproduced the alternating apparent acceleration and deceleration of the planetary

---

† Aristotle, *Physics*, Book II, Chap. I.

motions. Thus for Aristotle the naturally circular motions are those of the heavenly spheres, and the naturally radial motions are up and down, centripetal and centrifugal. Since the natural tendency of each terrestrial element is toward its place, with the heavy states at the center and the light just under the sphere of the moon, Aristotle faces a problem that reminds one of a modern thermodynamic problem: why terrestrial processes do not run down. His answer, not very clearly worked out, is the inward transmission of the circumambient celestial motions. These explain the terrestrial cycles of day and season, and they induce transmutations, so that what rises as air falls as water. If it were not for this constant input of motion from the heavens, the equilibrium of processes on the earth would deteriorate to the equilibrium of death. Aristotle's is the first steady-state cosmology.†

The concept of natural motion, contrasted with motion externally induced, was not really at stake in the scientific revolution of the time of Galileo and after.‡ Indeed, the statement that a body on which no force acts does not change its velocity is precisely a statement that such inertial motion is natural and needs no explanation in terms of external agency. The rock or the javelin, on the other hand, is a crucial problem for Aristotelian science; for its lateral motion, though not natural, continues for some time after the external motive force has ceased to act. What was lost in the physics of Galileo and after was not the contrast between natural and induced motion, but the contrast between different *kinds* of natural motion as connected with different *kinds* of matter. What is natural is the constancy, what is induced is the change, of *any* motion. Differences between terrestrial and celestial motion are not natural in Aristotle's sense but are connected with the milieu of the moving object and its mode of interaction with that milieu. If we wish, then, to introduce the concept of dynamical law into the Aristotelian system, we can say that for Aristotle every kind of thing had its own appropriate law of motion. In the science of mechanics, on the other hand, there is only one law, or set of laws, applicable indifferently to all material things. In Aristotelian thought this would imply that all material things are, to that degree, of the same nature.

Aristotelian natural philosophy is primarily a philosophy in which essences, natures, are appealed to as explaining motions. But it does not wholly lack resources for dealing with interaction. The concept of action and passion—the active and the passive—provides a means of explication. One thing acts upon

† See especially Book II, 9, of *De Generatione et Corruptione*.

‡ A. N. Whitehead, in his *Science and the Modern World*, Chap. II, claims that Galileo's profoundest innovation was the conception of the "isolated system." But Aristotle has the idea fully formed. The novelty is not in the form, but in the content.

another in a manner that expresses its nature, and the other is affected in a manner that expresses *its* nature. The way in which a body is accelerated by a force (in Newton's second law) is, in Aristotelian language, of the nature of that body. But again differences of kind are eliminated, for all that counts is the *mass* of that body, the *measure* of Newton's "quantity of matter." The way in which a body acts can again be said to characterize its nature, as in impact or gravitational attraction. But again differences are of measure rather than of kind. In the seventeenth century the special forces of electricity or magnetism might still have been regarded as expressing an ultimate difference of natures, but in the later development of physics even these were universalized and quantified.

Thus, although the Aristotelian concept "nature" can be accommodated to the new physics, it loses, in the process, part of its apparent explanatory power. It can no longer explain differences but only similarities. The differences among things can now be thought of in two ways, one external and one internal. Things differ because they exist in different environments, are acted upon differently; or they are different structures or organizations. Their ultimate parts are not different, but those parts are joined differently; their internal interactions are different, and therefore their gross behavior. Internal differences are explained as external to the parts of things. What Aristotle took to be different natures are differences of organization and environment—what the physicists of a later generation would call boundary conditions.

This is the place to speak of Aristotle's teleology. If the nature of anything can be described by reference to its characteristic behavior when free, when not constrained by external conditions, this nature can also be thought of as tendency or goal. Thus, because the center is the natural place of a stone, it falls toward the center when unconstrained. During the development of mechanistic science and the philosophy that went with it, Aristotle was often condemned for imputing purposes to nature, even to inanimate things. But the correct Aristotelian statement is that purpose in human life, function in the biological realm (as of teeth to grind food), and the centripetal tendency of earth or water are all instances of a generic concept, that of *final cause*. Purpose in human affairs is a kind of final cause, but final cause is not a kind of purpose (as though just like human purpose but non-human). Aristotle is not animistic or anthropocentric in his philosophy. He had to create a technical terminology out of the common tongue; hence "goal," "end," etc. A rock tends toward the center, but it does not wish to be there.

Now one of the consequences of this doctrine is that, if it were not for final causes, there would be a kind of indeterminacy in the processes of nature. What Aristotle calls the efficient cause of any thing or process is coupled to a final cause, again by analogy with means and ends; if it is not so coupled, the thing or process is a matter of accident or chance. The attempt has often been made to describe the early modern shift to a mechanistic pattern of thought as a change from emphasis upon final causes to emphasis upon efficient causes, identifying the latter with the force concept of mechanics. But this is quite wrong. Just as the idea of final cause was transformed into the idea of *generic* law applying equally to all material things, so the idea of efficient cause was deprived of its specificity. It is not the *kind* of force that matters, but only its direction and magnitude. The really significant causal concept in mechanical thought was not that of efficient cause, but was more nearly identical with what Aristotle called the *material* cause.

The material cause of anything, that from which and of which it is made, is formed into the thing, as clay into the pot or earth and water into the tree. It is formed either by artifice or by nature. The material cause is itself formed matter, however, and has *its* nature. From this point of view Aristotle sees the idea of causal *necessity* in terms of the material cause. A saw must be made of something like metal; a large animal with disproportionately big bones must have much "earth" in its diet; the bricks must antedate the house built of them. Antecedent material conditions are necessary, but not sufficient, in explaining what is. Causal necessity derives from the persistence of the material cause and its properties as formed matter. But the saw, or the animal, or the house, is not explained by, or predictable in terms of, its material cause.

Aristotle reserves heavy irony for those who think that the material cause is the whole explanation of anything:

> "People talk about things being 'necessarily generated' much as if they thought that a wall would come up in the necessary course of things because what is heavy naturally descends and what is light is naturally on top, so that stones go down and make the foundations, while the lighter adobe rises above them, and the timber, lightest of all, roofs them above." †

Aristotle's is a philosophy of "integrative levels." At every level of organization the components are formed into a whole; but these components are formed of more elementary matter, and so on down to the four elements, which are differentiations of a prime matter. It is this differentiation or organization that requires the idea of specific final causes to account for it. When the props are

---

† *Physics,* Book II, 9, in the Loeb Classical Library (Harvard University Press).

pulled and "natures" are replaced by "laws of nature," the sense of levels disappears.

It is a curious and significant fact that Aristotle sees the consequences of this way of thought in one special case.† The "nature," or final cause, of circular, celestial motions is already very much what we call law. Here, since there is no possibility of chance interference, a celestial sphere, in its uniform rotation, is constantly and automatically "expressing its nature." The idea of necessity can be applied to it: to be at A now, a planet must have been at some earlier time at B. But, by symmetry, we can also say that it must again, at some predictable later time, be at B. In this case, and only in this case, Aristotle recognized a way of thought that later would come to be called dynamical determinism. Given the final cause (law) and the state of affairs at one time, the state at all other times, past or future, is determined. But, if the idea of specific celestial natures and agencies is generally replaced by the idea of universal laws, the same view can be taken of the affairs of the terrestrial world: given the laws of nature and the state of affairs at a particular time, it will be possible to say that the house necessarily assembles itself. This proposition came to formulation by the eighteenth century.

It is clear, then, what had happened. The monistic concept of universal law was the end-product of Aristotle's pluralistic final causes; but the concept of specific natures, as autonomous and explanatory, disappeared. The explanation of things is reduced to the laws of motion of matter; the behavior of complex things is reducible to the behavior of their elementary parts with given boundary conditions. Thus the material cause, matter with a nature defined by universal laws, is not only a necessary but a sufficient condition of what is, not only a partial explanation but a complete one. If "materialism" is taken to mean a belief in the sufficiency as well as the necessity of Aristotle's material cause, the philosophy of the new science is well described as materialism. Final causes as laws, and efficient causes as forces, are still part of the apparatus of ideas, but they characterize matter as such, and do not serve to distinguish this or that kind of matter.

The Science of Mechanics

The conclusion of the previous argument is that the new physics that began with Galileo did not so much contradict the Aristotelian natural philosophy as subvert it. The Aristotelian categories of cause are still there, but they have

---

† *De Generatione et Corruptione*, Book II, 338ª–338ᵇ.

been transmuted. The most dramatic consequence of this was the dissolution of the old and cherished distinction between heaven and earth. The dissolution had hardly begun in the thought of Copernicus and Kepler, was incomplete in the mind of Galileo, but was fully developed in the physical speculations of Descartes and the analyses of Newton. To treat the planets simply as massive bodies, centripetally accelerated by their gravitational interaction with the sun, and to show the detailed agreement of their motions with the same laws that could be confirmed in the laboratory with weights, springs, and clocks—this was a solvent of the most confirmed belief in the distinction between celestial matter and terrestrial. The classical problems of astronomy—the problems of Eudoxus, Ptolemy, Copernicus, and Kepler—were solved, and they were solved in terms of the humble, but refined and precise, ideas of terrestrial mechanics. Out there is just like here, and the earth is not the center, but only a sample, of the universe. The materialists among the Greeks had said this, but they had to stand on arguments of plausibility and were rejected. The physicists of the seventeenth and eighteenth centuries said it and could supply endless and detailed evidence to support the statement.

One may regret the vanishing of that extraordinary medieval cosmography inherited from Aristotle and Ptolemy, which lent itself so readily to double interpretation, by physics and by religion. But the novel implications of the new physics went deeper than that. They derived from two remarkable features, one a feature of the laws of mechanics themselves, the other a statement in the prose text that accompanies the equations. The two features are temporal reversibility and completeness.

The claim that the laws of mechanics provide the framework of a *complete* description of nature has the following meaning. The motions of matter are predictable, with arbitrary accuracy, in terms of the generic laws of motion and the particular state of affairs to which the laws apply. The forces that link the motions of one part of a system to those of another are, in turn, completely determined by those parts and their motions. Thus there is a closed logical circuit, open to no extraneous influence. In Newtonian physics only a force can cause the acceleration of a mass, and only a mass can exert a force. The third law says that whatever acts (to use again the Aristotelian terminology) is acted upon, whatever moves is moved. Aristotle had classified movers as moved and as unmoved. The movers not themselves moved were his final causes, and God was *the* unmoved mover. But, unless one could speak of the generic laws as unmoved movers (in which case they moved all things indifferently), the laws of mechanics said: all movers are moved. This contradicted the belief in miracles, and it contradicted the belief that a non-material mind or soul could move the body. It said that whatever is causally effective in the material world is itself a part of the material world.

One could, of course, remark that these laws of mechanics are only well-tested scientific hypotheses being mistaken for metaphysical dogmas. But the remark is not very useful, for it is the logical structure of the laws, and not the tenacity with which they are believed, that gives rise to the conception of completeness. If we want to make room for other ways of explaining the processes of nature, we must modify the laws so that they no longer exhibit completeness. Until that is done, we may say that the laws of motion are not the whole truth, but we cannot bring them into fruitful relation with other modes of thought. Aristotle had accomplished what was required by taking for granted the insufficiency of the material cause and the necessity of an unmoved mover. But this was a position that Aristotle could afford because he was not troubled by knowing about the logical completeness of Newtonian physics—a luxury of ignorance.

The second characteristic of the laws of motion, implicit in their algebraic form, is their remarkable temporal symmetry, by which the dependence of mechanical motions on time involves no essential reference to the direction of time. This is supplied from the outside, so to speak. For every kind of motion that is dynamically possible, the exact reversal of this motion is also dynamically possible. An approximate reversal of time is represented by the familiar device of a motion picture run backward; it is approximate in the sense that we are always able, by careful scrutiny, to tell that such a picture is being run in the wrong direction; but the manner of making this deduction—to be discussed later—owes nothing to the laws of mechanics.

We must distinguish temporal symmetry from the existence of special cyclical processes in which every motion is periodically matched by the reverse motion, so that the average during the period of the process is zero. It is possible to show that in any isolated mechanical system the motion will, when taken over a long enough period, be nearly cyclical in this sense. But in an "open," infinite world there need be no cycles; all that temporal symmetry implies is that for such a world both its actual history and the temporal reversal of that history are equally possible. And, of course, if everything—including motion-picture cameras and live observers—were reversed, nothing would be different.

This seems to reduce temporal symmetry to a distinction without a difference, but that would not be correct either. For the temporal symmetry of the laws of motion permits the possibility that some processes could be the reverse of what they are while others were not. The sense in which such a reversal is impossible is to be found, not in its violation of mechanical laws, but in its inconsistency with the boundary conditions that prevail.†

The contrast between the temporal symmetry of the basic laws of motion and the actual asymmetry of history suggests that one look again at the first characteristic of dynamical laws, their completeness. Evidently there is more to be said about the world than the laws of mechanics say; these would be consistent with many different worlds, with many different histories; and they say nothing about the temporal asymmetry of history. In any of an infinite class of worlds the laws of mechanics would be similarly complete—that is, would leave open no avenues of influence from non-mechanical laws.

But this remark, in turn, suggests a second look at Aristotle's final causes, for he thought—and said—that these had very much to do with the asymmetry of past and future. He conceived of each celestial sphere as ideally isolated and subject to no chance interaction from other things. In this case, as we have observed, his *telos,* or final cause, is synonymous with what we call law. But in such a case it had lost the significance it predominantly had for Aristotle as that which explains the perpetuation of order and organization in the sub-lunary world against the chance jostlings and interactions of things that would otherwise break down that order.

> "A thing, then, will be affected by time, just as we are accustomed to say that time wastes things away, and that all things grow old through time, and that there is oblivion through the lapse of time, but we do not say the same of getting to know or of becoming young or fair. For time is by its nature the cause rather of decay . . ." ‡

In the terrestrial world final causes are needed to explain the stability of order against known tendencies toward "decay"; in the celestial world they are needed as a matter of metaphysical principle, but not as a cause running counter to degenerative changes. There they signify what we call dynamical laws, and are temporally symmetric. Perhaps, then, a part of what Aristotle covered by the concept of final cause was what we call law, and a part covered something that we relate not to basic laws but to boundary conditions, to the thermo-dynamic order of nature rather than to the laws of motion. And this is a subject I shall resume in a later chapter. It is evident, at any rate, that modern classical physics discovered a mode of analysis and of abstraction that permitted

---

† One has to be careful here. The Lorentz transformations of special relativity are not *per se* invariant to a reversal of time. See Chap. 6.

‡ *Physics,* Book IV, 221ª, in the Loeb Classical Library (Harvard University Press).

it to ignore those aspects of nature in which temporal irreversibility is a conspicuous feature. The philosophers might justly complain, yet in the ignoring were laid foundations upon which, long after, time's arrow would acquire a new and deeper meaning. There is a deviousness here, a style of indirection and even of opportunism, that is characteristic of the history of science. It suggests one of the reasons why science needs philosophic criticism, and why philosophy needs the challenge of science.

Determinism and Causality

With the development of Newton's laws it became possible to say that the motions in any system of bodies are determined by, and predictable in terms of, the forces of interaction within the system and the external forces acting on it. The nature of these forces is restricted by the third law, which says that the forces acting between any body in the system and the rest of the system are equal and opposite. External forces, in turn, are internal to a more inclusive system. In the imagined limit to which any isolated system could be expanded—in the universe as a whole—all motions are determined by the material interactions of bodies according to the laws of motion, and all the material interactions of bodies are determined by their motions.

In a later chapter I shall point out that an idealized economic system may be described in terms of production and circulation in such a way that production determines circulation and circulation determines production. From the assumption that there is no free play in these interconnections it follows that an economy's course through time may be defined solely in terms of production or solely in terms of circulation; these are two equivalent descriptions. In the case of classical mechanics, likewise, it was possible to describe the history of a system of bodies in terms of kinematic variables or of dynamical variables; at any given point in time the state of affairs could be pictured in terms of motions from which later motions could be predicted, or in terms of force patterns from which later force patterns could be predicted.

In the economic analogy the empirical source of one of the two pictures is to be imagined as observers stationed in every factory, while the source of the other is thought of as observers on every route of transportation. Both sets are needed to establish the laws of the economy; but these laws, once established, make it possible to dispense, for practical purposes, with either set.

The situation in Newtonian mechanics is logically similar. Here the contexts are, respectively, static and kinematic. Force and mass are meaningful concepts in purely static contexts; static experimental arrangements suffice to give them meaning and measure. Forces are associated with strains of solid bodies (springs, for example), and a unit force is defined by a unit stretch of a unit spring, two units of force by a unit stretch of two unit springs, etc. Mass is defined statically by something like the equal-arm balance.

Both concepts can, on the other hand, be defined in dynamical terms provided the laws of motion are accepted as already established. The equality of action and reaction (conservation of momentum) permits us to measure the ratio of the masses of two bodies by the inverse ratio of the accelerations when the bodies interact. The product of acceleration and mass, so defined, gives a dynamical definition of force. Thus a concise statement of the two laws in question is that the two kinds of mass and likewise the two kinds of force—the static concepts and the dynamic—are equivalent.†

It is possible, however, in the description of purely dynamical systems, to forget the static concepts altogether. This has been popular in the traditions of physics, since it leads to a certain formal elegance and reduces the number of "fundamental" measuring instruments to two, the clock and the meter stick. But this elegance and simplicity—of great importance in the formal elaboration of theoretical dynamics—also have the effect of cutting off the theory of dynamics from the rest of physics—from the mass concept of the chemists, from the theory of gravitation, and from the theory of the structure of matter.

The duality of kinematic and static ideas has another kind of significance, however—one related to the possibility of isolating mechanical systems for study. The forces acting on a system may be conceived as independent variables, the masses within the system as constants specifying the system's response—that is, its accelerations. We then ignore the system's reaction upon its environment. The result is a *causal* description, in which force causes acceleration. The framework of ideas is that of Aristotle, of action and passion. But it must be noticed that the distinction depends upon the cut that has been made between the system and its environment. And the roles of these concepts may be reversed by a different way of isolating things. In Einstein's accelerated elevator (nowadays a rocketship) the force felt or measured as weight is the dependent variable and acceleration the independent variable. So the relation of force and acceleration is a reciprocal one.

Since causality is usually thought of as involving an asymmetric relation be-

---

† For Newton's conception of mass, see Leonard T. Pockman, "Newtonian Mechanics and the Equivalence of Gravitational and Inertial Mass," *American Journal of Physics*, vol. 19 (1951), 305–12.

tween cause and effect—a logical, and perhaps also a temporal, asymmetry—
it is doubtful whether such laws as the laws of motion should be described as
causal. In a two-body collision the acceleration of each body may be described
as the effect of a force exerted by the other; but these forces may be described,
in turn, as caused by the respective accelerations. In action at a distance a time
lag introduces temporal asymmetry, but in this case the general laws permit
the lag to be either positive or negative (temporal symmetry).

Physical causation runs both ways; if it does not seem to, this is only because
of the way in which we have isolated the system being investigated. The distinction between independent and dependent variables is a practical or an
epistemological one, but is not a meaningful characteristic of physical laws
per se. On the other hand, these laws are causal in the sense of deterministic,
implying a strict connection between the earlier and later states of a system.
In Chapter 8 I shall argue that the causal relation, with its characteristic logical
asymmetry between cause and effect, is physically meaningful independently
of human intervention in nature, but that it is so only in a thermodynamic
context. This is to say, not that causality is a statistical concept—although the
paradox is tempting—but that it is meaningful only in situations having certain thermodynamic, statistical characteristics.

There remains, for Newton's laws as well as for "causal necessity" of the
asymmetric sort, the problem raised by Hume as to the sense in which the
relations involved are to be called necessary. Aristotle had commented on
the analogy between the necessity of the material cause and the necessity with
which conclusions follow from premises. Philosophers such as Leibniz and
Spinoza had accepted the analogy as an identity of meaning. Hume's corrosive
skepticism about this analogy has undoubtedly been one of the major turning-
points in the history of modern philosophy.

The essence of Hume's argument† is the observation that the causal relation
can be said to hold only when it is *not* a logical connection, when the things
connected are logically distinct, and when, in consequence, the things causally
connected may be, in fact, logically unconnected. A square is necessarily a
rectangle because the criteria for identifying something as a square include,
among others, the criteria for identifying it as a rectangle. The ideas of square
and rectangle are, in Hume's language, not distinct ideas, and the relation of
logical necessity holds for that reason. But if, again in Hume's language, the
idea of the cause must be distinct from the idea of the effect, the connection

---

† David Hume, *An Enquiry Concerning Human Understanding*, section 7.

between them has no necessity unless of a kind that experience itself discloses.

What experience discloses, however, is not any kind of necessity in the connection between cause and effect, but only the regularity of association between what we *call* cause and what we *call* effect. If the connection were like that of logical necessity, it would always hold; but we do not know that it will always hold in cases we have not examined, and there is no way of demonstrating (logically) that it will.

Hume's argument does not establish the meaninglessness of the causal relation, but only its essential difference from the analogous logical relation. In an age dominated by a rationalistic philosophy, full of necessary truths, this was important enough. It established, as firmly as anything in philosophy can be established, that arguments that imply any matter of observable fact must depend, not on reason alone, but on hypotheses that may, because they imply facts, be refuted by facts.

> "Experiment escorts us last,
> His pungent company
> Will not allow an axiom
> An opportunity." †

The idea of necessity implicit in causal laws cannot be interpreted, therefore as implying necessary truth. Causal laws are valid only on sufferance of fact. What distinguishes such laws from mere generalizations is, rather, the claim of unconditionality. Bodies interact, and the behavior of any particular body is contingent on the environment of other bodies. But the way in which it is thus contingent is specified *completely*. This completeness is, we have seen, equivalent to the claim that a mechanical system can be isolated, that, when the forces acting on it are specified, no other aspects of its environment are relevant to its behavior. The rationalistic philosophers thought, or at least talked, as if the appeal to causal necessity put the conclusions they drew from it less at the mercy of fact than mere contingent generalizations would be. On the contrary, statements affirming necessary connections must be stronger, in their implied factual claims, than those not making such claims. The classic textbook example of the latter is "all swans are white," presumably once credible to Europeans. The claim of necessity—here withheld—would entail the whiteness of swans past and future, independently of any conditions of selec-

---

† Emily Dickinson, *The Complete Poems,* edited by T. H. Johnson (Cambridge, Mass., 1960), No. 1770, with the permission of the Belknap Press of Harvard University Press.

tion or breeding, even those—and this is an odd thing to say—that are so un-likely that they would, perhaps, never be realized.†

A logical comment is in order here although it anticipates a more extensive discussion in the following chapter, in connection with probability. A conditional proposition, expressed in English by the if-then conjunction, functions in two rather different ways. In one of these it links propositions and is thus a compound, or molecular, proposition. In the other it links propositional forms, incomplete propositions, which, in being linked, form a complete proposition. Of the first function there are two types, material implication and entailment. If p and q are propositions, $p \supset q$, defined as "either p false or q true," expresses the relation of material implication. If p entails q, or q is deducible from p—sometimes written as $p \Rightarrow q$—the material implication also holds, a fortiori. Concerning the first type there is a paradox—namely, that a false proposition implies any proposition. In American one can say, "If the square root of two is rational, then I'm a monkey's uncle." One makes the statement only under the assurance that the antecedent cannot be truly affirmed. One may also say, "If the square root of two is rational, then an odd number is an even number," and one can make this statement without knowing—and in Euclid's proof, indeed, it is the basis for affirming—that the antecedent is false.

The second function involves the use of a blank or variable sign, and has the form "if x is A, then x is B," subject to the rule of substitution: that, if a meaningful sign is substituted for x in one place, it must be in both. Here we understand A and B as constants, as naming traits or classes. In English the double blank often signifies "anything" and "it" in the two positions. One can

---

† A good deal of attention has been paid, in recent years, to the fact that statements that seem to claim some kind of necessity are often expressed in a subjunctive conditional. See William Kneale, "Natural Laws and Contrary-to-Fact Conditionals," *Analysis,* 10 (1950), p. 123, and "The Problem of Counterfactual Conditionals," *Journal of Philosophy,* 44 (1947), pp. 113–28. Several writers have tended to the conclusion that the sense of the subjunctive mood is to tag the statement as a deduction within some more general system of statements constituting a theory. See Henry Hiz, "On the Inferential Sense of Contrary-to-Fact Conditionals," *Journal of Philosophy,* 45 (1948), pp. 17–22; Roderick M. Chisholm, "Law Statements and Counterfactual Inference," *Analysis,* 15 (1955), pp. 97–105. Such a conclusion may well be correct, but it avoids the question why we build systems of statements, theories, about some ranges of fact and not about others. The description of the gravitational field has the sense of necessity, but it is not a deduction from any more general law. I should say that theories are built only around generalizations that are worthy of being thus enshrined, for which the claim of unconditionality has some *other* kind of support. For generally similar statements of the view I thus question, see also R. B. Braithwaite, *Scientific Explanation* (Cambridge, England, 1954), and, most recently, Ernest Nagel, *The Structure of Science* (New York, 1961), Chap. IV.

maintain that this form of statement is a conjunction of many statements, each a material implication, with a different filling of the blank. Thus to say "if *x* is human, then *x* is sinful" means "if *a* is human, *a* is sinful, and if *b* is human, b is sinful, and . . . ," where *a, b,* . . . are constants, independently defined designations, signifying each object in turn. This analysis can be maintained only if it is tacitly presumed that any *x* with the trait *A* is one of the independently designated objects in the sequence *a, b,* . . . But, when we *state* this presumption, it is *another* statement of the form purportedly being analyzed. The double-blank conditional is equivalent to a conjunction of material implications only if another double-blank conditional is conjoined to the material implications. This means that we cannot reduce the double-blank conditionals to conjunctions of material implications.

I have avoided giving the double-blank conditional its usual name and interpretation, "generalization" or "generalized conditional." † This is implied, but there are other ways of talking about it. One of these is to notice that the *x* is not an independent sign with a pre-established referent, but a blank that functions as a referential sign because it is connected to the constant *A*. The expression "*x* is *A*" means "*x* which is *A*"; it designates something of which *B* is then predicated. Let us write such a subject-predicate statement in the form *A x B*, so that the *x* serves as copula. When the conditional is interpreted in this way, it may be prefixed by quantifiers like "all" and "some" or by modal terms like "necessarily" and "probably." Since the quantifiers do not refer to a list of *independently* designated *x*'s, however, their function is really not distinct from that of indicating modality. Let *N* be some further but unspecified trait. To prefix *A x B* by "some" is rather like using *AN*, rather than *A* alone, as designator. *A x B* might be problematic, but there is some further trait, conjoinable with *A*, such that *AN x B* is assertable with confidence. To prefix *A x B* by "all," on the contrary, is to imply that no such reconstruction of the designator is needed; further designating conditions are inessential to the truth of the statement, it is unconditionally true.

Causal statements or law-like statements involve this sort of modality. "Necessarily" alleges, when it is attached to them, the irrelevance of *any* qualifications except those expressed or understood in the designative terms employed. Philosophers, in formulating principles of causality or of uniformity, have meant this kind of thing: that for any trait *B* that things may exemplify there

---

† See W. V. Quine, *Methods of Logic* (New York, 1950), pp. 12–17. Quine adopts the conjunctive interpretation, which is here rejected.

is *some* logically independent trait *A* such that the form "Nec. *A x B*" can be correctly asserted. It is not easy to see what we would mean by substantiating or disproving such a philosophical claim, but it is not an empty or tautological one, as is sometimes maintained. For it is logically possible that, for some *B* and *every A*, "Nec. *A x B*" is false. (I mean, of course, to exclude two trivial counter-examples: one is the example in which the traits are so defined as to restrict exemplification of them to well-defined finite sets; the other is that in which the trait *A* is defined as "whatever will designate an *x* that has the trait *B*," for in that case "*A x B*" is a tautology.) Such principles as causality and uniformity of nature are regulative or programmatic. We seek to reduce the independent variety in nature by establishing unconditional connections. We postulate such principles, and our attitude toward them is that of the postulant. They are not beyond modification, for with the growth of knowledge our definition of what we hope for in the order of nature may evolve. And they are certainly not empty or tautological.†

One final comment, on conditionals and unconditionality, is appropriate here. Both for material implication and for deducibility there is a valid principle of transposition:

$$p \supset q \equiv \sim q \supset \sim p$$
$$p \Rightarrow q \equiv \sim q \Rightarrow \sim p$$

For the double-blank conditional, however, this is not necessarily so. *A x B* and *~B x ~A* are not identical in meaning, as I shall show in the next chapter. They do not designate the same object or set of objects, and they may have different modalities. As we shall see, they may, for example, have different probabilities. It is possible that we have here a clue to the asymmetric causal relation. For the causal relation is likewise not transposable. The wind causes the trees to move, but the immobility of trees does not cause the wind not to blow. One may object, of course, to interpreting "cause" as analogous to a logical modality. As we shall see, however, the shift from one manner of designation to another may involve us in a shift from one physical, thermodynamic context to another and thus also from one modality affecting the statements

---

† A strong kind of unconditionality is implicit in the description of actions at a distance, the propagation of actions with a finite velocity. One may *define* velocities greater than that of light— for example, the velocity of a distant star that daily circumnavigates the earth, as measured in the terrestrial frame of reference. But, according to an essential proposition of relativity, no *effect* can be transmitted faster than light. In contemporary high-energy physics the postulate of causality—that the claim above holds true of small (5×10^{-14} cm) distances—is a crucial theoretical tool. It says that no field effect can precede what propagates it.

we can make to another. The invalidity of transposition under some circumstances gives us the freedom to express such shifts.†

My interpretation of causal necessity as unconditionality explains its analogy with logical necessity. For logical necessity implies unconditionality: if a theorem follows from certain postulates, it follows unconditionally, independently of any other postulates we may make.

This interpretation is at variance with what some philosophers have had to say about the idea of causal necessity. A fashionable interpretation used to be, and in some circles still is, that such propositions as Newton's laws contain a kind of escape clause that makes it impossible to refute them. Consider the simplest case, that of Galileo's law, the conservation of momentum. If a body is not acted on by a force, it shows no acceleration. Suppose that a body is observed to accelerate, but we identify no force acting on it. Is this a refutation of Galileo's law? No, one says, it is merely the occasion for postulating an otherwise unobserved force, and Galileo's law is restored. Now, if one were to treat such a law in such a way under all circumstances, one would be treating it as a mere tautology, and the interpretation we are opposing would be correct.

But the postulation of a force carries responsibilities with it. Forces have static effects. They will explain accelerations, but they will also cause tell-tale distortions of shape in rigid bodies. The one effect without the other leaves the postulated force without logical efficacy. An example is the Coriolis force, postulated to go with a veering of projectiles. The Coriolis veering is an artifact that results from using the spinning earth as if it were a stationary frame of reference. The force is not a respectable force in Newtonian theory, for it has no static manifestations by which to demonstrate its reality. If we inhabited a cloudier planet, with no heavens to mark our rotation, the Coriolis acceleration would have been a challenge to Galileo's law, whether or not we postulated the face-saving force. Science is not word magic.

There are other examples of this alleged face-saving technique, notably in the history of the law of the conservation of energy. According to the face-saving formula, when one finds a system in which energy is not conserved, one postulates that for some reason the system is not really isolated. But always, so far,

---

† For a discussion of "The Logic of Causal Propositions" see the article of that title by Arthur W. Burks, *Mind*, 60 (1951), pp. 363–82. The failure of transposition is discussed especially in Herman A. Simon, "The Logic of Causal Relations," *Journal of Philosophy*, 49 (1952), pp. 517–28, and "Causal Ordering and Identifiability" in *Studies in Economic Method* (New York, 1953), pp. 49–74. Simon's analysis leads him to express the causal relation in a metalinguistic form, explicating the causal character in terms of logical relations between the particular causal statement and a law from which it is deduced. An alternative viewpoint, on causality in economics, is that of Herman Wold, "Causality and Econometrics," *Econometrica*, 22 (1954), pp. 162–77.

the postulate has been independently verified or, as in the case of the Einstein mass-energy equivalence, taken care of by a subtle restatement of the laws of physics.† A recent case is the experimental confirmation of predictions based on the assumed reality of the neutrino, which was postulated originally to protect the laws of the conservation of energy and of momentum.

The basic physical laws have led, in fact, not a protected existence, but one exposed to all the buffets of fortune. Since every application of physical laws to particular situations depends upon a host of special assumptions as well as upon the laws themselves, it is good intellectual strategy, when predictions fail, to question the special assumptions before one questions the laws themselves; but philosophers have mistaken the practice and the intent of physical research when they interpreted such strategy as face-saving casuistry.

To save face by postulating the existence of new entities or species of entities is a special case of this strategy. Three planets (Neptune, Pluto, and Vulcan) got postulated in this way; two of these were, in fact, found, and the non-existence of the third confirms an emendation of the law of gravitation within the theory of relativity. Neutrinos are well established, and the species has become a genus in the expanding list of particles in contemporary physics. The hereditary mechanism of the gene was postulated to account for a genetic orderliness analogous to the orderliness that led John Dalton to postulate the chemical atoms. Today one copies genes *in vitro* as one fabricates atoms in the high-energy machines. Philosophers have debated the meaning of "reality" in such contexts. Are atoms real? Or are they only quasi-real, hypothetical constructs that are convenient in a successful theory? I shall not enter the debate here. "Real" is a potent word, emotionally and epistemologically. I dealt with it earlier, in discussing the problem of universals. There the discussion was keyed to two modes of reference, demonstrative and propositional. Here I would only make one suggestion: To assert the reality of something referred to propositionally (as new planets and elementary particles must first be) is to assert the propriety of admitting them to the same universe of discourse as tables, chairs, and persons. It is to declare (rightly or not) the irrelevance of the fact that we cannot practically treat them as objects of every-day demonstrative reference, or can do so only by suitable extensions of hand and eye.

An even stronger example of necessity in the sense of unconditionality is given by physical laws of equivalence or identity, such as Einstein's mass-energy

---

† On the general issue see the pointed remarks of Pierre Duhem, *The Aim and Structure of Physical Theory* (Princeton, 1954), pp. 208–18.

relationship or the proposition, assumed and tested by Newton and basic to the general theory of relativity, asserting the equivalence of gravitational mass and dynamical mass. Such laws assert the unconditional identity, up to an arbitrary unit of measurement, of two quantities independently measurable. Such a relation is not a causal relation even in the sense in which Newton's second law may be taken to state a causal relation. The relation between any two variables in Newton's law is conditional upon the third, whereas in physical identities there is no such dependence. Either of the laws cited might turn out, of course, to be only conditionally true.

The Isolated System: Essence and Accident

The conception of law in physics, of unconditional generality, involves that of an isolated system, and vice versa. The changeable features of a system, represented by dependent variables, are dependent *only* upon external variables of a certain kind, and it is these that must be accounted for in any correct application of the law. The total momentum of a system is constant unless it interacts with some external system; the total energy of a system is constant unless there is some exchange, with its environment, of work or heat.

As these examples suggest, an unconditional generalization that prescribes a relation among variables may always take the form of a conservation law, for the relation may be expressed by the statement that some function of the variables is constant. And, when the energy or the momentum or the charge of a system is not constant, it is implied that the system is a part of some larger system for which the relevant quantity is conserved.

Since, moreover, the dependence of an isolated system is a dependence upon only certain external variables, the law must be invariant with respect to a transformation of any other variables that may be involved in its formulation. The laws of Newtonian mechanics, for example, are invariant with respect to a transformation of viewpoint from one unaccelerated coordinate system to another. Einstein derived the special theory of relativity by adding a new postulate, that of the invariant velocity of light, to the basic Newtonian laws. This postulate is inconsistent with the earlier formulations of mechanics and electromagnetic theory. The inconsistency was removed when he replaced the Euclidean geometry of motion by a non-Euclidean geometry in which neither time nor distance is invariant with respect to a transformation of coordinate systems. Time and distance are replaced by a new invariant, the four-dimensional space-time interval.

Thus the concept of isolation involves those of conservation and invariance. There is a fourth concept involved in an equally intimate way, that of symmetry. In both classical and relativistic physics space is homogeneous and isotropic; that is, there is nothing intrinsic to distinguish one location or one orientation in space from any other. The description of physical realities must therefore be invariant with respect to any mere transformation of physical coordinates. A recognition of this idea is implied in the *docta ignorantia* of Nicholas of Cusa.† The world (which he conceives as infinite) has, properly, no center; to say that one does not know where the center lies is to express learned ignorance. In the controversy between Clarke and Leibniz‡ the latter argues similarly about the "location" of the universe: that God should put the universe in one part of space rather than in another is not a statement of a real alternative, and therefore God has no burden of decision in the matter. This is another instance of Leibniz's principle of the identity of indistinguishables. In the same sense there is, Leibniz argues, no difference between our world and a mirror image of it. As H. C. Oersted discovered, there is an asymmetry, which apparently violates Leibniz's dictum, in the linkage between the electric and the magnetic field. If a negative charge moves away from an observer, a north magnetic pole in the neighborhood is accelerated in the counterclockwise direction, which in the mirror image would be clockwise. If, however, the magnetic pole is described in terms of the electron orbits in the magnet, these also are reversed in the mirror image, and Leibniz's symmetry is restored. It is in just this connection that the recent discoveries of Tsung-Dao Lee and Chen Ning Yang§ are highly significant; experiments to test the principle of parity demonstrate that in certain weak interactions the particles of modern physics display differing properties depending on their Leibnizian "handedness," suitably defined.

The importance of the ideas of symmetry and invariance in physics is not only, or not primarily, that they make possible a very elegant formulation of laws, but also that they provide powerful tools of theoretical investigation, often enabling the theorist to discern the form of a law in advance of detailed ex-

---

† This fifteenth-century philosopher gave early expression to the idea, important in the later history of physics, of the relativity of position and motion. See Nicolaus Cusanus, *Of Learned Ignorance* (London, 1954), and the Introduction by D. J. B. Hawkins.

‡ See the footnote on p. 53.

§ T. D. Lee and C. N. Yang, "Question of Parity Conservation in Weak Interactions," *Physical Review*, 104 (1956), 255, and C. S. Wu and others, "Experimental Test of Parity Conservation in Beta Decay," *Physical Review*, 105 (1957), 1413. For a popular discussion see Philip Morrison, "The Overthrow of Parity," *Scientific American*, 196, 4 (April 1957), 45–53. In weak interactions, for which conservation of parity fails, there is a weaker symmetry—face-saving, again, and perhaps deep—involving the product of parity, charge conjugation, and time direction.

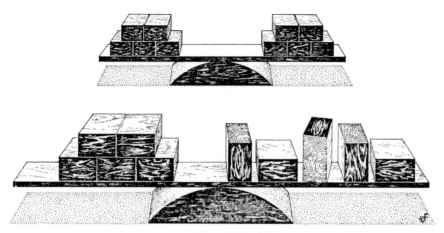

Fig. 13. Symmetries of Balance

perimental findings. The classical example of the argument from symmetry in mechanics is the Archimedean law of the lever. If equal weights at equal distances were unbalanced in one direction, they should, if interchanged, be unbalanced in the other direction. Hence any possible argument for an imbalance is matched by an equivalent argument for the opposite imbalance. If any statement about the lever is possible, it is a statement that the lever balances. If an actual balance did not work in this way, one would simply have to deny that the system was isolated, and look for the offending asymmetry. These conclusions do not follow, of course, if the balance is unstable; but in that case we come to the argument (postponed until Chap. 6) that the balance ought to tip in either direction with equal probability. A somewhat less trivial symmetry argument is the one that proves that the magnetic lines of force surrounding a wire carrying an electric current can only be in circles round the wire as center and perpendicular to it; for any other paths are excluded by the unconditional dependence of the magnetic forces upon the relative motion of the electric charges and the magnetic test-pole. If, for example, the lines were supposed eccentric in one direction, rotation through 180 degrees would make them eccentric in the opposite direction; if they were not perpendicular, there would be equivalent but contradictory arguments about the direction in which they tilted.† In modern quantum mechanics deductions are even more dependent upon symmetry arguments.

In all such arguments we must distinguish two components: one a physical hypothesis subject to ultimate empirical test and in no way guaranteed, logically,

---

† In point of fact, the field lines cannot form ideally closed loops. But symmetry prevents you from saying just *how* the closure will fail.

to be correct; the other a purely logical principle, which, although often of great power, imports, of itself, no contingent assumptions about the physical world. The physical hypothesis is that the behavior of a system does not depend upon any but certain prescribed variables. The logical principle is that two alternative —mutually incompatible—propositions are both false if they can be distinguished from each other only with respect to inessential variables: "the left side of the lever goes down" and "the right side of the lever goes down" must both be false, for any argument for the one could be converted into an argument for the other by an interchange of what are, by hypothesis, details inessential to the description. If there were an argument for either alternative, it would be self-contradictory within the system. A straightforward elementary deduction from a set of hypotheses often leads only at length to the solution of a problem, but symmetries in the statement of the problem, if noticed, lead directly to the solution or to a greatly narrowed class of solutions. A concern for symmetries and invariance is, consequently, an indispensable part of good scientific discipline.

The techniques of dimensional analysis, which are important in applied mathematics, stem from the same logical root as the symmetry principles. If we know that a certain physical phenomenon depends only upon certain variables, the requirement that its dependence on these be linear, and be invariant with respect to variation of any other variables, is often sufficient to prescribe the law of dependence. Since, for example, the velocity of gravity waves of water can depend only on their height and the acceleration of gravity, it must be a pure number times the square root of the product of these quantities; for only such an expression has the right dimensions.

By what right, however, can one make this extraordinary assertion that the behavior of a system depends wholly upon certain specified variables and upon no others? The only possible answer is that the claim of unconditionality is an empirical claim, which has been verified, so far as possible, by our failure to detect any violation of it within the range of observation and experiment that has been explored. A certain boldness has often marked the great advances. And here we come to a point that is of great importance for understanding the history of science and for prophesying its future. The widening of the range of observation and experiment generally leads, eventually, to situations in which the abstractions on which laws are based simply become inapplicable. The Galilean law of falling bodies breaks down for distances not negligible compared with the radius of the earth; the acceleration is not a constant but depends upon the location of the accelerated object and, ultimately, upon the distribution of masses throughout the universe. The Newtonian law of gravity breaks down at high velocities. The chemists' law of the conservation of mass breaks down in regions of sufficiently strong interactions, dramatically so in the transformation that creates an electron-positron pair from the energy of a gamma ray. The law of the conservation of charge is almost the only nineteenth-century formulation that has proved unexceptionable under the bombardment of twentieth-century experimentation. The recent breakdown of the principle of parity has already been referred to.

The history of the claim of unconditionality has been a history of retreat from previously established positions; but it has not been a rout, and it is not a proof of error. It has been, rather, a retreat before advancing knowledge, a gain rather than a loss. A law may be valid over a wide range of its independent variables, but, if it is pushed too far, we encounter deviations that can no longer be dismissed as minor or accidental deviations from the ideal case. As we vary the sizes, the time intervals, the energies of interaction, either toward the extremely large or toward the extremely small, we find that the minor and accidental interactions with the rest of things become, finally, major and essential. Again let us take an example from classical mechanics: the behavior of falling bodies in a resisting medium, described by Stokes' law, finally becomes inappropriate for bodies not large compared with molecules, for at that size the very concept of a resisting medium must be replaced by that of a random molecular chaos, in which the body in question no longer has a completely well-defined motion. And under sufficiently intensified interactions, the very concept "body" becomes inappropriate.

Instead of supposing, as one tends at every stage to do, that that stage is the last, one might self-consciously adopt as a kind of metaphysical axiom the proposition that isolation is never, in principle, complete, that unconditionality is never perfect; that all laws, in that sense, break down when extended to some region of experience or of possible experience; that nature is, in that sense, infinite.† Such an axiom implies, not that nature is unintelligible, but that intelligibility is always relative and approximative.

In recent decades attention has been fixed, by its spectacular progress, upon the revision of classical laws required in the attempt to extend their range to the

---

† Questions about the spatial or temporal infinity of nature are on the borderline of empirical science. Twentieth-century cosmology has demonstrated that hypotheses involving the actual infinity of space and time, and their contraries, may be as fully testable as other basic propositions in science. Our postulate is, rather, that of the infinity of experience, the inexhaustibility of the universe as the object of knowledge and as the source of novelty. Cf. Spinoza, *Ethics,* Book I. A close contemporary approximation is to be found in David Bohm, *Causality and Chance in Modern Physics* (New York, 1957).

scale of the very small and the very rapid and energetic phenomena of atomic dimensions. At the present time it has become clear that the previous ultimates of atomic theory are ultimate only in the sense in which the chemical atoms were once ultimate. Electrons, protons, and neutrons are stable entities only over a range—wide, but not unlimited—of times not too short or too long, and of interactions not too strong or too weak. At the limits of modern experimental probing, new particles appear, and the older simplicities are gone. At the level at which it may be meaningful to explain the nuclear forces of the atom, there have already been found a profusion of new particles, and of interaction phenomena among them, which defy description in terms of the now "classical" physics of the thirties.

As we go in the other direction also, toward the large and the slow and the weakly interacting, new perspectives are suggested. With the discovery of the essential mechanisms of chemical evolution—the aggregation of other atoms from hydrogen by "slow cooking" in stable stars and by fast "pressure cooking" in supernovae—the hypothesis of Prout† and the evolutionary speculations of T. H. Huxley‡ are vindicated. At the present time the cosmical origins of hydrogen itself are up for speculative investigation; in this framework it is natural, also, to seek new generalizations that will explain, in the sense of embedding them in a cosmological context, the classical principles of gravitation and inertia.

Because of the subject matter of my final chapters, it is worth considering the extent to which the concept of physical law—unconditional concomitance of variation—is important in the biological and anthropological sciences. That the concept is relevant is obvious at the level of biophysics and biochemistry. At the more molar levels, however, those that concern us in biology, psychology, and the social sciences, the relevance of this mode of formulation of our knowledge is decidedly a controversial matter. No science is conceivable without laws in one sense, without some breadth of generality in statement. In these areas, however, the possibility of finding exact and unconditional concomitances is, in many ways, doubtful—not, indeed, because we are ignorant or because they seem hard to find, but because our knowledge is, in many ways, remarkably great, and be-

---

† Early in the nineteenth century William Prout observed that atomic weights cluster near integral values (hydrogen = 1). This suggested the hypothesis that all elements are intra-atomic compounds of hydrogen. If we use twentieth-century atomic weights and forget to distinguish isotopic subspecies, the average difference from the nearest integer is about 0.1, whereas for points randomly chosen on the line it is near 0.25.

‡ Contained in a remarkable essay of 1887, in which Huxley states as a problem for the future the "evolution of the chemical species." See T. H. Huxley, *Methods and Results* (London, 1893; New York, 1896), "A Half Century of Science." The essay was a sort of supplement to William Whewell's *History of the Inductive Sciences*, published fifty years before.

cause what we know about life in general, and about man in particular, reveals an almost overwhelmingly complex responsiveness to environment. Conditionality rather than unconditionality of behavior is an essential trait. Some degree of isolation there certainly is, and in a field like economics we may achieve formulations of concomitance among a small number of aggregate variables. These concomitances are, however, quite obviously idealizations of a fairly bold sort. The knowledge of physical laws may lead, through the further discoveries that they promote, to their own qualification; in economics the qualifications are obvious from the beginning, and "laws" are justified only because they give sharpness and power to our thinking about an otherwise unmanageable complexity. Value theories in economics are, formally considered, conservation laws. (This is the main subject matter of my last chapter.) But even after many generations they are not accorded by economists the status that laws have in physics texts; they are too obviously relative and provisional. There are "laws" likewise in psychology; in the proper place we shall look at the claims made in behalf of them and their role, whether central or only peripheral, among the organizing principles of these sciences.

For the present it is my purpose only to suggest that the claim of unconditionality, from which the physical sciences have characteristically retreated as knowledge has advanced, is not, in the biological sphere, a very impressive claim to begin with. For we already know enough to qualify the claim severely. Our ignorance of the laws that govern in these areas is, to use once more the phrase of Nicholas of Cusa, of a rather learned kind; and it implies, not that the progress of our knowledge in these areas is doubtful, but rather that, through our very understanding of the limitations of one kind of descriptive tool, we may learn to use others that are more appropriate to the subject matter.

6

CHANCE AND PROBABILITY

The idea of dynamical lawfulness discussed in Chapter 5 provides a particular standpoint from which to describe things, and from this standpoint have flowed, historically, the great achievements of physical science in its modern classical period. The events in a physical system are connected in the order of time and predictable from one time to another, throughout nature and not only, as the ancients had thought, in the heavens. But the picture of nature as ordered in accordance with this temporal determinism is, despite its impressiveness, only a partial picture; for even within the framework of classical physical science there is another aspect to things—that of sheer spatial multiplicity.

Events are connected in time, but they are unconnected or more weakly interconnected in the order of spatial coexistence. A physical system described in classical language always has some number of what are called, significantly, "degrees of freedom," and these must be independently measured before the state of the system at any one time is known. If contemporaneous events in a system are causally coupled, so that their defining coordinates are not independent, it is nevertheless possible to transform these coordinates as functions of coordinates that are normal, that represent dimensions of causal independence. The vibrations of atoms in a crystal, for example, are strongly coupled to one another, but the normal modes of vibration, each of which may occur independently of the others, are the same in number as the spatial coordinates of the N atoms, are thus $3N$. The possibility of this simplifying representation illustrates the importance of the condition of linearity, which was mentioned in Chapter 3. Representation by normal modes breaks down with non-linear interactions.

In the physics of the twentieth century this sharp dichotomy between temporal determinism and spatial independence has been subtly but profoundly modified. In consequence of the quantum principle there are both a non-temporal lawfulness and a temporal non-lawfulness, both of kinds unfamiliar in classical physics. For the general purposes of the present discussion, however, the old ideas will suffice. Our conclusions will hold *a fortiori* in the world of quantum physics. In some ways, indeed, they will come into their own.

Law and Chance

Even within the world of classical physics it is possible to give a definite physical meaning to the concept of chance. To predict the behavior of a physical system requires information, the measurement of boundary conditions. If we assume the ideal of absolute precision in measurement, the behavior of the system can be predicted with absolute accuracy. But it is possible to ask what can be known about a system whose boundary conditions are *incompletely* specified. There is a trivial † answer: the system will be found in some state that is not inconsistent with the (incompletely) known boundary conditions. In terms of dynamical laws alone, nothing further can be said; by measurement the system is known to be confined to some set of alternative states, and the laws of motion map this set into other sets at later or earlier times. But much more can be said if the saying of it can be cast in the language of probability.

Probability is a very old concept, familiar to common sense and philosophy, but only a century old in the context of dynamical law. The obvious and natural interpretation of probability in this context is that it introduces, not something that has to do with the nature of the physical system, but something that has to do with the incompleteness of our knowledge. With more information we should have less need of probability; with perfect information we should not need it at all. We may liken perfect information to the knowledge that an angel has of things, and we conclude that in the angelic mind there is no place for the concept of chance. Hence the belief in the subjectivity of chance: "chance is a name for ignorance."

But this opinion turns out to be false. Ignorance of dynamical regularity may be a *motive* for resorting to probabilities, but it does not explain the probabilities

---

† The answer is trivial, but in dynamical systems it leads to interesting consequences. See p. 196 *et seq.*

to which we resort.† Determinism and chance appear as alternative and incompatible, but in fact they are not. They are independent ideas and define independent aspects of nature. The angel whose duty it is to describe nature *completely* cannot do without the concept of chance. For this concept expresses the characteristic mode of relationship among a multiplicity of independent causal processes that are, although coexistent, not co-determining. That just this mode of relationship should obtain is not implied by the laws of classical physics, nor does it contradict them.‡ The completeness claimed by Newtonian physics (or its counterpart in quantum physics) is completeness in the dynamical mode, but not completeness in an unqualified sense. Chance exists between the deterministic motions of stars in a galaxy, in the formation and history of those stars and their planets, in the life of society. It characterizes the processes of biological metabolism and reproduction and of all chemistry. It is the essence of heat, but even at absolute zero it reappears as the randomness of the uncertainty principle in quantum mechanics. It is involved, as we shall see, in the very conception of a being who can make measurements, hypotheses, or paintings, who can commit the ancient crime of which Socrates was convicted, that of introducing novelties.

Logical Preliminaries

One of the reasons for the disputes over the meaning of probability is that the language of probability—as part of ordinary speech—turns out to be ambiguous when the demands placed upon it become exacting. To review all these difficulties, and all the controversies over them, would require a volume in itself. The present chapter is designed rather to avoid difficulties than to face them. It is a dogmatic presentation of a single interpretation. The reader who is

---

† See Yves R. Simon, *Prévoir et savoir* (Montreal, 1944), I, "Le Hasard."

‡ The conception of chance in terms of causal independence is developed in Augustin Cournot, *Essai sur les fondements de nos connaissances et sur les caractères de la critique philosophique* (Paris, 1912), as well as in Simon, *op. cit.* In the famous quotation from Laplace [*Essai philosophique sur les probabilités* (1814); see the translation reprinted by Dover (New York, 1951), p. 4] about the intelligence that can predict everything one finds the reason for Laplace's subjectivistic interpretation of chance. As Simon points out, an intelligence capable of knowing all the forces of nature, and the position and motion of everything in nature, is described by Laplace as embracing all the movements of nature "dans la même formule." We might grant rigorous predictability without granting, as Laplace does, a single and unique immanent law. Laplace's attention is upon this unicity; hence chance has no place. The ancient Stoics denied chance for a similar reason: the belief in a single immanent purpose of nature. Even though Aristotelian pluralism is ruled out for Laplace, he still could have given chance a certain objective status by shifting attention from the law to the plurality of boundary conditions, of things given. Purpose eliminates degrees of freedom; mechanical law does not.

familiar with the subject is asked to postpone critical judgment until he has understood the main argument of the present chapter and of the later chapter on probable inference. Some of the main problems and issues are, in fact, dealt with in these two chapters, in a way that I hope will be found adequate.

Probability theory, as it is employed in the sciences, presents itself as the appropriate discipline for formulating and justifying inferences based upon certain kinds of evidence, but such inferences are not, except as a limiting case, deductively certain. Probability theory is thus allied with, and in a sense is a generalization of, formal logic.† But in actual use the theory must be interpreted in terms of certain non-formal, empirically vulnerable rules of measurement, and at this level it is more nearly related to the subject matter of science than to its abstract methodology. Pure mathematicians have interested themselves in developing the theory on a rigorous axiomatic basis; and, so conceived, the theory has no necessary connection with either the content of science or the logic of inference, but is simply a part of mathematical measure theory.

The interests of applied mathematicians, pure mathematicians, statistical-minded investigators in various fields, logicians, and philosophers have resulted in a variety of terminologies. Fortunately the number of terminological decisions is small. In all discussions of mathematical probability one needs to distinguish some fundamental set of alternatives, to which probabilities are ascribed. To mathematicians who want to put probability in the context of measure theory, these alternatives are merely subsets of a given set, not further defined. By statisticians and applied mathematicians the alternatives are called events, and a set of mutually exclusive, exhaustive alternative events is called a sample space, the latter term deriving from the interest in population sampling. In statistical physics the term "phase space" is often used synonymously with "sample space," each point in the phase space representing a possible state of the physical system under discussion. In logical and philosophical writings probability is usually ascribed, not to events or possible states of a system, but to the propositions or statements involved in the specifying of such events or states—to descriptions of events or of states.

The difference here may, but need not, be consequential. It may only represent a shift from a naturalistic object language to a metalanguage in which one talks about the object language. Instead of saying that events do or do not occur, one may as well say that descriptions of events are true or false. The difference becomes consequential if probability is ascribed to propositions that are true or

---

† Developed in great detail by Rudolf Carnap in *Logical Foundations of Probability* (Chicago, 1950) and in *The Continuum of Inductive Methods* (Chicago, 1953).

false under conditions that would not be called events. Thus the logical terminology presents a potential generalization of the scope of probability theory.†

In texts on statistics the term "event" is taken as primitive, and the way of
applying it is communicated rather by example than by precept. A good deal
of confusion can be traced to this usage, however, and here I want to be more
analytical. In the end I shall reject the term for a technical one. The relevant
meaning of "event" is propositional rather than demonstrative. An event in
probability must be something we can talk about as a possibility and not merely
something we define by pointing to it. Thus a particular lightning flash, Jupiter's
Red Spot, and the Trinity Bomb Test may be called events; we refer to these as
we refer to more permanent objects, by demonstrative pronouns or adjectives,
descriptive phrases, or even proper names. But a possible event—or, more
properly, each of a set of alternative possible events—is not something we talk
about by exhibiting or pointing or proper-naming. What happens, rather, is that
we make a statement that *would* be a description of an actual event if just *that*
event occurred; and the "that" in italics is not a demonstrative adjective referring
to a physical actuality but an adjective referring to a previous statement.

One of the perennial philosophical issues comes to the surface here—one that
I have already treated in Chapters 1 and 3. Whereas a demonstrative adjective
refers to an actuality ("Did you see *that* lightning flash over there?"), a propositional adjective ("Did *that* event occur?") refers to a potentiality. Confusion of
the two modes of reference leads us to invent, alongside the actual world, a
richer world of potentialities, a sample space or phase space surrounding the
actual world, which is merely a point in that space. In one case the meaning of
the pronoun or adjective is completed by something in the non-linguistic,
physical context of discourse; in the other case it is completed by something in
the linguistic context, a previously enunciated proposition, a possible event. In
the idealist tradition such referents are conceived as existing in a separate realm
of pure potentiality, apart from and metaphysically superior to the spatio-
temporal order of mere existence and occurrence.

The discovery of confusion never quite settles any metaphysical issues, since
a bad argument can lead to a true conclusion. What it does, however, is to help
avoid merely silly conclusions. Like numbers, potentialities are not there
(where?) to be named or to complete the meaning of demonstrative pronouns or
adjectives, but there in the discursive context, there in the meaning of a statement that can be made without being made true, and that completes the meaning of a propositional pronoun or adjective. The confusion arises because we

---

† Or, if "proposition" is taken in the sense of "proposing," see p. 227.

form a sort of image of a strange new world, which we look at through a window or from behind a guard-rail, like visitors at the Mint: there is a unicorn; there is a coin falling heads up, and there it is falling tails up; and there is the non-occurrence of the Trinity Test.

What is bad in this is not our accrediting of potentiality as essential to an account of the nature of things, but, on the contrary, our suppression of it by treating it as a kind of quasi actuality. Even worse, potentialities get separated from actuality. The possibilities we can define are not definable except by reference to an actual, non-linguistic context of discourse; if a proposition defines a possible event, *some* of the terms in that proposition have their meaning completed by demonstrative reference to things or occurrences within the context. Possibility is within actuality. This is not a metaphysical pronouncement from on high, but a statement of what is rather obviously implied in the patterns of our cognitive procedure. Whether it is metaphysical is a matter of definition. In the major traditions of philosophy such *is* the meaning of metaphysics.

The possible events of applied probability theory are possibilities within some actual situation, not merely what are labeled as possibilities within an abstract mathematical formalism. The sample space is defined by reference to this actual situation, itself taken as non-problematic and non-probable. These alternatives are the possibilities. The context may be wider or narrower, but acknowledgment of it is what determines the range of possibilities to be considered.

But the recognition of this fact leads to a difficulty, which is that possible events are not related in a simple way to actual events conceived as objects of demonstrative reference. The semantical counterpart of any actual event is not a single proposition, but a whole class of propositions; the relation is not one-one, but one-many. For there are statements that, though not logically equivalent, nevertheless say the same thing. To see how this is so, we must eliminate, first, the fact that language is redundant enough to permit the use of synonymous terms in statements that are identical in meaning. We can, in fact, define a proposition as an equivalence class of statements identical in meaning. We can do this because identity of meaning is a symmetrical, transitive, and reflexive relation (Chap. 1). But there is, in addition, what may be called conditional equivalence among statements that are equivalent, for example, within the framework of a theory—such as statements about gravitational mass and inertial mass in physics. There are also equivalences that arise from ambient circumstances, which are taken for granted.

Any lightning flash, toss of a coin, or fission of a bacterium or a plutonium nucleus, considered as an actual occurrence, involves the simultaneous verification of many propositions, without limit as to their number. Lightning flashes vary as to date, duration, color, energy, shape, location, relation to clouds and houses and other lightning flashes, etc. Any event occurs in a specific natural context, which gives rise to an inexhaustible supply of relational facts about that event, of statements that its occurrence verifies. The event, as a given fact, is, then, a potentially inexhaustible source of information. The class of all statements verified by its occurrence is an equivalence class, since the relation among them is an equivalence relation.

It is not necessary, however, to get involved in this topic in its full generality. I shall restrict our discussion to a more narrowly limited set of equivalences. For this purpose I define a sort of event that *is* the direct counterpart of a single event-proposition statement. It is what Mill called a *collocation,* and it involves the possession by a single object of two characteristics of which one characterizes the object uniquely and functions to designate it while the other is predicated of the object so designated. Logically, we express such a collocation by the double-blank conditional discussed in Chapter 5: "If x is ϕ, then x is B." But ϕ is designative rather than predicative. The statement form of a collocation is "The x having the property ϕ has the property B" or, in shorthand, "ϕ x B." Now we are interested in the fact that the same object x, which is designated by ϕ_i, could have been designated in a variety of ways ϕ_i ($i = 1, 2, 3, \ldots$). The classical example, from Bertrand Russell, is the statement form "—— is the author of *Waverley,*" in which we substitute for the blank "Sir Walter Scott" or "The author of *Marmion*" or something else. Since all these statements predicate the same thing of the same person, they are equivalent, but only because *in fact* the different designations do designate the same person. We do not mean to emphasize the designations, usually, and employ any that are uncontroversially equivalent.

The equivalence relation holding among all ϕ_i x B, for which the ϕ_i designate the same x, may be called a relation of *contingent equivalence,* and the term "event" may be regarded as the name for what all collocations of a given contingent-equivalence class have in common—namely, that they predicate the same property of the same object, however designated.

The collocations of such a class are, however, not *logically* equivalent, and there is, in particular, no reason why they should have the same probability. It is easy to give examples, moreover, to show that contingently equivalent collocations may have different probabilities. Suppose that a man N years old is selected by some sampling procedure. Actuarial statistics now justify the argument that the probability of his death within x years is p. The man's name is

John Smith. It does not follow that "John Smith will die within x years" has the probability p. The proposition may have a quite different probability. In the following section I shall return to this topic after developing the relevant theory. For the conclusion to the present section it is sufficient to emphasize that the term "event" is unobjectionable as a technical term only if properly understood, the proper understanding being that an event, in the colloquial demonstrative sense, is an equivalence class of collocations, and that different collocations, contingently equivalent to one another, may have quite different probabilities. In what follows, therefore, I shall speak not of events but of collocations, and not of sample space but of collocation space, in which the alternatives under consideration are possible collocations of a uniquely designated x with the various alternative properties that that x may possess.

The Mathematics of Probability

The alternative collocations to be considered on any occasion have been referred to as a *space* and the term needs amplification. Let ϕ be any designating property, x the thing designated, and F any property predicated of x. Then an elementary collocation is expressed by the propositional form $\phi \, x \, F$. Generally we wish to consider several designations or designated objects and several properties that each of them may possess: for example, several spins of a roulette wheel and for each spin the various properties resulting, such as number, color, and parity. We represent the different designations by ϕ_i $(i = 1, 2, 3, \ldots m)$ and the properties predicable of any ϕ_i by F_{ij} $(j = 1, 2, 3, \ldots n_i)$. The properties predicable of any particular ϕ_i may be represented by points or intervals on a line, and for all m of the ϕ_i the corresponding lines represent the coordinate axes of an m-dimensional Euclidean space. If we select a point or region on each of the axes as representing the collocation of the corresponding ϕ_i with a particular predicate F_{ij}, then the m-dimensional point or region determined by these coordinates represents the simultaneous realization of the m collocations in question. Hence the terms "phase space," "sample space," and "collocation space." Conversely, any m-dimensional region represents some logical combination of possible collocations involving the m designata and the properties predicable of them.

The point of this representation is not merely one of convenience. It demonstrates that any logical combination of collocations may be described as a single collocation. Even when the number of designations increases without limit, as when we talk about an infinite sequence of tosses of a coin, their composite behavior may still be represented by a single point (or region) in an infinite-dimensional Cartesian space.

We can therefore say, without any restriction as to generality, that probability always qualifies a *single* collocation, something expressed by a singular proposition of the form "The x having the property ϕ has the property F." It may also qualify a whole class of such collocations by abstraction, as when we say that *any* normal toss of a coin has probability $1/2$ of falling heads up; but this means that it holds for *each* toss. We may likewise discuss the probability that a million coin tosses will fall heads up 50 ± 1 percent of the time; this is represented as a *single* collocation in a million-dimensional space.

The details of formal definition depend on the kind of problem, on whether we are dealing with properties that can be represented by continuous or discrete variables, etc. But the general form of representation is the same in all cases. The principal logical operations by which collocations can be combined are conjunction (both A and B, represented by AB), disjunction (either A or B or both, represented by $A \vee B$), negation (not A, represented by $\sim A$ or $\bar{A}$), and implication (if A then B, or either not A or B, represented by $A \supset B = \sim A \vee B$).

Probability is a number in the unit interval associated with each collocation or region in collocation space. We define two special collocations: the sure collocation, which is the disjunction of all collocations in the space and therefore certainly occurs; and the null collocation, which is the negative of the sure collocation and therefore cannot occur. By definition the probability of the one is 1, of the other 0.

If A is an unspecified collocation, we call probability a function of A and write "$0 \leq P(A) \leq 1$." The essential formal property of this function is that it is additive, by which is meant that, if two collocations A and B are mutually exclusive, then $P(A \vee B) = P(A) + P(B)$. In particular, if A and B are also exhaustive, so that their disjunction is the sure collocation, then $P(A) + P(B) = 1$. On the other hand, "$P(A) = 1$" need not mean that A is the sure event (what is the probability that an ideally sharp pencil will fall over when we balance it on an ideally hard surface?).

These properties define what is called an additive measure function, and the whole of the mathematical theory follows, in essence. A very important set of theorems, however, is concerned with the consequences of a special hypothesis, which is that the probability measure is not only additive but also multiplicative in a certain sense. Specifically, this means that, if A_1 is a collocation in one collocation space and A_2 is a collocation in another space, then in the Cartesian product space of higher dimensionality the conjunction of the two collocations, A_1A_2, has the probability $P(A_1A_2) = P(A_1)P(A_2)$. This corresponds to the definition of area as the product of two linear dimensions, of volume as the product of three linear dimensions, etc., and permits us to represent probability by the ordinary geometric measure of area, volume, etc. Two collocations A and B, whether belonging to distinct subspaces or not, may be such that $P(AB) = P(A)P(B)$, and in that case they are called independent. Three or more collocations A, B, C,... may be independent when taken in pairs, but it does not follow that, for example, AB is independent of C.

Since we can write

$$P(AB) = P(A) \cdot [P(AB)/P(A)]$$

we can give a special name to the expression in brackets and call it the *conditional* probability, that of B granted A, written $P(B/A)$. We then always have

$$P(AB) = P(A)P(B/A) = P(B)P(A/B)$$

The conditional probability $P(B/A)$ is evidently the probability of B when A is treated as defining the whole collocation space. Independence means that $P(B/A) = P(B)$, and it follows that $P(B/A) = P(B/\overline{A})$.

The operational symbol "/" used here is interesting because it raises some difficulties already discussed (pp. 122–25) in connection with conditional statements. The logical operations of conjunction, disjunction, negation, and implication are sufficient to express *all* the possible combinations of statements with respect to their truth and falsity. Yet "/" is not identical with any of these standard operations or definable in terms of them. It can nevertheless be read in English as "if." In particular, let us compare $P(B/A)$ with $P(A \supset B)$. Let A be "it is raining" and B "the sun is hidden." Then $A \supset B$ can be read as "either it is not raining, or the sun is hidden" or as "if it is raining, the sun is hidden" or as "the sun is hidden if it is raining." We ought therefore to be able to read $P(A \supset B)$ as "the probability that the sun is hidden if it is raining." But we can also certainly read $P(B/A)$ as "the probability that the sun is hidden if it is raining." Yet the two expressions are not the same in meaning and have different probabilities. For

$$P(A \supset B) = P(\overline{A}) + P(AB) \qquad \text{since } \overline{A} \vee B \equiv \overline{A} \vee AB$$
$$= P(\overline{A}) + P(A)P(B/A)$$

Now it follows from this equation that $P(A \supset B) = P(B/A)$ only if they are equal to 1 or if $P(A) = 1$. But, if two probabilities are not or need not be identical, they cannot be the probabilities of identical collocations.

A possible way out of the confusion is to suggest that the symbol $P(B/A)$ is misleading because B/A is not a meaningful combination by itself, but only when inside $P(\quad)$. It should be read, not as "the probability of 'B if A,' " but as " 'the probability of B' if A"; A is not a condition on B, but a condition on $P(B)$.

But this interpretation is patently wrong and leads to direct contradiction. For consider the case $P(B) = 1/2$, $P(B/A) = 1/4$. If the second is read as "$A \supset [P(B) = 1/4]$," it follows that $A \supset (1/2 = 1/4)$. A not uncommon fallacy also arises from this interpretation. The probability of 5 on each of two throws of a die is the product of the separate probabilities, and, since these are equal, it is the square of the probability of 5 on a single throw. In other words, these are independent collocations. This is true both of a fair die and of a loaded die. If we interpret the condition as above, and L means "loaded,"

$$L \supset [P(\text{'5' '5'}) = P(\text{'5'})^2]$$
$$\bar{L} \supset [P(\text{'5' '5'}) = P(\text{'5'})^2]$$

and we can assert, unconditionally, that $P(\text{'5' '5'}) = P(\text{'5'})^2$. But this is not true; for, if we do not know whether or not the die is loaded and there is a finite chance that it is, the occurrence of one 5 makes another more probable; they are independent on either of two hypotheses considered separately, but not on the disjunction of the two; and this is a logical absurdity.

There remains a third interpretation, which is, in fact, the correct one: the expression "B/A" can be defined outside the probability bracket and is the statement of a collocation. The property A is not a condition on B and not on $P(B)$, but on a part of B—namely, the designating characteristic ϕ. Let the two collocations be $\phi x A$ and $\phi x B$. Then the operation $\phi x B / \phi x A$ gives the collocation $\phi A x B$, in which the property A is conjoined to ϕ as *part of the designation* of the x, of which B is then predicated. The sign "$/$" does not mean an operation that combines statements by constraining their possible truth values, but an operation by which one statement alters the meaning of another. If "$\phi x A$" is, in fact, false, "$\phi A x$" does not designate anything, and neither "$\phi A x B$" nor "$\phi A x \bar{B}$" is true.† Some philosophers would like to say that under these condi-

---

† The interpretation of "$/$" is an example of a modal rather than a material relation, as discussed in Chap. 5. It is a relation of meaning rather than a *de facto* constraint upon truth combinations. But the use of the English "if" to interpret both "$/$" and "$\subset$" is explained as an isomorphism between modal and material. For consider the following theorem of elementary propositional logic: If p, q, and r are propositions, then

$$(p \supset q)(p \supset r) \equiv (p \supset q)\{(p \supset r) \subset (p \supset q)\} \equiv (p \supset q)(pq \supset r)$$
$$\equiv (p \supset r)\{(p \supset q) \subset (p \supset r)\} \equiv (p \supset r)(pr \supset q)$$

Here the expression in braces has been written in reversed order. Now, if we drop the interpretations the statements in question must be meaningless, but this seems wrong; they rather have no referent, they belong to a set of excluded possibilities. They may still have meaning, however; we may, for example, still talk about what their probabilities *would be* if the designating condition *were realized*. The use of the subjunctive conditional in English implies that we cannot make use of such excluded possibilities for direct prediction, but the probabilities are still perfectly defined.

In summary, the ordinary concept expressed in English as "event" is ambiguous and must be replaced, for the purposes of the theory of probability, by one for which we use the technical term "collocation." By a sufficiently unambiguous statement of designating and predicative properties we may define "collocation space" in such a way that each collocation has a single fixed probability. And, rather than say that this probability is relative to various conditions, we say that the collocation space itself is relative—that is, differently designated with reference to various conditions. But the probability is not relative once the collocation space is defined.

Probability and Determinism

We are now in a position to see why the ideas of chance and determinism are compatible. We interpret determinism according to the following postulate:

> For every event E there is some set of conditions C such that, whenever conditions C are realized, event E occurs.

The event mentioned here is not what we have called a collocation, but what we have called a contingent-equivalence class of collocations. We imagine something as happening, and then we say, "Any such thing could have been predicted." But there is no magic about determinism; it is not fatalism. In order to predict event E deterministically, we must *describe* it in such a way that it can be predicted in accordance with some rule or formula or law. But laws establish connections between conditions and events, and this means that event

---

tion of ϕx as "x designated by ϕ" and treat it as a simple propositional form, "x has the property ϕ," as though x could somehow be independently assigned a referent, then what we have written by the shorthand $\phi x B$ would be equivalent to $(\phi x) \supset (B x)$: "x has the property ϕ" implies "x has the property B."

Let p, q, and r represent, respectively, the three propositional forms ϕx, $A x$, and $B x$, whereupon it will be seen that the equivalences above correspond exactly to those below:

$$(\phi x A)(\phi x B) \equiv (\phi x A)\{(\phi x B)/(\phi x A)\} \equiv (\phi x A)(\phi A x B)$$
$$\equiv (\phi x B)\{(\phi x A)/(\phi x B)\} \equiv (\phi x B)(\phi B x A)$$

Here the symbol "/" in the braces is the counterpart of "$\subset$."

E, to be predicted, must be described *with reference to* some antecedent conditions in such a way that, when the statement of these conditions is plugged into the statement of a law, something else is predicated of the event. In short, the deterministic *description* of an event is a statement of only one particular collocation in the contingent-equivalence class of collocations that we call event E.

Let us consider now the following postulate of probability:

> For every event E and probability p there is some set of conditions C^* such that, whenever conditions C^* are realized, event E has probability p.

Again E refers to an equivalence class, and we are postulating that in that class there is an infinite set of collocations and of conditions with respect to which they can be defined, each set of conditions implying a well-defined probability. For each such collocation its *probability* is now unconditional and has the character of necessity discussed in connection with causal necessity in a previous chapter. The particular case of probability 1, in the postulate of probability, is equivalent to the postulate of determinism.

Let us now return to a standard worry about chance, its subjectivity. Consider the problem of tossing a coin. If the conditions implied in the designation of this toss are the standard ones, the probability that heads will turn up is $1/2$. According to the probability postulate, one can specify conditions with respect to which the collocation has any other probability one pleases—remembering that the collocation here is not the stated collocation but another one, with the toss differently designated, which *may* be realized in the same event. There are, in particular, a set of conditions C_t such that, if C_t is realized, the result will be tails with certainty, and another set C_h such that the result will be heads with certainty. By our mode of designating the toss—and thus of singling out a specific collocation—we commit ourselves to ignoring these possible deterministic antecedents. To say that $P(H) = 1/2$ does not contradict the statement that the conditions C_h were in fact realized; it only commits us to the further statement that $P(C_h) = 1/2$.

Thus, even in a Laplacean world of absolute determinism, the concept of probability *can* have a perfectly good objective meaning. Consider any event A in such a world, and let C_a be the complex of deterministic conditions—which may have obtained throughout all past time—that are sufficient to the occurrence of A; from the statement "$P(A) = p$" there follows no contradiction with determinism when p is neither zero nor one, but only the consequence "$P(C_a) = p$." This does not show, of course, that probability *does* have a perfectly good objective meaning. The argument that it does must now be presented.

The Measurement of Probability

The probability measure is a physical measure construed as a function over a collocation space, a space of disjunct logical possibilities. But, of course, we cannot measure something that is merely a possibility. The measure is a measure of some *actual* set involved in the definition of a *potential* collocation.

The nature of the probability measure is illustrated by simple examples. If a sheet of paper is placed in the rain, the probability that a drop hitting the paper falls on a marked region of the paper is the area of that region divided by the total area of the paper. Gambling devices usually offer some set of discrete alternatives of which a certain proportion comprise the collocation one is interested in. In blackjack, for example, the probability of drawing 21 with two cards is $64/1{,}326 = 0.048$, for 1,326 distinct pairs of cards can be drawn, and 64 of these give the required sum.

Fig. 14. The Probability Measure

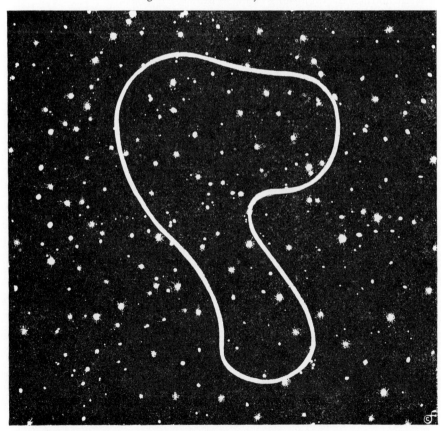

In all such cases some process of selection of an object from among a set of objects is defined, and the possible results of this selection enable us to define a collocation space. The assumption that permits us to identify as probability a physical measure (as of area or as number of distinct pairs of cards) is a symmetry assumption, an assumption of the causal irrelevance, to the outcome, of any differences that may exist among the alternatives in question. What distinguishes, in blackjack, an ace of clubs and a king of diamonds from an ace of hearts and a king of spades is assumed to be without causal relevance to the outcome. Any small element of area of the paper placed in the rain is causally indistinguishable from any other congruent area, and their differences are irrelevant to the outcome.

A set of alternatives, in the absence of causally relevant distinctions among them, form an equivalence class with respect to probability—they must all have the same probability; for the assignment of a greater probability to one alternative than to another would imply some causal asymmetry, some causal relevance inherent in their distinguishing characteristics.

The principle involved here, which is generally in disrepute, has been variously named the principle of insufficient reason, of non-sufficient reason, and of indifference. It was formulated by Laplace,[†] but it is implicit in earlier writers —for example, Bernoulli.[‡] I propose to rehabilitate this principle, since the objections to it are largely irrelevant to my intended interpretation.

The principle states that two alternative events are equally probable if there is no reason why one should occur rather than the other. The difficulty is in interpreting the term "reason" in this context. If it means cause, the principle is applicable only on pain of denying the deterministic principle. If it means knowledge, it inevitably makes the application of probability depend on the extent of our ignorance concerning causes and, in the extreme case of virtually absolute ignorance, still leads to a different assignment of probability. If the principle is inapplicable at both extremes, that of perfect knowledge and that of perfect ignorance, there is no obvious reason why it should be applicable in between. I have argued that chance is an objective concept independent of the degree of our knowledge or ignorance; I am committed by the same arguments to the view that the quantitative measure of probability is equally non-subjective. Carnap, with whose views I deal in a later section, uses the principle of in-

---

[†] Laplace, *op. cit.*, Chap. 2.

[‡] Jakob (or Jacques) Bernoulli (1654–1705), *Ars Conjectandi*, translated into German in Wilhelm Ostwald's *Klassiker* (Leipzig, 1899), No. 108. There is a short section in English in James R. Newman, *The World of Mathematics* (New York, 1956), pp. 1452–55.

sufficient reason in another form and regards it as pointing to a sort of symmetry that is neither subjective nor physical but is, rather, a logical symmetry among alternatives stated in a certain formal language.

My analysis of the meaning of "chance" and of "events" leads me, however, to a different interpretation. When we examine the cases in which the classical writers applied the principle of insufficient reason, we do indeed find that they involve certain essential, and quite physical, symmetries—those of coins, dice, playing cards, etc., as well as those involved in many natural phenomena. An amino acid molecule may be formed in two ways, each form being a mirror image of the other, and under classical conditions of the chemical laboratory the two forms are equally likely. In analyzing the raindrop example, we see that there is a symmetry between two equal areas of the paper, within which a drop may fall. In the absence of such symmetry conditions, as I shall show presently, it may be very difficult to ascertain probabilities by any methods. Obviously, however, these mere geometrical symmetries are not sufficient. In spite of them we may have excellent reason to believe that one alternative will occur rather than another, as in the case of biologically synthesized amino acids, which are of one "handedness" only.

When we turn to the dynamics of such systems, however, there is another kind of symmetry, which may or may not be involved. For there are cases—indeed, many cases—in which we know, or may plausibly hypothesize, that geometrically symmetrical alternatives differ only in respects that are irrelevant to the causal description of the system. This does not mean that the behavior of the system on any particular occasion could not have been predicted from a sufficient knowledge of antecedent conditions. It means that those very antecedent conditions, from which one of two symmetrical alternatives could have been predicted, are themselves equiprobable. This was the concluding argument of the last section. In the tossing of an ideally symmetrical coin, for example, we may suppose that we could determine, from a sufficient knowledge of the exact dynamical conditions under which it is spun, whether the result would be heads or tails. The equiprobability of heads and tails is then simply transferred to the dynamical conditions; the set of all possible conditions leading to heads would define, in the phase space defined by the relevant variables, a certain region; the set of all possible conditions leading to tails would define a set symmetrical with the first. But now we may suppose that the system is expanded to include the human being or machine that tosses the coin, together with an arbitrarily large part of the environment of the process, extending arbitrarily far into the past.

Predictability of the event from the now perhaps enormous set of relevant conditions is still, by hypothesis, possible. But this does not contradict the statement that the two alternatives are equally probable, for the statement only implies that regions of this new and enlarged phase space, or collocation space, defined with respect to the final alternatives, heads and tails, *also* satisfy the symmetry condition. We might suppose, however, that *outside* any such system conditions that destroy symmetry prevail. There might be a demon, for example, bent on frustrating our use of symmetry arguments, who would manipulate the conditions so as to make one alternative more probable than the other. A hypothesis of equal probability therefore implies that there is no such demon and no other natural mechanism operating in the same way. And this is not *a priori* certain.

If there is any such mechanism, one that destroys the symmetry of alternative states of a system, I shall speak of this causal coupling as a reason that would lead us, if we knew about it, to ascribe a greater probability to one state than to the other. The absence of such coupling is, I take it, what is hypothesized when we decide that there is no reason why one alternative should occur rather than the other. Thus, and in this sense, two alternative collocations $\phi x A$ and $\phi x A^*$ are equally probable if the two sets A and A^* are symmetrical and have the same measure, and if the causal sequence that selects an x, and thus designates it, is not coupled with, is causally independent of, any properties distinguishing A and A^*.

The standard objections to the principle of insufficient reason do not apply to the formulation above, for it does not purport to be a principle that bestows finality upon probability judgment; it is the form of a hypothesis that, however final in a practical sense (and in many cases it certainly has such finality), is always, in principle, subject to empirical tests of one kind or another. It resembles, in this respect, any other form of statement about physical realities of such a kind that its implications extend beyond the range of the immediate and the obvious. And, though there are many cases in which the principle of insufficient reason can be applied with an almost dogmatic assurance, there are countless others, particularly in such fields as the social sciences, where the known causal relations are insufficient, not only for exact prediction, but even for the kind of probabilistic description we have been considering here.

In Chapter 9 we shall consider the principle of insufficient reason again and see that it does have a logical, or decision-theoretic, meaning quite distinct from that here considered. Controversy is explained, I believe, by the confusion of the two interpretations.

Symmetry and Independence

The principle of insufficient reason applies only to two or more alternative collocations. Its application in particular cases gives rise to a hypothesis about the probabilities of those alternatives. A more restricted symmetry argument, possible in many cases for which our knowledge is insufficient to assign a probability measure over the whole collocation space of alternatives, is the argument for *independence*. Where two or more such spaces are to be combined into a single space, the measure over the product space is the product of the respective measures *if* the respective sets of collocations are independent. If V and W are variables ranging respectively over two independent collocation spaces, independence means that $P(V/W) = P(V)$ for every V and W. If a set of n collocation spaces have two-fold, three-fold, ... and finally n-fold independence, the probability measure on the product space is the product of the corresponding measures.

An argument for independence between two collocations A and B (prototype of all more complex judgments of this type) is an argument to the effect that we can restrict the designating characteristic ϕ of ϕ x without altering the probability of a collocation defined in terms of it. In the language of symmetry, the difference between collocation ϕA x B and collocation $\phi\overline{A}$ x B is inessential to the metrical and dynamical conditions with reference to which the probability of ϕ x B is defined. The result of a previous coin toss is assumed to be independent, in this sense, of a later one. "Heads previously" or "tails previously" may be imposed as a designating condition on the next toss, but any argument of the form " '—— previously' increases the probability of heads the next time by an amount d" would be an equally good argument whether the blank was replaced by "heads" or by "tails"; hence $d = 0$. Perhaps this symmetry is not prevalent under all possible conditions to any arbitrary accuracy. We often resort to such judgments, in fact, when we know they are not completely right. In practice, indeed, we sometimes resort to them when, though they are quite wrong, they permit the use of textbook formulas that give the appearance of being scientific.

The formulas in question are based on theorems that follow from the assumption of independence or from more complicated assumptions equivalent to near independence. They are the so-called *large-number theorems*. Suppose that a particular collocation space S is reproduced a large number of times under the same conditions C^*, and that these spaces are independent. Then in each space S_i there are collocations $\phi_i \times B$, in which B is a variable representing the properties or subsets of that space. The spaces are isomorphous with one another, and $P(\phi_i \times B)$ is the same in all. Then in the product space there is a collocation whose predicated characteristic is a particular *relative frequency* of the subspace collocations $\phi_i \times B$. Let us call this frequency $FR(\phi \times B)$. There is in the product space one collocation, in particular, that is defined by the property that $FR(\phi \times b) \approx P(\phi_i \times b)$, the symbol "$\approx$" meaning approximate equality, with arbitrarily small error. This collocation we may call the *statistical image,* in the product space, of the *probability* in the isomorphous subspaces. Then the theorems in question state, in one way or another, the conclusion that the probability of *this* collocation—the statistical image—is an increasing function of n and approaches 1 as a limit. In what are called the *weak theorems* the conclusion is stated for any particular value of n, whereas in the *strong theorems* it is stated as holding simultaneously for *all* n greater than a given one.

Among a vast number of tartaric acid molecules, for example, some will be of the left-handed form and some of the right-handed form. We define for the ith molecule a collocation space S_i, of two alternatives, and B means either left or right. Suppose that the probability of the left-handed form is $1/2$ under some specified conditions. Then the collocation, defined by that statement that the relative frequency of left-handed forms is approximately $1/2$, has a probability very near 1. This illustrates the weak theorem of large numbers. The strong theorem is better illustrated by a time sequence. If we could concentrate attention on a particular molecule, we should observe that random collisions with the environment occasionally kicked it from one form to the other. A possible collocation is defined by the statement that the relative frequencies of left and right are nearly equal (that is, with a small discrepancy, which we are at liberty to specify) after a certain calculable time, and remain nearly equal thereafter, *no matter how long the sequence of observations continues.* The strong theorem of large numbers says that, if successive changes are independent, the collocation above has a probability very near 1.

A more elegant statement of the laws makes the stipulated errors decrease slowly to zero with increasing n; then the strong law says that, with probability 1, the relative frequency of $\phi \times b$ approaches $P(\phi_i \times b)$ as a limit.

But these conclusions follow only from the hypothesis of independence or slightly weakened hypotheses of the same general sort. They do not follow from, and indeed may be radically false on, other assumptions.

The great practical utility of these theorems arises from the fact that there are collocation spaces for which we have no ability to define the relevant symmetries, no way of applying the principle of insufficient reason. If essentially similar spaces can be examined repeatedly, and are independent, we can infer the probabilities in the subspaces, with high probability, from the *observed relative frequencies* in the product space.

Consider the following example. The arguments of symmetry break down in the face of conspicuous physical asymmetries. Mechanical gambling devices are designed to exhibit such symmetries, but do so only approximately. How well do the six faces of a die, for example, exhibit the equiprobability usually attributed to them? For the study of this question an unsymmetrical wooden die was constructed and thrown on a linoleum floor. The die had two square faces and four rectangular faces, the distance between square faces being 1.2 times the distance between rectangular faces. The die landed on a square face 54 times out of 300.† Since different throws are independent, we resort to large-number theorems. We find that the probability of only 54 square faces, on the hypothesis that all faces are equally probable, is extremely small, about one in a billion. The statistical evidence points to a probability of about 1/10 for each of the square faces and 1/5 for each of the rectangular faces. The logic of the inference is that probabilities very different from those would be unlikely to produce the observed results. But this is a subject for later discussion.

The same conclusion *can* be derived by an argument that applies the principle of insufficient reason to a collocation space defined by the physical variables in the deterministic description of the motion of the die bouncing on the linoleum floor. Although the detailed argument is probably beyond human capacity because of its numerical complexity, plausible simplifications can be made. The faces of the die correspond to calculable areas on the surface of a circumscribed sphere, slightly less than 1/6 for each square face. From this point on we can show that the probability that the die will land on such a face varies from that value down to zero, depending on the elasticity of the die and the floor. I mention this trivial problem to combat the widespread belief that such probabilities can be derived only *a posteriori,* from statistical evidence.‡

A final example will now be given, one in which the conditions of independence are false, and false in such a way that large-number arguments are invalid. (I shall refer to this example later, in connection with Carnap's ideas on the nature of probable inference.) Suppose that there are two marbles, black and

---

† Data privately communicated by E. U. Condon.

‡ The same simplified arguments, supported by several other experiments, give an answer to the old question "What is the probability that a coin will land on edge?"

white, in a box. One is drawn out and replaced by *two* of the same color. The drawing and replacement is repeated n times. In finding the probabilities, we can rely on some symmetry conditions, but others are lacking. Let B_i be the statement that the ith draw is black. Then, by symmetry, $P(B_i) = 1/2$ for all draws. This follows from the fact that the words "black" and "white" can be interchanged without altering the description of the process. Furthermore, $P(B_iB_j) = 1/3$ for any $i \neq j$, $P(B_iB_jB_k) = 1/4$, and so on. The result is that after n draws all *relative frequencies* of black are equally probable and no prediction of relative frequency is possible.

The large-number theorems define one very general characteristic of systems with many independent chance collocations. Another sort of theorem on independent collocations has been expressed, rather vividly, by the phrase "the impossibility of a gambling system." † To consider only the simplest case, suppose that there is a long sequence of collocations B_i with $P(B_i) = 1/2$. A gambler chooses to believe that there is some perhaps very complicated pattern in the sequence of B_i with respect to their occurrence or non-occurrence. He therefore bets each time on the collocation $\phi_i \, x \, b$ or on its negative, deciding which bet to make each time by some rule or strategy based on the statistics of previous collocations in the sequence. The probability of a correct prediction is still $1/2$, and the sequence of wins or losses is a sequence of independent collocations, each with probability $1/2$. No matter what his system, he can do nothing to improve (or worsen) his probabilities of cumulative gain. As we shall see later, this sort of argument and conclusion is deeply connected with the second law of thermodynamics, which has long been characterized as "the principle of the impossibility of a perpetual-motion machine of the second kind." Indeed, the two are, in essence, the same principle.

The Frequency Interpretation

Many writers on probability who have been impressed by criticisms of the principle of insufficient reason, including the quite legitimate criticism that it does not establish probabilities with finality, have decided that probabilities should be defined *solely* in terms of empirical relative frequencies, without recourse to symmetry arguments, tainted as the latter are with "rationalistic" associations.‡ I agree with proponents of the frequency theory that recourse to

---

† Richard von Mises, *Probability, Statistics and Truth* (New York, 1939).

‡ But the work of Richard von Mises, partly so motivated, led to the formulation of interesting and important problems.

statistical information is the only adequate test of hypotheses about probabilities. It does not in the least follow, however, that statements of probability are statements about empirical relative frequencies, any more than statements about Babylonian mathematics are statements about the clay tablets in our museums.

One may, indeed, define the word "probability" in any way one chooses—for example, as the long-run relative frequency with which an "event" occurs. But there then remains the question of the relation between this measure and the characteristics of the *individual* collocations in the sequence, in virtue of which the long-run relative frequency could, in fact or in principle, be predicted. Before one can define the frequency measure, one must be able to say whether or not a particular collocation space belongs in the sequence or not. The sequence is a sequence of collocation spaces that have in common some defining characteristics with which relative frequency can reliably be associated. Otherwise there is no prediction. In some cases these characteristics are well understood and are related to metrical and dynamical characteristics of the situation within which collocations are defined. They are the symmetry conditions discussed earlier in this chapter. In other cases they are not well understood, but we look for them, again as hypothetical symmetries of the sort we have discussed.

The essential conditions with respect to which we can define sequences that will have stable relative-frequency characteristics are themselves defined in terms of probabilities! It is true that the assumptions of independence involved here can themselves be tested statistically, but it is also true that they can be so tested only in a logical context defined by *further* assumptions of independence, not then and there tested. For every assignment of probabilities or statement of independence we may imagine a product space within which the statistical image thus defined has, in the limit, probability 1; but in the very definition of the product space and its probability measure new assumptions of independence are involved. One may make the cut that stops this otherwise infinite regress either with the empirical relative frequencies or with the symmetry assumptions that make those frequencies meaningful; but to claim that the one or the other is fundamental, ultimate, etc., is to be a fundamentalist in the bad sense, to make a claim that cannot be related to the procedures of knowledge and inquiry.

The word "probability" may be defined as I have defined it or, on the other hand, in terms of the statistical image, of relative frequency. This is arbitrary. I have chosen the first definition because it is related to individual collocations; because it is always about individual collocations (whether in a subspace, a product space, a product space of product spaces, etc.) that we make probable *inferences;* and because "relative frequency" is a perfectly good term for relative frequency! But what is not arbitrary is the *connection* between the two, the fact that relative frequencies are correlated with other, non-statistical variables involved in the description of individual collocations. Without this connection there could still be a formal theory of probability, but it would be inoperative in the formulations and procedures of human knowledge.

The general topic of the statistical testing of hypotheses is taken up in Chapter 9, although I have appealed to familiar ideas on the subject in this chapter. But there is one point that may be made here in connection with the frequency theory. If the *only possible* evidence for or against such hypotheses lay in statistical data, the meaning of the principles of symmetry would be trivialized; they would appear merely as a blank form to be filled in by subsequent, purely statistical information. Their content would consist, in effect, of nothing more than empirical relative frequencies, and we should have, in essence, just the frequency interpretation in disguise. Some writers, wedded on philosophical grounds to the frequency interpretation but wedded also to the classical way of thought, have taken this view: probability as a symmetry measure has been used as a kind of fiction, which gets its sole meaningful content from the observation of relative frequencies. Against this view it must be urged that many kinds of information besides direct statistical information are relevant to the supposed truth of a symmetry hypothesis. It is in the nature of any physical hypothesis that, in the context of the rest of our knowledge, it is subject to an endless variety of affirmative or negative evidence.

As an example that gets away from the stereotypes of games of chance, consider the probabilistic relation between the size of air molecules and the blueness of the sky. From the theory of the behavior of gases it is predictable that there will be endless fluctuations of pressure and density in sufficiently small volumes of air. The sunlight, traversing any such region of non-uniform density, will be slightly bent in accordance with the laws of refraction, blue being dispersed more than red. As a result of many such interactions a small portion of the sunlight will be widely scattered and its direction randomized. It is this light that we see as the brightness of the sky, predominantly blue. Regarded as a chance mechanism for scattering sunlight, the atmosphere can be characterized by symmetry measures depending on certain measurable quantities, among them the size of the air molecules. But this quantity is subject to many kinds of independent determination, some of them non-statistical. Thus the size of molecules determines the brightness and color of the sky, or, conversely, a knowledge of the latter enables one to determine the size of air molecules.

Statistically Isolated Systems

In Chapter 5 we explored the connection between the idea of a dynamically isolated system and various other conditioning principles of physics, such as the search for conservation laws and the idea of invariance with respect to inessential variables. In the present chapter we have been at pains to establish the proposition that probability measures depend upon certain dynamical and spatio-temporal conditions with respect to which they can be defined unconditionally. It is a natural generalization of the idea of an isolated system to extend it to include any system of such a sort that, whether or not its actual behavior could be predicted by exact laws, a probability measure could be predicted for its state at any particular future time. This prediction could be verified, then, not by a single observation, but only by a statistical image built from repeated observations of many essentially similar systems. If systems can be isolated in such a way that we can predict their probability measures ideally for any future time, such systems can reasonably be called statistically isolated.

There are also physical systems of many elements whose average behavior at any moment *is* a statistical image, predictable by means of the large-number theorems, and verifiable, to a high degree of precision. The classic example is the gas law.

The conditions of statistical isolation are both weaker and stronger than those of complete, dynamical isolation. They are weaker in that not all dynamically relevant variables are controlled or measured but some are left to chance. But the dynamically relevant variables that can be left to chance are those *not* relevant to the *probabilities* in a suitably defined collocation space. Which variables are left to chance and which are, on the contrary, regarded as designating conditions, is in some degree a matter of choice. But there is one limitation upon this freedom of choice that goes very deep and shows the sense in which the conditions of statistical isolation are stronger than those of dynamical isolation. When we ignore any variable that is dynamically relevant to the behavior of what we are studying, we must be willing to assume its randomness, its lack of causal relation to the variables that define alternatives within the collocation space under consideration. In describing the behavior of a symmetrical die, for example, we ignore the elasticity of the floor on which the die rolls or bounces, for it affects all alternatives in the same way. If the die is significantly asymmetrical in shape, however, we cannot leave out the effect of elasticity. The probability measures depend upon it, yet this elasticity is not itself a chance variable.

The fact that each mode of isolation is in one respect weaker and in one respect stronger than the other marks them as complementary abstractions; each pays attention to one type of natural regularity, which the other turns attention away from, and each does so by a selection of one aspect of things, an aspect irrelevant to the concerns of the other. This is the justification of my statement, made at the beginning of the chapter, that an angel whose duty it was to possess a complete account of the order of nature could not ignore the chance aspect of things any more than he could ignore the dynamical aspect. Nothing in the logical requirements of dynamics says that a system should, in the course of its uncontrolled interaction with the rest of things, exhibit a standard statistical order. And, likewise, nothing in the concept of statistical order-disorder requires that a system be describable in deterministic terms. I have assumed, for the sake of argument, that physical systems are describable in both sets of terms. Whether they are so in fact is left an open question.

The field of psychology offers us a rather striking example of the complementarity of statistical and dynamical descriptions, which may make what I have been saying a little more clear intuitively. Because the behavior of animals is highly adaptive, the patterns of such behavior may correspond closely to the statistical regularities of the environment. If, on the other hand, our laboratory investigation subjects an animal only to statistically abnormal situations, we may emerge with a description that, although correct as far as it goes, offers almost no basis for generalizing about behavior in the wild state. To isolate an organism after the model of physics, to surround it with an envelope of deliberately controlled conditions, which are then systematically varied, will reveal information about the dependence of behavior on this set of variable environmental conditions. What it will not do, however, is to throw light on the significance of that dependence as an adaptation to the statistical characteristics that happen to prevail in the uncontrolled natural habitat. One may, in particular, observe, under laboratory conditions, responses that appear stupid or irrational but that would, in the wild state to which they are an adaptation, be highly appropriate. Animal behavior is, in some of its aspects, a statistical image of the normal animal environment, developed through variation and selection of the genotype, or learned in the life span of the individual. Both these processes take place in uncontrolled interaction with the environment. To isolate an animal, as a physicist would isolate what he studies, may be necessary at some stages of investigation. But to regard such isolation as the ideal aim of animal (and, *a fortiori,* of human) psychology is to ignore the incredibly rich system of interactions that gives the concept "environment" its unique place among the concepts of biology and psychology.†

---

† An optimal strategy for gaining information about the environment may be adapted, through evolution or learning, to the statistical distribution of environmental variables. For the implications of this fact for psychological theory and experiment, see Egon Brunswik, "The Conceptual Framework of Psychology," in the *International Encyclopedia of Unified Science,* Vol. I, No. 10, Chap. 9 *et seq.*

CHAPTER

7

ESSENCE AND CONTEXT
IN TWENTIETH-CENTURY
PHYSICS

In Chapter 5 we reviewed the development of the science of mechanics and its conditioning hypotheses, the latter connected historically, through the European Middle Ages, with the Aristotelian philosophy of nature. The atomistic view of ancient materialism was revived, but with the additional and all-important hypothesis of dynamical lawfulness. As philosophy the view was one-sided, but as a guide to discovery it was fruitful, not only in those sciences to which we now think it appropriate, but also in its challenge to the founders of modern political and economic thought and of modern philosophy.

An Anticipation

In the late nineteenth and the twentieth century the evolution of physics has altered this implicit metaphysics. The alteration is connected with two major discoveries, relativity and quantum mechanics. Behind both of these lay the nineteenth-century development of electromagnetic theory, which paved the way for them by importing a new kind of fundamental reality, the electromagnetic field. Before, there had been particulate matter and empty space; now there were three irreducible realities: particles, empty space, and fields.

These three formed a sort of inconsistent triad, the logical instability of which has led to the radical reconstruction undertaken by relativity. This is the subject matter of the next section of this chapter.

The development of electromagnetic theory also created the framework for investigations of the interaction of matter and radiation, and it was out of these that the quantum limitations upon physical interactions—first those of matter and radiation, and later of all kinds—were discovered. The nature and consequences of these limitations are explored in the last three sections of this chapter. I introduced probability theory in Chapter 6 because, although its main relevance is such that it should follow the present chapter, the nature of quantum mechanics is best seen against the background of the classical division of labor between dynamical and statistical concepts. Quantum mechanics has been treated most often in relation to its partial relinquishment of classical deterministic assumptions and too seldom, I believe, in relation to the non-temporal, super-mechanical determinism it introduces, a kind of determinism unknown to classical physics. As I shall try to show, the new account of nature shows nature to be at once more orderly, more structured and rigid, in its potentialities and more radically chancy in its operation. The new picture of nature-in-the-small is no longer that of a steady deterministic flow of multiply interacting dynamic processes, but that of states and transitions, "flights and perchings," in which the perchings are more stable and the flights more abrupt than classical ideas would have allowed. The aspect of steady flow remains, but it is a steady flow in the macroscopic average, always marked by the fluctuation, the statistical noise, of elementary quantum interactions.

This picture provides, I believe, the indispensable background for the major interests that will occupy us in the remainder of the book. The quantum-mechanical description of nature is indispensable to an understanding of physico-chemical structure in general and of what has come to be called "molecular biology" in particular. But it has a wider relevance. Its development, along with that of relativity, has brought about a new way of thought in science, a revision—not a repudiation but a revision—of the implicit metaphysics of classical science. And this revision is such that terms like "life," "mind," and "purpose" seem more natural and less surprising than they would in the classical setting.

A wish that has appeared repeatedly in the history of our Western culture is that science should not understand the things represented by those terms; a hope has been expressed—with many supporting arguments—that it shall not, in principle, be able to understand them. One can sympathize. The implicit metaphysics of classical science is easy to make explicit; the guiding presuppositions have been proclaimed, sometimes, with finality. Success, even the most admirable, invites arrogance, and the practical career of modern science is not always an exception. Hegel said, expressing some ancient wisdom, that every part of the truth, to be recognized, must first be taken for the whole truth.

But science is not a school of metaphysics, committed once and for all to any set of presuppositions that the philosophical critics may label it with. What science is committed to is the truth of partial truths and the discipline of extending them. It is not a school of thought, but a succession, a history. When new and more powerful ways of unifying the description of nature appear, the critics must re-examine their criticisms. The limitations of science, at any particular date, are the boundaries of the territory that it then knows how to define for exploration. They are always real boundaries, not to be extended by fiat. The job of criticism is to keep alive the sense of these boundaries. I assume that the human need of guidance, insight, and understanding will never be wholly met within the framework of organized, discursive knowledge of nature or man. But, when criticism insists upon boundaries that science itself has already surpassed or redefined, the result is a misfortune. There can be arrogance in denying limits, but there can be arrogance, also, in drawing them.

In the chapters that follow I am trying to test and, in some measure, to deny the old limitations. The explication of quantum-mechanical concepts is a first step. A second is the examination of thermodynamical ideas, older than quantum mechanics but widened in range as a result of it. A third is the re-examination of teleological concepts in biology, in psychology, and in the social sciences. My conclusions are as clear and firm as I can make them; yet sometimes they remain unclear and infirm, suggestions only. Within this sequence of topics I have interpolated two chapters that seem to fit: one on an aspect of scientific methodology; the other on another sort of methodology, which we call ethics. I discuss the one in relation to thermodynamical and information-theoretic ideas, the other as an addendum to my treatment of psychology.

Relativity and Space-time

In Newtonian physics the behavior of any system was determined by interaction with its environment via specific forces. Apart from forces of direct impact, the only important force—in astronomy the only one—was gravity. Later, however, there came an extensive investigation of electric and magnetic forces, which proved to resemble gravitation in varying inversely as the square of the distance between charges or poles. With Oersted's discovery of the interaction between electric charges and magnetic poles in relative motion, and with Michael Faraday's more extensive investigation of these connections, the idea that electromagnetic forces represent a direct interaction (although at a distance) between bodies lost its simplicity. A moving magnetic pole could accelerate electric charges. In electrostatics one could speak of "direct" interaction between charges, but in describing electromagnetic phenomena one could not. The acceleration of a charge could be thought of in both cases, however, as due to the presence of an electric *field,* caused in one case by other charges, in the other case by the moving magnetic pole. The electric and magnetic vector fields were thus introduced as physical realities of a new kind, not concentrated in small regions, as particles were, but continuously distributed through space. The field around a charge or a magnetic pole is thought of as a material reality, although, of course, its existence and the forces it exerts in any given region of space can be verified only by the introduction of test bodies, whose resulting accelerations are then observed. James Clerk Maxwell developed the definitive classical theory of the coupled electric and magnetic fields and from this theory deduced the existence, in association with the acceleration of electric charges, of electromagnetic waves. The calculated velocity of this wave motion, depending upon the electromagnetic field strength per unit charge, agreed with the already known velocity of light. The wave nature of light had been hypothesized by Christian Huygens long before as a way of explaining the phenomena of optics, especially diffraction and interference. As a result of Maxwell's theoretic discoveries, light was identified as electromagnetic in character.

Out of the combination of Maxwell's discoveries with the laws of Newton there emerged, at the end of the last century, a consistent generalization of those laws. This generalization, now generally known as "classical physics," described the interactions between electric and magnetic fields, on the one hand, and electrically charged bodies, on the other. The laws of the conservation of energy, linear momentum, and angular momentum still held, with the proviso that at any given time some part of these quantities belonged to the field rather than to the particles, so that in this sense the field had the same kind of reality as the particles in it. This duality of field and particle has become a part of the intellectual apparatus of twentieth-century physics.†

---

† A very good discussion of the significance of modern field concepts in physics is to be found in Rudolf Peierls, *The Laws of Nature* (New York, 1956). See also David Bohm, *Causality and Chance in Modern Physics* (New York, 1957).

The twentieth century has produced two great emendations of classical physics, and both are consequences, although in different ways, of the extension of classical physics just discussed. The theory of relativity introduces the velocity of light as an essential constant in the laws of motion. Quantum physics introduces a new constant also, the quantum of action. Both of these constants play a limitative role, the first setting an upper limit to the range of possible velocities, the second setting a lower limit to the magnitude of interactions among material systems.

Newtonian physics had a principle of relativity, Galilean relativity, which was expressed in the proposition that the laws of motion are invariant with respect to a transformation of observations from any unaccelerated frame of reference to any other. This principle is connected, implicitly, with the old philosophical dispute concerning the nature of space and with the problem of spatial measurement. The issue concerns the meaning of *empty* space, of vacuum. The Epicureans had maintained an identification of being and non-being with atoms and the void, respectively. The Stoics, following Aristotle, had argued that any merely privative conception of space is absurd: space is a medium; a moving object *traverses* space, which is a plenum, not a vacuum.†
The difference between Stoic and Epicurean ideas is illustrated by the controversy over the swimming fish. According to the Stoic interpretation, water is not composed of discrete parts but is a "true" fluid and wholly fills the space it occupies. According to the Epicurean interpretation, water is composed of small atomic parts, solid, with empty space between. An Epicurean would say that the fish can move only because it compresses the water ahead and rarefies it behind, and that only after a time does the water replaced by the fish replace the fish. A Stoic would argue that no compression and rarefaction is possible, nor is it required for the fish to swim. In modern language, the Stoic would be using the idealization of the incompressible fluid, in which the velocity of sound is infinite, while the Epicurean would be somewhere along the road to a kinetic theory of fluids.

Similar alternatives are involved in early modern ideas about light. Descartes regarded light as a transmission of impulses through the plenum, Newton as a transmission of particles.‡ After Huygens the wave theory proved its superiority. It explained in quantitative detail all the known phenomena of optics

---

† See Max Jammer, *Concepts of Space* (Cambridge, Mass., 1954), Chap. 1.

‡ The story is more complex. Descartes worked at the corpuscular theory and Newton at the wave theory. But my priorities are right. Even in the seventeenth century we see the indecision that is now enshrined in quantum physics.

and in the end was shown to follow directly from the theory of the electro-magnetic field. On the other hand, the wave theory involved commitments that might or might not prove to be consistent with Newtonian relativity. Wave motion is motion in a medium, and a material medium, filling space, would seem to give meaning to the idea of absolute rest and thus to contradict Galilean relativity.

The idea of absolute rest is not inherently absurd from a cosmological point of view; motion need only be linked to some independently demonstrable, and pervasive, framework of reference that will take the place of the solid earth in primitive man's understanding of motion and rest. Motion is relative, but the motion of bodies with respect to one another involves a kind of symmetry that is lacking in the motion of bodies relative to a diffuse and pervasive medium.

Even without a tangible medium there are obvious frames of reference for motion that provide, cosmographically, a meaning for "rest." The velocities of stars within galaxies and of the centers of mass of nearby galaxies with re-spect to one another are all very small in comparison with the velocities of light and cosmic-ray particles; by this fact alone one has a practically rigid framework, in terms of which a kind of "absolute" velocity can be defined.[†] But this fact has acquired, so far, no deep significance in physics, and in the meantime the resolution of the problem raised by optics has proceeded in a different direction.

Wave motion is characterized by any two of three parameters: wavelength, wave velocity, and frequency. If a source of waves and an observer are at rest with respect to each other but moving with respect to some medium through which the wave motion occurs, the *frequency* observed will be the same as if both were at rest with respect to the medium, but the *velocity* will depend on the motion. It was this velocity dependence that was tested by the famous Michelson-Morley experiment and shown to be non-existent. The Michelson-Morley result is one that would be obtained for Newtonian light particles or for a source of waves at rest with respect to the medium. But the Newtonian (particle) model was inconsistent with data showing that the velocity of light is independent of the motion of the source (double stars), and the model of a wave source at rest was inconsistent with the fact that the same results were always obtained in the experiment, whatever the diurnal and seasonal variations in the cosmographic velocity of the apparatus. As a result of the Michelson-Morley experiment and others undertaken since, the conclusion that Einstein

† Cf. Albert Einstein, *The Meaning of Relativity* (Princeton, 1945), pp. 110–11.

took as a new postulate of physics—the invariance of the velocity of light with respect to frames of reference that are not accelerated with respect to one another—is firmly established. This postulate is inconsistent with both Stoic and Epicurean ideas of space.

Fig. 15. Surface Waves from a Moving Source (Courtesy, Educational Services Incorporated, Watertown, Mass.)

The physics of special relativity has been popularized more widely than the preceding development of electromagnetic theory out of which it sprang, and the result is a divorcement that makes relativity seem peculiarly unintuitive.†
This characteristic is increased by the popularization of the remarkable geometrical representation of Hermann Minkowski—undoubtedly of great importance in the further analysis of the ideas of space and time—in which time is represented as a fourth geometrical dimension, with invariant space-time distances in which a spatial distance x is made commensurate with temporal intervals t by the equivalence $x = ict$ ($i^2 = -1$, $c =$ velocity of light).

The representation of light first proposed by H. A. Lorentz and Einstein, and almost universally adopted since, is one in which light is not wave motion in a neutral medium, the "luminiferous ether." The electromagnetic field (as also the gravitational field) is not a stressed state of another—and hypothetical—medium, but is itself a material reality, having properties very different from those of particulate matter but, like the latter, capable—as was observed above—of transmitting energy and momentum. But fields are associated with particles by the very mode of their definition. Particles of matter are coupled by their field interactions, and there is no *independent* medium with respect to which light has an invariant velocity.

Laws concerning the frequency of light in this interpretation, like those describing its velocity, differ from what seems reasonable, either for wave motion in a neutral medium or for a varying flux of particles or a steady flux of internally varying, pulsating particles. To an observer moving toward a stationary source of sound waves with velocity v the intrinsic frequency of the source appears increased by the factor $1 + v/c$, in which c is the velocity of sound in the medium. To a stationary observer of a moving source, on the other hand, the increase is by the factor $1/(1 - v/c)$. The relativistic Doppler shift for light is, in the corresponding case, the geometric mean of the two formulas above (with c the velocity of light). Again learned ignorance: since we cannot detect an independent medium, we do not know which classical Doppler formula to use. Corresponding to our ignorance, in a sense, the correct formula is the average of the two indistinguishable competitors.‡

---

† It was important that Einstein explain the sheer geometrical consequences of relativity, apart from the special context of field theory; he himself introduced the imagery of trains passing each other and making observations of each other, etc. Nowadays high-speed space ships are *au courant*.

‡ The argument may appear glib, but it is correct. For a source traveling with velocity v_s and a mirror traveling with velocity v_m, the frequency shift observed, at the source, of the source reflected in the mirror is the product of the shift that would be observed at the mirror and the shift that would be observed if the mirror were originating the signals. (For the mirror we could

It is from this formula that the famous problem of the traveling twin follows. Twin A stays at home, while twin B goes to a nearby star and returns, finding himself younger than A by an amount that depends on the velocity and length of the trip. The two, during B's trip, send each other signals monitored by identical clocks. During the outward trip each receives the other's signals slowed down by the factor $(c - v)/(c + v)$, the Doppler effect. During the return trip the effect is reversed, v changing its sign. The recording tapes that the twins keep are, however, not identical when compared at the end. The twin who reverses his direction receives "slow" signals from home during the first half of the trip and "fast" during the second; while the twin who stays home receives "slow" signals for more than the first half of the total time and "fast" for less than half. The reason is, of course, that the "slow" signals, because the velocity of light is finite, keep on coming for a time after the traveling twin has reversed his direction. If each keeps a tape of both his own and the other's signals, the two sets of tapes will give the same record: A's elapsed time is greater than B's.† If such an experiment were attempted with sound waves

---

substitute a space ship that received radio signals from the source and relayed them back.) The compound shift is classically represented by the factor

$$\frac{c - v_m + v_s - v_s v_m}{c + v_m - v_s - v_s v_m}$$

If we require that this quantity depend only on the *relative* velocity $v_m - v_s$, we must suppose that one of the "absolute" velocities is zero. Since this cannot be maintained in general, the alternative is to adopt the relativistic addition of velocities, according to which the velocity of the virtual source is

$$v = \frac{v_m - v_s}{1 - v_s v_m / c^2}$$

With this definition of relative velocity v the classical shift above becomes

$$\frac{c - v}{c + v}$$

and the one-way shift is its square root.

† The problem has been much debated. A common objection is that the special theory of relativity does not hold for accelerated motion, and that the traveling twin must, in reversing his direction, be subject to strong forces. The answer is, in the first place, that the special theory does apply to accelerated motion; but the general theory imposes qualifications. In the over-all budget of the problem these effects become negligible if the trip is made very long. A neater solution is to have *three* space travelers, each recording the others' radar pulses. Travelers B, A, and C are lined up in that order, but with a greater distance between A and C than between B and A. Both B and C are traveling toward A at the same speed. The story begins when B passes A in going toward C. After a time B and C pass each other, exchanging special signals as they do so. After a further time C passes A, and the story is finished. There have been no accelerations and no forces acting. Hence no considerations of general relativity enter the problem. All Doppler effects are pairwise symmetrical. Since no two travelers pass each other more than once, ages cannot be directly compared. But, if all three transmit to one another the same recording of a symphony, A and B synchronizing when they pass, and C synchronizing with B when *they* pass, C's transmission will be retarded, compared with A's, at the end. And, since each records the others' music, all will agree that this is so.

during a journey on the earth at subsonic speed, there would be no such consequence. The effect of the finite time of signal transmission would occur but would be just compensated. The Doppler shifts observed by the traveling twin would not be the same as those observed by the stay-at-home, and tapes compared afterward would show the same elapsed time.

It is interesting that the retardation of time for the traveling twin is a consequence of the *identity* of Doppler shifts in the frequency at which each twin receives the signals of the other, the shifts thus *failing* to compensate for the finite time of signal propagation. Relativity restricts one kind of symmetry, that of a universal measure of time; but it does so only as a consequence of another and deeper symmetry, the symmetry of relative inertial motion in a world of invariant light velocity. This way of explaining the twin problem shows clearly that the temporal coordination between clocks (and, of course, between all other processes) at a distance involves not a universal time that, in Newton's language, "flows equably," but rather their material interconnection via the electromagnetic field. Einstein's technique of geometrizing physics, of translating laws of motion into inherent properties of space-time, has often been analyzed as leading toward a sort of Spinozistic eternalism as its implied metaphysics. One could just as well assert, however, that as a result of Einstein's work the pale cast of geometric thought has been rematerialized into a comprehensive framework of the physics of fields. The spatio-temporal order appears no longer as an empty vessel within which matter happens to be, but as the modality of the coexistence and interaction of things. In this sense the tradition of Aristotle and the Stoics rather than that of Epicurus, of Descartes and Leibniz rather than that of Newton, has won out.† But it has won along a historical pathway that Newton was the first to clear.

Einstein's extension of the relativity principle to the description of accelerated motion brought further modification to Newtonian physics, and only recently have some of these consequences received laboratory confirmation. The equations of general relativity are incomplete in the sense that they are consistent with some variety of unobvious boundary conditions. In special relativity Einstein relied upon the result of the Michelson-Morley experiment for his new postulate. In generalized relativity he relied upon a law mentioned in the previous chapter but not exploited in any fundamental way by previous theory: the equivalence of gravitational and inertial mass. The local effects of acceleration are equivalent to those caused by a static gravitational field, and both are in-

---

† See H. P. Robertson, "Geometry as a Branch of Physics," in *Albert Einstein, Scientist-Philosopher,* edited by P. A. Schilpp (Evanston, 1949), pp. 315–32.

terpreted as phenomena of field-coupling with the material environment of the body exhibiting these effects. The idea of a "natural" motion, which we traced from Aristotle to Galileo in Chapter 3, is extended in general relativity to motion in a gravitational field as well as to inertial motion, so that the mass of a star, for example, is sometimes said to "warp" or "curve" the space in its vicinity. A planet moving in the vicinity of the star is then said to move as it does, not because of special forces acting on it, but in a geodesic path in the "curved" space, corresponding to a straight line in Euclidean "flat" space.

As I remarked before, however, this mode of description is just as well said to be a physicalizing of geometry as to be a geometrizing of physical law. If the field is the medium of propagation of energy, linear momentum, and angular momentum in classical physics, it becomes, in general relativity, the medium of propagation, also, of the geometric properties of physical systems—for example, of parallelism. But a language in which such statements are possible is one in which the old dichotomy of matter and empty space is no longer firmly fixed

Quantum Physics

While, early in the twentieth century, the theory of relativity was revising classical physics to make it consistent with field theory, a series of new difficulties with the nineteenth-century synthesis were brought to light. Experiments with the emission and absorption of light showed that the classical picture was incorrect in some essential details. The classical theory predicted, for example, that, when electrons are ejected by incident light from a metal surface (the photoelectric effect), their energy will depend on the intensity of the light—that is, on the amplitude of the electromagnetic wave. Experiment showed, however, that the energy of the ejected electrons is independent of the intensity of the light, but dependent on its frequency, none being ejected by light below a certain frequency. It is the *number* of electrons ejected that depends on the intensity of the light.

Another and grosser difficulty came from the growing mass of evidence concerning the structure of atoms, which more and more certainly had to be pictured as systems composed of positively charged, heavy nuclei accompanied by matching sets of circumambient, planetary electrons. The classical theory, however, would not allow this obvious analogy between solar systems and atomic systems; the coupling between charged particles and the electromagnetic field implied that the former could not move in orbital paths without losing energy both to adjacent atoms and to the electromagnetic field. The resolution of these difficulties—a drastic one, whose consequences have required a revision of previously unquestioned concepts of theoretical physics—was the postulate, by Max Planck and Einstein, that interactions between matter and radiation take place only in quanta, in minimum, indivisible amounts. The postulate was later generalized to cover all physical interactions. Just as the acceptance of the invariant velocity of light introduced a new fundamental constant into physics and required the abandonment of the classical invariance of physical magnitudes, so the acceptance of the quantum principle required the introduction of another new fundamental constant and the reconsideration of another aspect of classical theory—the conception of physical processes as taking place continuously, with arbitrarily small changes occurring in arbitrarily short times. The photoelectric effect, mentioned above, was explained by the hypothesis of quanta of radiation, the indivisible energy of each quantum being determined by a relation expressed by Einstein in the formula

$$E = h\nu$$

in which ν is the frequency of the absorbed radiation and h is the new universal constant, called Planck's constant or the quantum of action. To expel an electron from the surface requires just one sufficiently energetic quantum; to increase the intensity of radiation is to increase the number of quanta, but not their individual energies; and this does not increase the energy, but only the number, of expelled electrons.

In the case of atomic structure, likewise, the quantum principle excludes transitions from one electron orbit to another by arbitrarily small interactions with the electromagnetic field. The orbital frequencies of the electrons are of the same order of magnitude as the frequency of the radiation absorbed or emitted by the atoms, which fact implies, by the Einstein energy-frequency relation, that the electron orbits can change energy only by relatively large amounts. There is, in particular, an orbit of minimum energy, and this energy the electron cannot, on quantum principles, lose. The next step in the development of theory was the postulation, by Louis Victor de Broglie, of a new type of field connected with the electron, in which there is a wave whose frequency is related, by the Einstein relation, to the energy of the electron, or—what comes to the same thing—whose wavelength is connected with the momentum of the electron. But, in general, wave motion in a confined space is possible only for certain resonant frequencies related to the dimensions of the confining space. Thus the orbits of an electron must be consistent with two independent sets of laws, one connected with the classical physics of orbital motion, the other with the Einstein equation.

The result is that, *from a classical point of view,* the variables of the system are, in general, over-determined; the frequencies of electron waves and electron orbits are inconsistent except for certain specific orbits. The electron can occupy only these orbits, and can move from one to others of these orbits only by dis-continuous transitions, gaining or losing well-defined quanta of energy.

Still later Erwin Schrödinger developed, by analogy with the electromagnetic-wave equations, an equation defining the de Broglie waves of electrons and also of other particles. I have not described the experimental confirmation of these theoretical developments, which are abundant and impressive. What is important for our purposes is that the Schrödinger equation is a differential equation, in which, as in classical physics, all quantities are continuously vari-able. The equation is, moreover, completely deterministic; if the wave function of an isolated system is specified at one time, the wave equation determines it for any later time. On the other hand, the energy changes involved in any physical interaction must go by definite quanta. Any attempt to interpret the wave equation directly in observational terms—that is, in terms of measurable quantitative variables, such as the classical physical quantities—would therefore result in a contradiction.† There is one interpretation, however, that avoids any contradiction and, at the same time, suggests a great variety of confirming experiments. This interpretation identifies the amplitude, the value, of the wave function at a particular time and position as a *probability* amplitude. This amplitude, as defined by the Schrödinger equation, is a complex number and may therefore be regarded as specifying simultaneously the amplitude in each of two associated fields. The probability interpretation defines the density of probability at a point as the absolute square of the wave amplitude, the probability being that of finding the particle in the neighborhood of the point. The probability distribution of a quantum event changes continuously and deterministically; the event itself, however, occurs discontinuously and indeterministically.

States

In philosophical discussions of this peculiar shift of classical ideas, emphasis has usually been put on the breakdown of determinism that it implies. In the present discussion I want to place the emphasis differently: quantum mechanics

---

† The contradiction here is not one that prohibits *any* reconciliation of the quantum principle with a determinism involving continuous change. But the change must be in newly postulated "hidden" variables, not in the classical variables of physics. For the views of a determinist see Bohm, *op. cit.,* Chaps. 3 and 4.

modifies classical physics by introducing a new kind of lawfulness, which is absent from classical physics, and as a *consequence* of this there appears also a new kind of non-lawfulness. These modifications enter through the fundamental postulate of quantum physics—namely, that any physical interaction between two systems has a minimum threshold, below which no interaction occurs at all. Thus the idea of atomicity, long since associated with the concept of matter, is made to characterize process as well. This process atomicity is a new sort of structural, non-temporal determinism in nature, and logical room can be made for it, so to speak, only by a relaxation of the older and more familiar type of temporal determinism. The necessary correspondence of the new theory with the old, in areas where the latter is well confirmed, is made possible by the fact that the quantum of action is very small compared with what is involved in the physical transactions that the classical theory described so well. When quantum mechanics is applied to such classical problems, it shows that the old laws still hold—not with infinite accuracy and perfect certainty, but with a degree of accuracy and certainty that renders the new and the old laws indistinguishable in their predictions.

The importance of the new kind of determinism is illustrated most impressively in its application to the theory of atomic structure, referred to previously. According to purely classical laws, the electrons in the atom ought to be coupled with the electromagnetic field and with adjacent atoms in such a way as to make any stable electron orbits impossible. Rigid bodies, which geometry and all of classical physics presuppose, are themselves found to be inconsistent with classical laws as soon as we penetrate far enough into the microscopic domain to investigate their structure. The quantum principle, on the contrary, leads to a satisfactory description of the atoms and their linkages in the structure of ordinary matter. The structure of a crystal is possible only for the same reason for which a single atom has stable structure: the work required to produce plastic deformation must be great enough to produce quantum jumps within the crystal, and short of this will produce no transitions at all.

Thus it is the quantum principle that explains both the extraordinary stability of the chemical atoms and the structures built of them. Examples of this same sort of positive restriction on classically possible states and transitions in nature can be multiplied almost endlessly. I have deliberately emphasized these positive implications before turning to the negative ones that have seized the philosophical imagination (of physicists as well as philosophers); for the negative implications are just the same positive implications seen in conflict with certain congenial classical ideas.

Transitions

Quantum mechanics involves a revision of both the classical conception of a field and the classical conception of a particle. In classical physics a field, as we have previously observed, is as much a material reality as a particle, but it is continuously distributed in space. To the material attributes of energy and momentum quantum mechanics adds the idea that wave motion in the field is always emitted or absorbed as individual quanta. In order to emit or absorb such quanta, however, particles must be capable of unclassical, discontinuous transitions of state. The equation that predicts the correct transition probabilities has the form of a field equation, formally resembling the equations of the electromagnetic field. Thus an account of the interactions between matter and radiation leads to a more complicated description of both, particles having wave-like properties and radiation having particle-like properties.

As a consequence of the quantum character of all material interactions, it follows that a system cannot be isolated in the classical sense and, at the same time, be under observation. For any act of observation requires a coupling between the system and some means of observation. This is true, of course, in classical physics as well as in quantum physics; but in classical physics there is no lower bound to the magnitude of the interactions that are necessary for determining the state of the system with any required accuracy, and this problem of observation can, in principle, be ignored. In quantum physics, on the other hand, the making of an observation implies a minimum and irreducible disturbance of the thing observed. The more accurate the measurement, the greater the ensuing disturbance. Since the measurement itself fixes the state of the system with respect to one variable, the disturbance produces an uncertainty in the conjugate† dynamical variable. Thus, the more accurately the time of an event is determined, the more uncertain is the corresponding energy transfer, or vice versa.

---

† The standard conjugate pairs are energy versus time, momentum versus distance, and angular momentum versus angle. In each case the product has the dimensions of action. The principle of indeterminacy (uncertainty) says that the product of uncertainties in measurement of conjugate pairs is at least $h = 1.2 \times 10^{-16}$ electron-volt seconds, or 6×10^{-27} erg seconds. In macroscopic interactions the relative size of this uncertainty is vanishingly small, and it is buried in the ocean of thermal and other sorts of classical uncertainty. An examination question for graduate students comes from the problem I mentioned in discussing the symmetry of chance. Balance a pencil on its point, arbitrarily well. To get rid of the thermal noise, which will be the first thing to knock it over, cool everything down to absolute zero. How long before the pencil must fall? Its angle with the vertical must be very nearly zero, and so must its angular motion. But the product of the uncertainties in these measures cannot be less than h!

The general fact that the laws of motion in quantum mechanics determine not events but probability distributions leaves open the possibility that a system so described could also be described in a classical deterministic fashion. For there are similar statistical laws in classical physics, and these are not incompatible with strict determinism. But the verification of deterministic laws requires measurement, and measurement involves coupling with the uncontrolled environment. In the case of classical statistical laws this coupling is independent, in principle, of the measuring process and could therefore be taken account of. In the case of quantum laws the same sort of coupling may be present, but we cannot take account of it by measurement, for measurement introduces further coupling of the same sort.

The standard phenomenon for illustrating the principle of indeterminacy, or uncertainty, is the interference of light waves. The wave theory of the nature of light explains why electromagnetic radiation fans out after passing through a slit. If there are two slits close together, moreover, the radiation fans out from each, and there is a region in which the diverging rays from the slits overlap. If this radiation is stopped by a screen or a photographic plate, the illumination has alternating bands of light and dark. These bands are explained by the superposition of waves coming from the two slits. According to the quantum principle, however, this radiation must be thought of as coming in definite and indivisible quanta. The interference is, moreover, an internal affair of each photon, or quantum of light energy; each is emitted by a single atom and absorbed by a single atom, but its absorption probability is low in certain bands (the dark ones) and high in the others, so that its transmission involves an interaction with both slits. Speaking un-picturesquely, "it" passes through both slits. If the source emits electrons rather than photons, essentially the same phenomenon will be observed. The wave here is not electromagnetic but is the de Broglie wave associated with any material particle. A paradox evidently arises if we conceive the electron as a particle in the conventional sense, for again we have to say that "it" passes through both slits; otherwise the interference pattern produced when many electrons are absorbed on the photographic plate, one after another, would not be explained. We may still believe, apparently, that the electron does pass through one slit or the other; for it is part of the implicit meaning of "particle" that a particle cannot be in two places at the same time. The crucial point, however, is that we cannot determine which slit the electron goes through without destroying, at the same time, the interference pattern itself. This is obviously true if we close one of the slits, for then the electron must go through the other if it gets to the plate at all. It is true for more subtle reasons if we try to determine which slit the electron goes through by measuring its interaction with the plate containing the slits, or if we try to watch the electron by illuminating it with light, etc. The point, deducible from the quantum theory, is that, when we locate the electron with enough accuracy to say which slit it goes through, we thereby destroy its interaction with the other slit. The location of the electron requires that it scatter, into some sort of camera, at least one quantum of light of wavelength short enough to distinguish the alternative positions. This interaction produces an indeterminate change in the momentum of the electron, and this change renders the wavelength of the associated de Broglie wave sufficiently indeterminate to destroy any interference phenomena on the photographic plate.

In the light of this and countless other examples, it is suggested that the principle of indeterminacy is not a principle that imposes on us an unavoidable ignorance; rather, the ignorance it imposes is a learned ignorance. What has a precise, and arbitrarily minute, spatial location is not the electron itself, but rather its interaction, under certain conditions, with other matter or radiation. To locate a particle is, literally, to localize it, and our ignorance of the location of an unobserved particle is, like our ignorance about the ends of the earth or the center of the universe, a negative statement of a positive fact. The incompatibility of a precisely defined location and a precisely defined momentum is not an accidental result of our observational techniques, but an intrinsic characteristic of the electron. The persuasiveness of this interpretation is easily lost sight of when attention is concentrated on the principle of indeterminacy alone; for it is merely one deduction from a theory that, in other contexts, implies in nature positive regularities having no counterpart in classical physics—the photoelectric effect, the Compton effect, and the detailed structure of molecules, atoms, and nuclei and of the spectra associated with them, to mention only a few examples. Even in the example considered, the uncertainty of position is a concomitant of a new effect, the interference patterns associated with particle radiation, a phenomenon that is incompatible with the classical concept "particle." The *positive* character of the principle of indeterminacy is explained very clearly in the following quotation from one of the founders of the quantum theory, Niels Bohr:

> "It must here be remembered that even in the indeterminacy relation we are dealing with an implication of the formalism which defies unambiguous expression in words suited to describe classical physical pictures. Thus, a sentence like 'we cannot know both the momentum and the position of an atomic object'

raises at once questions as to the physical reality of two such attributes of the object, which can be answered only by referring to the conditions for the un-ambiguous use of space-time concepts, on the one hand, and dynamical conserva-tion laws, on the other hand. While the combination of these concepts into a single picture of a causal chain of events is the essence of classical mechanics, room for regularities beyond the grasp of such a description is just afforded by the circumstance that the study of the complementary phenomena demands mutually exclusive experimental arrangements." †

The application of probability to quantum mechanics poses no problem that we have not already considered; the wave function that describes the character-istics of material systems provides the basis of probability calculations con-cerning their interactions with other systems. Since the time-dependence of the wave function describing any such system is completely deterministic, and since this determinism applies, in principle, to all material systems, including our-selves and our instruments of observation, the element of chance appears to enter quantum mechanics, as it enters classical physics, via the contingency of interaction between systems. Because of the quantum principle itself, however, there is no possibility of supplementing the wave-function's deterministic de-scription by a direct, deterministic account of events themselves, as in the language of classical physics.

Among the conclusions to which quantum mechanics leads, and that future modification of the theory can hardly set aside, there is a whole hierarchy of conclusions about the structure of matter, of which the explanation of the stability of atoms is only the first. Classical physics introduced a way of de-scribing nature in which all structure in matter appeared as essentially ad-ventitious, a consequence of arbitrary boundary conditions. It perforce accepted the variety of natural species, but as simply given. Quantum physics, on the other hand, has introduced a new kind of lawfulnes, which has to do, not with the succession of states in time, but with modes of coexistence in space. These laws, moreover, are coupled with the principle of indeterminacy in such a way that the gain in non-temporal lawfulness is balanced by temporal non-lawful-ness. One is tempted, indeed, to see in the quantum-mechanical way of thought a return to Aristotle's view, discussed earlier, that there is a temporal inde-terminacy when things are considered as the effects of material causes, an indeterminacy that is overcome, in a sense, by the prevalence of final causes—that is, of determining forms or patterns. The comparison may seem far-fetched,

† Niels Bohr, "Discussions with Einstein on Epistemological Problems in Atomic Physics," in Schilpp, *op. cit.*, p. 211.

but the twentieth-century way of thought has a certain formal resemblance to Aristotelian categories of explanation.†

Identity

A much-disputed doctrine of Aristotle's has been that of natural kinds, according to which all individual substances in nature fall into classes whose members do not differ in essence but only in their accidental characteristics. The classification of matter as ethereal or corporeal, of the latter kind as earth, water, air, or fire, and of composite terrestrial bodies as inanimate or animate, etc., implied that nature does not vary on a continuum of natural kinds, that there are, rather, qualitatively distinct modes of existence, each with its characteristic nature, and that between these are no intermediate varieties, none, at least, that are stable and self-perpetuating. The existence of intermediate varieties and, ultimately, of individual differences is allowed for by the doctrine of chance, which allows things to interact and leave their marks upon one another, but in accordance with no final cause.

It is a characteristic of quantum physics, too little appreciated in most philosophical discussions of it, that it restores the doctrine of natural kinds.

This doctrine is otherwise known as the principle of identity, and it embraces many familiar facts of nature as well as many that are unfamiliar. According to the Aristotelian belief, individual substances differ from others of the same species only in their accidental characteristics but not in those that are essential. This distinction between accidental and essential is never adequately defined by Aristotle. In quantum-mechanical identity the difficulty is removed by the stipulation, well supported by a wide range of evidence, that there are natural kinds, species, whose members are indistinguishable from one another in *all* respects that are relevant to the *causal* description of their behavior.

But the principle must be stated more precisely. It is absurd to say that two distinct objects differ in no respect, for, to be identified as two, they must be matched against some other pair of objects, and this fact alone distinguishes them as this or that, left or right, etc. But to state a difference between the objects requires that they differ in at least *two* respects: first, they must be differ-

---

† My thinking was stimulated in this direction several years ago by a mimeographed essay of, and by conversations with, Professor Laszlo Tisza of the Massachusetts Institute of Technology. Professor Tisza used the phrase "morphic determinism" to contrast with the "temporal determinism" of classical laws. Aristotle would have been happy with the expression.

ently designated; second, different characteristics must be predicated of the things so designated.†

The quantum-mechanical principle of identity asserts that no two differently designated members of an identity class can be distinguished by predicated characteristics that are relevant to the causal description of their behavior.

A relevant sort of characteristic might be called a mark, a small congenital or acquired difference that would distinguish one member of a class from the other. Any pair of billiard balls could be distinguished by a slight difference of mass or by the nicks and scratches they have acquired. But quantum mechanics assumes that two elementary particles are wholly indistinguishable, and that one of two composite structures of the same kind—two atoms of sodium, for example—can be "marked" only by a finite, quantum interaction below which there is no interaction at all. But two atoms that are in different states are not members of the same identity class. If one of two atoms is marked, for example, by absorbing energy, it moves to a different class. If it then loses energy, it returns to the original class, with no mark left in it of the transitions it has undergone.

Two uranium nuclei may be in the same energy state, but one will disintegrate before the other. While they are in the same state, they show no difference that explains why one disintegrates before the other. Any attempt to find a difference either will have no result or will, by interaction, *put* the two into different states, thus destroying symmetry. To revert to the language of the principle of insufficient reason, there is no *reason* why atom A should disintegrate before atom B. You will recall that in discussing probability I insisted that an event—a collocation—is not well defined except in terms of both designating and predicated characteristics. The difference between collocations in classical physics and those in quantum physics is this: In classical physics it is assumed that a collocation with probability $1/2$ is conditionally equivalent to one with probability 1 or 0; the same objective happening could have been predicted deterministically. In quantum physics this is not always so.

The most striking evidence of the existence of identity classes is statistical. In proton-neutron scattering experiments, trajectories after scattering can be paired; for any recoil motion of the neutron and proton there is a corresponding alternative, in which the paths of scattered neutron and proton are interchanged.

---

† Suppose that two objects differ *only* in spatial location or, more generally, in spatio-temporal history, but that all their qualities are identical. From a perfect qualitative description there would be no way of telling which object was intended. If twins could be identical in this sense, they would respond in the same way to all behavioral tests, including the question "Which twin are you?"

In proton-proton scattering, considered classically, there would still be this pair of alternatives; although the alternatives might be practically indistinguishable, counting them as two would still give the right statistical weight. But in fact the right statistical weight is found, by experiment, when one does *not* count "*A* goes to the left" and "*B* goes to the right" as an alternative to "*A* goes to the right" and "*B* goes to the left." Recognizing our inability to distinguish these two cases in any way, theory says that they are *not* distinct. Ignorance, once more, can be regarded as learned, and the meaning of it is that elementary particles lack individuality. Even for more complex systems this proposition remains true as long as it is possible to speak of pure quantum states. But the number of possible states of a system increases so rapidly with the number of its components that the probability of finding two very complex systems in identical states is negligible. In any given environment, moreover, the prevailing temperatures set a limit to the size and duration of structures that must be talked about in quantum terms; and only at very low temperatures can large masses exhibit the peculiar properties that are characteristic of elementary particles and atoms. A remarkable example of this is the phenomenon of superconductivity.

With respect to the building blocks of matter, nevertheless, there is no individuality; and the individuality of more complex things must still be described, from the point of view of quantum physics, as difference of state rather than difference of substance. There is a Christian theological doctrine to the effect that each angel of the heavenly host is a member, not of the species *angel*, but of his own species. Quantum mechanics brings us to describe everything in nature in the same way; individuality is a matter of form or pattern, but not of unalterable substance. Complex individuals are individuals simply in the sense that there are so many more species definable than there are entities to belong to them that the chance of indistinguishable entities is negligible; each is, indeed, of its own species.

On the other hand, what is most important about individuality in life can hardly be discussed in terms of pure quantum states. The individuality of cells and organisms, and, *a fortiori,* of persons, involves a kind of abstraction that is not reducible to the pattern of quantum states; it is a pattern of states and transitions, of "flights and perchings," so that it would not be biologically meaningful to speak of *the* quantum state of a living thing. It is curious that in the search for metaphors life has been compared, on account of its orderliness and structure, to the crystal, and, on account of its metabolic character, to the candle flame. Neither comparison by itself has depth; but—to anticipate a later discussion—it might be said that life is a remarkable sort of candle flame that can burn only in the presence of a remarkable sort of crystal. The crystal in question is the genetic material of the cell, which exhibits—although in a rather complex sense—the identity and stability of speciation projected—again in a rather complex way—from the quantum domain into that of vital process.

The Scala Naturae

One of the heritages of the philosophic past that quantum mechanics revives and alters is the idea of a *scala naturae,* a ladder of nature. The conception of levels of organization or integration was mainly a product of pre-scientific thought and had no stable place within the framework of mechanistic philosophy. At the same time it had an obvious basis, and it persisted through the eighteenth century.

The philosophic source of this idea, mainly in Hellenistic and medieval neo-Platonism, had been an attempt to work out the metaphysical consequences of the metaphor of craftsmanship. Matter is formed; form is imposed upon matter. The fascination of this metaphor, and the sense of its rightness, derive from what may be called common-sense thermodynamics, the belief that specific order and organization do not simply happen but are brought about; and the order of the thing formed is not *ex nihilo,* but is responsive to some antecedent order. This may be thought of as an idea in the mind of God or as an impersonal pattern inherent in the nature of things. The neo-Platonic element, responsible for the idea of a ladder in nature, is the belief that all such patterns are parts or fragments of one pattern, and that the more organized and complicated structures of nature are, so to say, closer to the original, more perfect in the sense of more complete. This idea of perfection was therefore not in any sense subjective, arbitrary, or relative to a standard; it was simply a matter of how much of the Original Pattern stood revealed in this or that species of things.†

There might be intermediate steps of creation: what more fully embodied the Form of Being could, in turn, produce things that less fully embodied it. There is a sort of causal principle implied here, which still dominated the metaphysical thinking of Descartes: the cause of anything must be at least as perfect as the effect. Later on, as we shall see, this principle was domesticated, brought to scientific formulation, as the second law of thermodynamics.

---

† Here I speak of part and whole. But compare Chap. 3, on universals. A classic study of the neo-Platonic idea is Arthur O. Lovejoy, *The Great Chain of Being* (Cambridge, Mass., 1956; paperback, New York, 1960).

In the eighteenth century the *scala naturae* showed up in the belief that the species of plants and animals could be ordered in a scale of perfection. The taxonomic system of Linnaeus lent itself to this view; it exhibited a single well-ordered series from man down to the lowliest zoophytes.

But the idea of temporal development over long periods of time leads to a different conception of hierarchy in nature and, in spite of superficial agreement, does not fit with the *scala naturae* of neo-Platonic tradition. In the one case perfection is something from above, reflected darkly in the mirror of nature; in the other case it is an expression of evolutionary potentialities within nature. The idea of a ladder, of a linear ordering of species, was rejected by Georges Cuvier, the great anatomist and paleontologist. Cuvier's taxonomy was based upon the metaphor of branching, his four great animal classes being simply four different types of anatomical structure, not related to one another as higher to lower. In Darwinian evolution, likewise, the idea of a linear ordering is discarded in favor of the evolutionary tree; and again the result does not suggest, as the neo-Platonic ladder suggested, a single *forma finalis*.

Fig. 16. The Tree of Life [*From the Nelson-Atkins Gallery of Art, Kansas City (Nelson Fund)*]

Perhaps the best comparison of ladder and tree can be found in the circumstance that in both cases there is a principle that we may call, following the older tradition, the principle of plenitude. This principle, still alive in the thought of Leibniz, says that all things possible in nature are actualized. In the older tradition this meant that there is a continuum in nature, from higher to lower. In the evolutionary tradition it has come to mean that the evolution of matter creates new potentialities, which are tried out in the course of further evolution; some appear but do not persist, while others achieve stability and define, in turn, still further potentialities. Nature tries everything.

In classical physics there is no place for concepts of hierarchical order. It operates with the abstraction of material particles interacting in various ways, but these particles with which it starts have properties that it does not explain when they reappear as properties of complex structures. Only atoms can be rigid and without internal degrees of freedom. Yet the very concept of the solid state is an abstraction from everyday experience. From the Greek atomists through the nineteenth century the atomic hypothesis, plausible as it was on other grounds, could not explain how atoms could be "felted" together to form macroscopic rigid bodies. Above all, it could not explain the sharp speciation of these structures. Nineteenth-century chemistry was founded on the axiom of pure substances. John Dalton's investigations, in particular, were founded on this axiom, but the atomic species that he demonstrated were ultimates of his science, not things that physics could throw any light on.

With quantum physics all this is changed. The old distinction between atom and compound is relativized, and today one may say, speculatively, that *every* atom shows itself, under suitable conditions, to be a compound, but that, conversely, any compound has a range of conditions under which it is atomic, participating in processes with a well-defined character and without internal alternatives. Its nature determines its interactions, but not its interactions its nature. Under different conditions, on the other hand, it shows itself as a complex, altered by interaction with its environment. These statements are speculative only in the sense that there is an unexplored frontier. In Chapter 5 the argument on this point was begun: laws of nature, it was argued, are unconditional generalizations, generalizations held unconditionally true because verified over a very wide range of conditions. But under a great enough change of conditions, it was remarked, the possibility of considering a system isolated and of studying the laws of its behavior disappears. In the picture offered by present-day quantum mechanics this pattern is very clearly exemplified. A system is quantum-stable as long as external disturbances are weak enough.

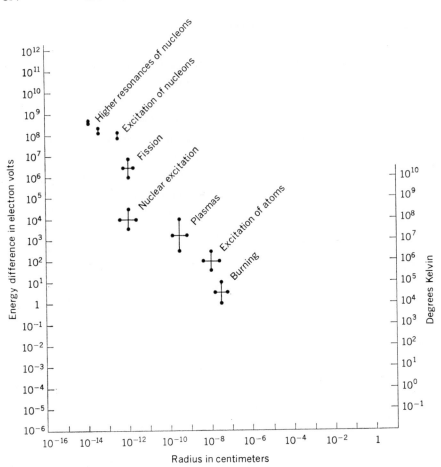

Fig. 17. The Quantum Ladder: the Relation of Size and Stability

Every system has, however, a threshold of stability, a characteristic excitation energy above which it does not remain stable. The quantum ladder (so called by V. F. Weisskopf)† is defined by the fact that this excitation energy varies inversely with the mass and the square of the radius of the system. This means that the larger and more complex systems can exist only at lower temperatures. Under the extremely high excitation energies produced by the large accelerators of today, even elementary particles such as the neutron, proton, and electron exhibit internal structure, and the new particles of recent discovery are connected with this structure in ways not yet understood.

The Aristotelian natural philosophy sought to understand things in terms of

† V. F. Weisskopf, "Quality and Quantity in Quantum Physics," *Daedalus,* Fall 1959, pp. 592–605.

qualities, of essences, which, in turn, determined characteristic forms of the interrelation of things. The mechanistic natural philosophy sought to understand the qualities of things as structural, but the structures that were possible within its framework of ideas were inevitably plastic and responsive, on a continuous scale of transitions, to the environment in which they existed. The clearest expression of this is the Boltzmann paradox, formulated just before the advent of the earliest quantum ideas. According to this paradox, the specific heat of any material substance ought to be infinite. If molecules or crystals consist of atoms, atoms of electrons and nuclei, and nuclei of still smaller units, and if there is no end to this subdivision, then the random kinetic energy called heat should gradually penetrate inward—that is, downward on the scale of sizes—to the smaller and smaller constituents. Equilibrium at a given temperature would have no meaning.

In quantum mechanics the Boltzmann paradox is avoided in a way that is elegant and that fits the facts of observation. The penetration of thermal energy into the minuter components of a system stops, and stops completely, at the point at which the excitation energy necessary for penetration of the quantum barrier is not available at the prevailing temperatures.

The quantum ladder is, of course, no replacement for the grandly metaphysical conception of the *scala naturae*. Yet it provides, in the form of empirically testable and, in fact, well-confirmed theory, a unitary account of those natural phenomena by which the older, metaphysical theory supported itself: structures that become units of larger structures through many stages or stories, structures that exhibit, at every stage, qualitative differences in their laws of behavior but that belong together, at the same time, in something like the old Aristotelian pattern of form and matter. But the quantum theory is only in one degree less abstract than classical physics: it provides for the possibility of wholeness and organization, as classical physics did not, but it does not explain the actuality. That question, which involves us in the idea of evolution and in the conceptual context of thermodynamics, will be resumed in a later chapter.

It is worth pointing out, in closing this account of quantum mechanics, that it offers a sort of paradigm for analyzing one of the most important metaphysical problems. The interactions among things are conditioned by their character as things, by their qualities. Things have their qualities, however, not in isolation, but in a milieu of relations with other things. The particle-field duality is the expression of this logical instability as it appears in modern physics. The field is a nexus of relations among antecedently defined particles. But it is more than that, for the quantum fluctuations of the field and the creation and annihilation of particles are described as potentialities of the field. The whole range of metaphysical impulses is displayed by physicists, some of whom would like to do away with the field as a fundamental concept and return to the ultimateness of particles. Others would like to "dissolve" particles, describing them as localized manifestations of the field.

Outside physics, philosophical thought has turned round this circle many times. G. W. F. Hegel, the master dialectician, saw it all and joked about it. His method was to play the one viewpoint against the other; essence was a function of context, and context of essence. But in the end the rational was real, and the real was rational. In Hegel's private language "rational" meant relational; context determined, the part expressed the whole, and particularity got swallowed up. Back at the beginning of modern physics Thomas Hobbes saw things differently. Men were bodies, with a well-defined character as intelligent and bound to self-preservation ahead of all other goals. The political state was the result. But, whereas individuals were fixed in their essential character, civil society was artificial, problematic, and fluid. It was as though the temperature had been raised (as, indeed, it had been in the seventeenth century) to a point where the larger structure was no longer stable and only its units were reliably constant. This is the conceptual source of Hobbes's atomistic mode of thought, of his psychological egoism and his theory of the social contract.

Hegel saw the duality. Men were the products of changing institutions, but institutions were expedients devised by men. It was only at the metaphysical summit that he defected in favor of the Absolute. In some present-day cultural anthropology one sees contextualism without a struggle: human beings are expressions, local embodiments, of culture, and culture is absolute; men are wholly plastic to culture as their "second nature," and a first nature, an original nature that sets bounds to culture, does not exist.

How shall we learn to think well about this range of questions? Surely not by mere analogies from physics. But we cannot ignore analogies, for then we use them uncritically. The new analogies of quantum physics are important because they are analogies neither of essence simply, nor of relation simply. Nor are they eclectic mixtures. By one of the most extraordinary intellectual syntheses yet accomplished they show how it is possible to combine opposed but complementary abstractions within a single and logically rigorous theory.

8

THE IDEA OF ORDER

Each of the previous chapters has been concerned with some species of order: number, form, continuity, law and causality, the invariants of measurement, and the kind of order, equivocally called disorder, that is the subject matter of the theory of probability. In the present chapter the general meaning of the idea of order is examined, with specific attention to one of the most significant intellectual developments of the nineteenth and twentieth centuries, the *thermodynamic* conception of order.

L'ordre Naturel

In the revolt against Aristotelian traditions, which was essential to the independent growth of modern physics, not all the old questions were equally well resolved. From the point of view of Aristotelian natural philosophy, the mechanistic philosophy represents the ascendancy of one mode of explanation, that of the material cause, over the others. But along with this philosophy—in an Aristotelian sense, materialism—there developed another and complementary philosophical view, which represented a superficially Aristotelian reassertion of final causes. This was the belief in a divinely appointed natural harmony, an *ordre naturel.*†

---

† Jacob Bronowski, *The Common Sense of Science* (New York, 1952), contains a brief but perceptive account, entitled "The Eighteenth Century and the Idea of Order," of the period between the triumph of Newton and the discoveries of the nineteenth century.

It was one of the commonplaces of seventeenth- and eighteenth-century deistic thought, both in Newton's circle and on the continent, that the world is the best world possible. The same idea appeared in the eighteenth century as a presupposition of some political and economic philosophers, notably in the economic theory of François Quesnay, inventor of laissez-faire and of economic science. This philosophy is not really Aristotelian. For Aristotle, natural purposes, final causes, were not diffuse cosmological principles, but as individual and plural and empirical as the many natural kinds of things that we do, in fact, find; and, as I said earlier, the order of nature as a whole is loose enough to include chance; the interactions of things, each with its own characteristic ends, are not controlled by an all-embracing end. Aristotle's First Cause is, indeed, a final cause and not a temporally first cause; it is, perhaps, the finality of Nature as an individual whole, but it is no Providence of a sort to give secret meaning to each event. Aristotle was probably not unacquainted with such ideas; he may have thought them in his youth, but he was too much of a natural scientist to be interested in inscrutable causes.

Now this global teleology could be put to use of a kind. While it was ostensibly opposed to the materialism that accompanied the development of mechanical science, it could be accommodated to that philosophy without mutual embarrassment. The science of mechanics might explain the operation of things within nature, but it could not explain the order within which these operations took place. The automaton operated with clockwork and levers, but the organization of these into an automaton implied a design. So the operation of mechanical laws could explain all within its province, but it could not explain the existence of just *this* world from among the set of all possible worlds—to use again Leibniz's famous phrase.

What is literally mechanical—machine-like—is also teleological. A machine—in the standard image of it—is an assemblage of parts so constrained, mechanically, that it transmits motion from some source to some use; its functionality and its dynamically degenerate character, with no degrees of freedom, mark it as the work of design. Medical physics in the early modern period was cast in this form. The skeletal and muscular system was described as a machine, and speculation extended the metaphor to functions not understood. The capital discovery, of course, was William Harvey's discovery of the circulation of the blood; and it made possible a theory of pathology, in which illness could be linked to the impairment of circulation.

This particular chain of developments led to Quesnay's description of the circular flow of goods and services and to his conception of wealth as good circulation rather than as the sheer amassing of gold. In the natural order there were good circulation and good health unless ill-conceived policies of taxation depressed the rate of flow and thus of production. Quesnay's proposal to tax only the owners of land was, conceptually, a kind of iatrophysics applied to the diseases of the French monarchy. By removal of the hindrances to circulation the natural order would be spontaneously restored. Nature was the best physician; the human doctor could, at best, remove alien and disturbing factors and wait for Nature to do the rest.

Adam Smith, although a follower of Quesnay, shifted attention from the circular flow to the market mechanisms—in today's terms, from macro-economic to micro-economic questions. In the market behavior of individual producers and consumers Smith found the equilibrating mechanisms by which the natural order, once established, would maintain itself. Smith's famous "invisible hand," so often appealed to as a justification of laissez-faire economic policies, was no mystical harmony, postulated once and for all, but the direct and traceable effect of a multitude of individual decisions based upon principles of rational self-interest. Nevertheless, Smith's account of the wealth of nations is not yet developmental and historical in character; it takes the order of commercial society, with its markets, as a given and, in a sense, providential order.

The recognition that science had made its great gains in an understanding of the processes and mechanisms that operated within some established order, but was powerless to understand the order itself, marked a true, but not fixed, limitation. Hence the maxim, never very clear but still popular, that science can answer *how* but not *why*.

The beginnings of the attack on the problem of order occurred in the nineteenth century, in two great innovations. One of these was the theory of evolution, revolutionary in its conceptual form and dramatic in its implications. It is the subject of Chapter 10. The other was the growth of thermodynamics and statistical mechanics, highly formal sciences with almost no impact on popular thought. Today, out of the partial fusion of these two developments, there begins to emerge, in outline at least, the conception of a new and vastly enlarged science of order, which stands to seventeenth-century physics as a living thing stands to the clockwork automata that were admired in the polite society of the post-Newtonian era.

The nineteenth-century revolutions of scientific thought are past, yet their full implications, in science and the philosophy of science, have hardly been realized. In the remaining sections of the present chapter my main concern is to elucidate the propositions and habits of thought that are germane to thermodynamics. In Chapter 10 these propositions are brought into relation to the problems of biological order. The result, in part, discredits the eighteenth-century idea of order, but also, in part, gives to that idea a new meaning and a new status among the topics of scientific inquiry. The notion of a fixed and providential arrangement of things in a harmonious "system of the world" temporarily filled a gap in the scientific description of the world, while accommodating itself to a gradual accumulation of information in biology, chemistry, geology, and cosmography. This accumulation prepared the way for the work of such men as Charles Lyell and Charles Darwin. The growth of physics, meanwhile, continued to the point where students of heat developed the intellectual tools that would, in the end, bring about a recasting of the whole seventeenth- and eighteenth-century framework of scientific thought.

Thermodynamics

The crucial development, within physics, was the conception of heat as a form of energy and the formulation of the law of the conservation of energy. Both the conception and the law were derived from investigation of the connection between heat and mechanical motion. The conservation law can be applied, retrospectively, to the problems of Newtonian physics, and there are earlier formulations of it, notably in the writings of Leibniz. But its greatest value was in the connection it provided between the laws of motion and a phenomenon to which those laws had no obvious relevance—heat.

When the conservation of energy was so formulated, it led to a problem that was quite novel in the history of physics. Mechanical energy could be converted into heat, and heat into mechanical energy. But, whereas the conversion of mechanical energy into heat was easy, the reverse conversion was difficult. The former was spontaneous and, in the normal course, inevitable; the latter was contrived and subject to a major qualification, which it became the business of thermodynamics to study.

The earliest investigations concerned the steam engine and the reason for its low efficiency in converting heat into mechanical energy. The problem was solved by reasoning from the general empirical fact that heat will not flow uphill—that is, from a colder to a hotter body. This proposition, or any one of several more careful but essentially equivalent statements, became known as the second law of thermodynamics. The law expressed only a familiar fact of experience; what gave it importance was the conservation law, which made it necessary to think of the total energy of a system as partitioned into two parts, a part available for work and a part not so available.

The second law had one peculiarity that distinguished it from all previous formulations of physical law since the time of Galileo: it took account of time direction, and they did not. The difference between past and future, however overwhelmingly obvious and decisive in the scheme of things, was inessential in the basic formulations of Newtonian physics, as we have seen earlier. This is true not only of the dynamics of particles, but also of the nineteenth-century extension of the laws of motion to cover the interactions of matter and radiation. The acceleration of an electric charge causes electromagnetic radiation, which spreads out spherically from the locus of the particle; Maxwell's equations, however, are time-symmetric and include also the possibility that a converging spherical electromagnetic wave is absorbed and manifested as acceleration of the electric charge. The second law, on the other hand, implied that physics, by its own means, was finally moved to acknowledge one of the most pervasive features of experience, the difference between "before" and "after." A simple example (to be used later for a more sophisticated purpose) will illustrate this. A cylindrical metal disk has a hole in it (Fig. 18); into the hole we insert a plug that is at a higher temperature. The subsequent temperature gradient is shown in Figure 19. The second law is illustrated by the obvious fact that the time reversal of this flow does not occur. A formally

Fig. 18. Metal Disk and Heated Plug

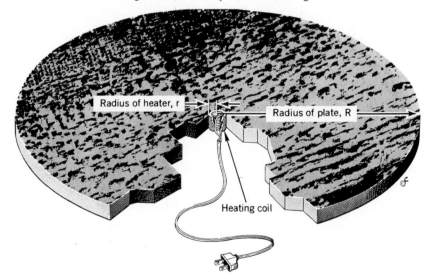

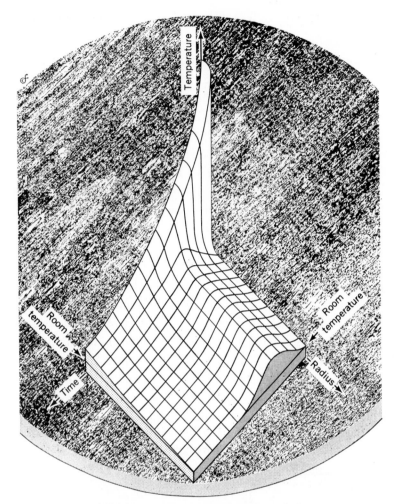

Fig. 19. Disk and Plug: the Temperature in Time

analogous case in mechanics is the motion of a planet in its orbit; for every such motion the time-reversed motion is equally possible.

Now, if the equations of heat diffusion in the disk were derivable solely from the laws of mechanics, we should have found a contradiction, having deduced a time-irreversible process from laws invariant with respect to time direction. But, as I have already shown (Chap. 6), the laws of mechanics do not give a *complete* description of natural phenomena, even within the framework of classical physics. The processes of heat flow must depend, on pain of contradiction, upon something beyond the equations of motion.

Heat flow is only one example of such irreversible processes; the production of heat by friction, the freezing of supercooled liquids, and chemical reactions (most obviously the explosive ones) are other examples. In all such cases it is possible to show, by a variety of more or less ingeniously thought experiments, that, if any such irreversible reactions were in fact reversible, one could continuously transform heat into mechanical energy, and the heat energy of the world could be transformed at will into useful work.

An alternative formulation of the second law is useful in a wider range of cases than the one that refers merely to heat flow. In any system that is isolated (and in which, therefore, the total energy is constant) we may subdivide the total energy into two fractions. One of these is able to perform work and is called free energy; the other is bound, or unavailable, energy. The second law, formulated in these terms, says that the bound energy of an isolated system can only increase, the free energy only decrease. For a still sharper formulation the degree of unavailability of the energy of a system is given by the measure called *entropy*. For systems in which changes take place at constant temperature—that is, for *isothermal* processes—the entropy is simply the total bound energy divided by the temperature of the system, and is thus measured in calories per degree. If temperature changes are involved, the entropy *change* is defined as the *change* in the quantity of heat divided by the temperature (which, for small enough changes, is virtually constant). Gross entropy changes are thus defined by integration over a sequence of smaller ones. The entropy change for a whole system is the algebraic sum of changes for all parts of the system.

In a steam engine, for example, if a quantity of heat Q_1 is removed from the boiler at temperature T_1, and if a quantity Q_2 is added to the condenser at temperature T_2, the entropy changes are, respectively, Q_2/T_2 and $-Q_1/T_1$. If W is the work done by the engine, the first law of thermodynamics requires that $W = Q_1 - Q_2$. The second law states that the entropy change $Q_2/T_2 - Q_1/T_1$ must be positive. If W is positive as well, this evidently leads to the conclusion that

$$W \leq \frac{T_1 - T_2}{T_1} Q_1$$

By means of the entropy concept it is possible to resolve the threatened contradiction between the reversibility of the elementary processes of classical physics and thermodynamic irreversibility. The feature of the second law that does not depend upon the laws of motion lies in the distinction between free and bound energy, and thus in the entropy concept. Entropy is a physical variable; but, as was discovered toward the end of the nineteenth century, it may be represented as the product of a physical constant and a dimensionless variable, the latter having a meaning outside the province of dynamical law. The constant is called Boltzmann's constant, and it represents the increase of energy in a gas, per molecule, for a one-degree temperature rise. But the dimensionless variable represents the intrusion into physics of a radically new element, described below.

Statistical Mechanics

In the chapter on probability I argued that the reality of chance is not contravened by the hypothesis of exact, deterministic laws of motion, for these do not give a complete account of physical systems, which also have a certain number of degrees of freedom represented by spatio-temporal variables. In the previous section I pointed out that, if the laws of thermodynamic irreversible processes were deducible from the laws of motion, a self-contradiction would result. I thus suggested that the non-dynamical premises of thermodynamics are of the kind—namely, premises of probability—that complement the laws of motion.

Just this connection, in fact, was developed in the nineteenth century, primarily through the work of Maxwell and Ludwig Boltzmann, as an elaboration of the kinetic theory of heat. The most remarkable consequence of this development was that entropy reappeared in the new theory, not as a phenomenological variable measurable in the heat laboratory, but as a parameter of the probability law describing the statistical behavior of large systems of particles, and was definable far outside the experimental range of ordinary calorimetry. As a result, thermodynamics received an extension of the range of phenomena to which it could be applied, becoming a truly universal science. The dimensionless variable referred to in the previous section reappeared in the formulation of statistical mechanics as a non-mechanical variable—namely, as a parameter of the probability law characterizing the phase-space distribution of the system being described. In the meaning of this parameter was hidden the final explanation of the apparent contradiction between the symmetry of time direction in dynamics and its asymmetry in thermodynamics.

One result was a logical weakening of the second law, which could no longer be taken to describe what would happen on every possible occasion, but only what would happen on the average and apart from improbable contingencies. There was no empirical contradiction, however, for the new theory ascribed wholly negligible probabilities to a spontaneous decrease of entropy big enough to be observable by calorimetric techniques. On the other hand, it did predict measurable statistical fluctuations in microscopic systems, and these were verified in such phenomena as Brownian motion. It also provides today the basis of the theory of turbulent motion, a kind of motion conceptually between laminar fluid motion and Brownian motion. It gives meaning, moreover, to entropy as a time-dependent variable of systems not in equilibrium, something that ordinary calorimetric measurements, by their very nature, cannot be used to deal with.

A historical curiosity connected with these fluctuation phenomena is the prediction of Brownian motion (actually observed in the nineteenth century) by the Roman philosopher Lucretius, who perhaps transmits it from the earlier Greek tradition of Democritus and Epicurus. Lucretius believed he had verified this prediction from the atomic theory by watching motes in the sunlight (Fig. 20); what he actually observed was turbulence, no less a consequence of the atomicity of air.

The interpretation of the second law as statistical rather than dynamical solved one kind of problem, but it provoked another. It explained the partial unavailability of heat as a source of mechanical work; but it explained this unavailability by arguments of probability. Confusion about probability had bothered only the philosophers before; now it threatened the foundations of physics as well.

Fig. 20. Motes in Sunlight

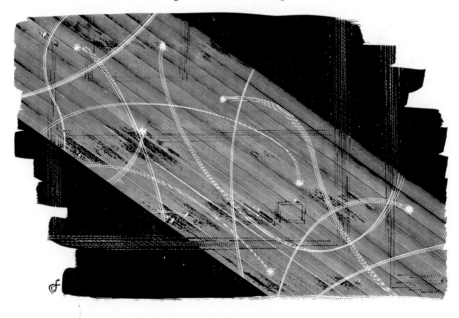

The theory begun by Maxwell and Boltzmann deals with processes that have come, today, to be called *stochastic*.

Dynamical laws map the state of a physical system at one time into the phase space of that system at any other time; and the mapping is unique, one-to-one. In the laws describing stochastic processes, on the other hand, the mapping is not one-to-one, but one-to-many, many-to-one, or many-to-many. A familiar example is the random-walk problem—for example, of molecules of one gas diffusing through another. A simpler example is card-shuffling, in which it is possible at each step to go from the given arrangement of the cards to one of several alternative arrangements, and in which any given arrangement can have come from a variety of possible arrangements in the previous step.

In statistical mechanics all processes such as diffusion and mixing, as well as all transfers of heat, are stochastic processes. So also are the flows of highway traffic or of telephone calls, and the behavior of stars in a galaxy.

In the transition from deterministic description to stochastic description there are unresolved theoretical issues of a sort I have discussed earlier, issues that arise when one tries to build a bridge between two conceptual schemes that seem, on the surface at least, mutually incoherent or contradictory. Such is the issue concerning the discrete and the continuous in mathematics, and the issue concerning fields and particles in dynamics.

A theorem in dynamics, the Liouville theorem, provides a way of defining the issue in the present case. In classical dynamics the state of an isolated physical system is represented by a point in phase space, and the laws of motion prescribe a continuous, one-one mapping of this space into itself. The temporal sequence of states, in other words, is represented by a point that moves through the phase space, like a billiard ball on a frictionless table. Suppose that the state of the system at time t is contained within a small region, R, of the phase space. The laws of motion map region R into region R', which is such that the system is in R' at time t' if and only if it is in R at time t. The Liouville theorem asserts that the volume measures of R and R' are identical. If the measure of R is used as a measure of our uncertainty about the system at time t (we know it is in R, but we do not know more than this), the theorem implies that our uncertainty about the system does not increase with time.

In point of fact, however, our uncertainty about such a system does increase with time. If we know, at time t, the position and motion of a mark on the periphery of a frictionless spinning wheel, each with a small uncertainty, our uncertainty of prediction clearly increases with time. Our uncertainty about the velocity remains unchanged, but after a long enough time we can make no prediction of the position of the mark.

The resolution of this apparent contradiction depends on the fact that it involves two ways of defining the measure of uncertainty. The Liouville theorem applies, in a very special case, to the three-dimensional volume measure of an incompressible fluid, whose motion at time t is defined at every point in the container. This application provides a visual analogy for the general case, an analogy first presented by Willard Gibbs. Here the space in question is a real space filled with fluid rather than a logical space filled with alternative possibilities. We now let R represent a drop of ink in water at time t, and we see what happens to it at time t'. We conceive both water and ink as ideal incompressible fluids, not composed of discrete molecules but Stoic fluids, fluid all the way down on the scale of size. The drop of ink characteristically sends out filaments that become thinner as they spread out, streamers that penetrate eventually to every part of the container. But the water never dilutes the ink, and the ink never tints the water. The drop never separates into a multiplicity of drops, and, although its surface area increases without limit, its volume remains constant (Fig. 21).

If we are asked after a time to say *where* the ink is, we have a choice as to the meaning of the question. The unchanging volume gets harder and harder to

Fig. 21. Drop of Ink in Water

define; still we can always define it, in principle, by knowing the laws of motion and the initial state of the fluid. If we try in any *other* way to circumscribe a volume that will contain the drop, we shall have to make that volume larger and larger with increasing time.

Let the drop of ink, in this visual analogy, represent the uncertainty with which we have ascertained the initial state of a dynamical system. Then the constant volume of the drop represents the deterministic conservation of our initial uncertainty, and its increasing surface area represents the stochastic increase of our uncertainty. If you will review the remarks in Chapter 6 on the probabilistic and the deterministic postulates (pp. 145–46), you will see that this is merely a case in which two different systems of collocations belong to the same family of "events." In the deterministic case the collocation is defined with respect to a region R' that is the deterministic image, at t', of the given region R at time t. In the stochastic case the collocation is defined with respect to a region S' at time t', S being chosen independently of the exact nature of R at time t. After a long time R' has penetrated almost equally into almost all regions S that might have been chosen. In the stochastic sense, then, the location of the representative point is almost completely uncertain.

We describe this eventual equilibrium by saying that the probability density (like the ink density in our analogy) is uniform throughout all the cells into which phase space may be divided. But within each cell, if we looked minutely enough, we should still find the filament-like projections of the original region R. What we should like to do, at this point, is to introduce into the description of phase-space transitions something analogous to the interdiffusion of ink and water when these are considered as molecular in character rather than as ideal incompressible fluids. The quantum-mechanical emendation of classical laws does this, in a sense, for the uncertainty principle sets a lower limit to the size of cells, in phase space, within which a physical system can meaningfully be said to exist. In principle this does not help, perhaps, since the time-dependent equations for the wave function of the system are deterministic. But it is no longer possible to keep the system isolated unless it remains unobserved. In terms of observation, conversely, the wave function has to be read as a generator of probabilities. Thus there is still a slight logical bump when the wheels go over the bridge between deterministic and stochastic descriptions. There is no damage, either to the wheels of the vehicle or to the passenger; but there may linger some uneasiness in the logical conscience of the latter.

Another way of looking at the relation between chance and determinism arises when we look at the path, through phase space, of the point that represents the state of a system. Many systems are *ergodic*. This means that, for all initial states of the system except a quite exceptional set, the representative point eventually comes as close as you please to every point in the phase space, as an endlessly moving billiard ball would to every point on the table. It spends the same amount of time, moreover, in every neighborhood. At any time designated independently of the initial time, therefore, the system is as likely to be found in any state as in any other. Again there is no contradiction between the two descriptions; they involve logically independent families of collocations.

A simple mathematical mechanism of this sort of process is the following.[†] Take a number x_0 between 0 and 1, and double it. If $2x_0$ exceeds 1, subtract it from 2; otherwise leave it untouched. Call the resulting number x_1. Repeat with x_1 the operations performed on x_0, and call the result x_2. Continue indefinitely. One can now prove that, for almost all real numbers x_0 in the unit interval, the infinite sequence of x's will have perfectly random properties. We may, for example, replace each x by H if it exceeds 1/2, and otherwise replace it by T. Then we have a sequence resembling that of heads and tails. There would be no statistical way of distinguishing between the two cases. The numerical process is completely deterministic, but it gives a result that cannot be distinguished from that of a completely indeterministic process. This result seems very odd. Let us look at it more closely. In the coin-tossing method of producing the sequence there is no law of generation; the collocations are not defined by deterministic means. In the other method the sequence is defined deterministically, but the initial condition $x = x_0$ is not given. And, when we talk about the set of real numbers $0 < x_0 < 1$ that might be plugged in to start the process, we are, in a sense, leaving just as much to chance as we should be in a sequence of coin tosses that was infinite. We could, in fact, define an arbitrary number x_0 as that which would give the same *H-T* sequence as one that had been provided by tossing coins. Figure 23 represents the numerical process graphically. It is clear that, with certain exceptions, each x_i can have come from either of two values of x_{i-1}, one of them an H and one a T. It is also clear that an H (or a T), not further defined, may lead either to an H or to a T in the next step. And this remains true no matter how many initial H's and T's are given.

What would the sequence look like, defined by specific x_0? For $x_0 = 2/3$, $x = 2/3$ thereafter. What about an initial $\sqrt{2} - 1$ or $1/\pi$? Here it seems

---

† Which I owe to Dr. Stanislaw Ulam.

Fig. 22. Chance or Determinism?

plausible, but is by no means certain, that the resulting *H-T* sequence would be statistically normal.† Is there perhaps some irrational number, such as the two above, already defined somewhere in the mathematical literature, that would give a hundred *H*'s in a row among the first few thousand values of *x*? Is the class of numbers designated in this way in any sense a random sample of irrational numbers? All, in fact, have rather special mathematical properties, without which we could not even define them individually. We should unhesitatingly predict that in any honest sequence of tosses of a coin there would

---

† Cf. p. 38.

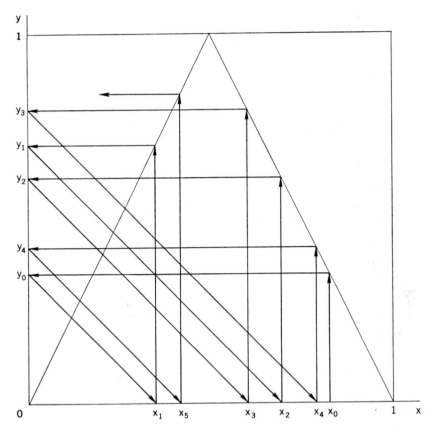

Fig. 23. Iterated Mapping of the Unit Line onto Itself: Deterministic and Random

not occur a hundred heads in a row.† (No one feels quite so strongly about the same question in the Platonic domain of number.) Deterministic and stochastic descriptions are not incompatible, nor does the validity of the one entail that of the other. And from an ultimate metaphysical point of view each is problematic in the range of things to which it applies.

Having discussed the meaning of uncertainty in relation to stochastic processes, I wish to bring this closer, by one more example, to the statistical interpretation of thermodynamics. I use again the example of card-shuffling, a case intermediate between coin-tossing, which gives independent events, and purely deterministic processes. Let the method be the simple one of removing a card from the top of the deck and replacing it in the deck at random. The

---

† Some people do get nervous about this. But a hundred heads in a row has about one chance in 10^{30}. The odds are overwhelming that no one has ever honestly tossed a hundred heads in a row, either on earth or, for that matter, in the Galaxy.

initial well-defined order of the deck is now changed to one of 52 alternatives, each still bearing a strong resemblance to the original. After a large number—compared with 52—of repetitions the original order will have been almost totally destroyed. Qualitatively, the process is one of increasing disorder, and the question arises whether there is some convenient numerical measure of this disorder.

The answer, of course, is that there is an endless variety of measures as long as we only require invariance of the measure up to an arbitrary, monotone transformation. Special measures, however, have additional properties, and one of these is overwhelmingly significant. This is a measure first found by Boltzmann; its special property is that, when it is used, the propositions of thermodynamics can be deduced, and in the *deduced* equations this measure of disorder corresponds, in the *empirical* equations of thermodynamics, precisely to the measure of entropy. The only difference is that the statistical measure of disorder is a dimensionless variable and must be multiplied by the dimensional constant k, already referred to, known as Boltzmann's constant.

Boltzmann's measure of disorder, if A_1, A_2, ... A_n are any complete set of alternative collocations, with the corresponding probabilities P_1, P_2, ... P_n, is given by the expression

$$H(p_1, p_2, \ldots p_n) = -\sum_1^n p_k \log p_k = \sum_1^n p_k \log \left(\frac{1}{p_k}\right)$$

in which the base of the logarithm is arbitrary. The more detailed properties of the function H will be discussed later, but it is easy to see that it is a minimum when one of the P_i equals 1 and the others equal zero, and a maximum equal to $\log n$ when all are equal to $1/n$. This measure is invariant up to the chosen logarithmic base. A zero of entropy is provided by Planck's postulate that the entropy of a perfect crystal at absolute zero is zero. Thus it is possible—subject to minor emendations of no concern here—to identify thermodynamic entropy with Boltzmann's H, up to a constant that depends upon the units of energy and the temperature.

When this interpretation is made, we may regard all thermodynamic processes as stochastic processes and deduce their general laws from dynamical laws plus certain postulates about the underlying probability distributions. But the interpretation works the other way as well: all stochastic processes may be regarded as thermodynamic, as describable in terms of empirical concepts, suitably extended, that originated a century ago in the investigation of the steam engine. Specifically, we may define not only the increase in the entropy of a deck of playing cards after n shufflings but also the decrease of free energy associated with this process. The notion that a deck of cards, just by being in an independently defined order, can have the capacity to do work that it cannot do when that order is shuffled, appears bizarre. The theoretical energy involved is, indeed, small, being comparable to that of a system containing only a few molecules. Or, putting it the other way, a mole of playing cards (6×10^{23}) would contain, very roughly, as much free energy in its ordering as a firecracker. As will be seen later, there are cases in which such examples are far from bizarre.

This bald assertion that energy is available in the mere ordering of the cards is often met with disbelief. The difference between the two sets of cards is, indeed, negligible. The firecracker's worth of free energy in the one deck and not in the other has to be contrasted with the totals, and a mole of cards would use up all the atmospheric oxygen in burning. The experiment is a thought experiment, however, to test a question of principle. The size of the deck is not crucial. What is crucial is the heat engine that will demonstrate the reality of the free energy of information. Used to stoke the fires of an ordinary heat engine, the two decks will, indeed, do the same work. But the heat engine of my thought experiment is designed to work at maximum efficiency when the cards are in a specific order. It anticipates correctly where the spots of ink will be on each card in succession and thus, in the burning, extracts work from little temperature differences that it would miss in a random deck. One operation has a greater theoretical efficiency than the other.

Now let us imagine the size of the playing cards reduced. The free energy of information remains the same, but the total free energy decreases. When the playing cards are reduced to molecular size, we discover that the firecracker's worth of difference, in a mole, between ordered deck and unordered deck is comparable in magnitude to the total. What is even more surprising is that such decks exist, as do the well-informed heat engines for burning them. But that subject I postpone to Chapter 10.

The Maxwell Demon

Our subject, so far, has belonged to the nineteenth century. But, as matters stood at the end of that century, the subject still had latent paradoxes. These are connected with the probabilistic interpretation. The first is that grave doubt seemed to be raised as to the status of the second law by the purely probabilistic interpretation of entropy. A sense of puzzlement, or embarrassment, can be detected in many older writings on the subject. This was owing to the long-standing uncertainty about the status of the probability concept itself, specifically to the prevalence of a subjectivistic interpretation. Ignorance *appears* to be involved in the definition of probability, at least in relation to deterministic alternatives. It was this appearance that made necessary the careful definition, in Chapter 6, of "collocation." If entropy could be defined in terms of subjective probability rather than as a property of a physical system, the result threatened the objectivity of thermodynamics as a science. For it implied that the whole science of thermodynamics was a commentary, not on the nature of things, but on human limitations. Maxwell borrowed Laplace's demon for a thought experiment that displayed very clearly the logical limitations of his own statistical formulation, or appeared to.

> "Clerk Maxwell supposed two compartments, *A* and *B*, to be filled with gas at the same temperature, and to be separated by an ideal, infinitely thin partition containing a number of exceedingly small trap-doors, each of which could be opened or closed without any expenditure of energy. An intelligent creature, or 'demon,' possessed of unlimited powers of vision, is placed in charge of each door, with instructions to open the door whenever a particle in *A* comes toward it with more than a certain velocity *V* and to keep it closed against all particles in *A* moving with less than this velocity, but, on the other hand, to open the door whenever a particle in *B* approaches it with less than a certain velocity *v*, which is not greater than *V*, and to keep it closed against all particles in *B* moving with a greater velocity than this. By continuing this process every unit of mass which enters *B* will carry with it more energy than each unit which leaves *B*, and hence the temperature of the gas in *B* will be raised and that of the gas in *A* lowered, while no heat is lost and no energy is expended; so that by the application of intelligence alone a portion of gas of uniform pressure and temperature may be sifted into two parts, in which both the temperature and pressure are different and from which, therefore, work can be obtained at the expense of heat. This shows that the principle of the dissipation of energy has control over the actions of those agents only whose faculties are too gross to enable them to grapple individually with the minute portions of matter which are the seat of energy." †

Such was the unsatisfactory state of the statistical interpretation of thermodynamics at the beginning of the present century. It revived, in a new form, a metaphysical problem that had been much debated in the seventeenth century and after: man's place in a world describable by deterministic law. From an epistemological point of view, thought, self-conscious intelligence, did not appear part of the same universe of discourse as the human body and its physical

---

† Joseph Larmor, "Energy," *Encyclopaedia Britannica,* 11th edition, Vol. IX. For Maxwell's own account see James Clerk Maxwell, *Theory of Heat,* 10th edition (London, 1891), p. 338.

Fig. 24. The Maxwell Demon

environment. Descartes had tried, as a sort of afterthought, to connect mind and body anatomically, but Spinoza and others denied the meaningfulness of the idea of such connection. In the nineteenth century, with the principle of the conservation of energy, the problem became crucial. If the mind acted on the body, either it was itself a physical system that exchanged energy with the body, or it was not a physical system, and its interaction with the body violated the conservation principle. Or it neither acted on the body nor was acted on by the body, in which case the body was all-sufficient and the mind just a show, an epiphenomenon or, for whatever the statement might mean, an unreality.

The Maxwell Demon aggravated the problem but shifted its locus. The

Demon has as much physical reality as a thought experiment requires, a wisp, at least, of mass and muscle; his existence involves no violation of the conservation principle. He does not even have to be very bright. Yet his coupling with the box in which he lives creates, apparently, a perpetual-motion machine of the second kind, in which he earns a living via the free energy that his intelligence constantly gives rise to.

It was not wholly within the range of nineteenth-century physics to resolve the Maxwell Demon paradox, but its later resolution was a remarkable example of the way in which later developments in science seem, in retrospect, to have been required by earlier ones. The resolution was possible only through a full account of the Demon's interaction with the gas he manipulates, and the basis of this account was not available until the advent of a better understanding of the interaction between matter and radiation. Part of the heat energy inside the box must be present as random electromagnetic radiation, black-body radiation, in thermal equilibrium with the gas and the walls of its container. Under these circumstances, however, the Demon cannot see anything at all, even with his "unlimited powers of vision." What he can see is a uniform "white" mist, pure electromagnetic noise. The visual perception of objects depends upon some non-chance inhomogeneity of the electromagnetic field, and precisely this is excluded by the condition of thermodynamic equilibrium. In order to see, there- fore, the Demon must have something like a radar beam; the better he is to see, the better his signal-to-noise ratio must be, the more such energy he must dissipate into the system. Must he waste more energy in this way than he gets back by trapping fast molecules? This question was raised for the first time, and answered, in a now famous paper of 1929 by Leo Szilard, who showed that the energy made available by the Demon's trap-door was, in principle, no greater than what he expended in getting the *information* he needed in order to decide whether to open the door or leave it closed.

Szilard's analysis does not depend upon the quantum-mechanical principle of indeterminacy; the noise background against which the Demon must work in order to store free energy is not quantum noise (the statistical consequence of that principle) but ordinary thermal noise. But the analysis does involve the idea of a statistical equilibrium between matter and radiation, an idea that is meaningful only in terms of the quantum principle, which makes it possible to describe the radiation field inside a closed container as having only a finite number of degrees of freedom.†

---

† Apart from the quantum principle the number of modes of vibration in a closed system would be infinite.

In the same paper Szilard laid the foundations of information theory, rooting it in thermodynamics. The Demon exchanges potential energy stored in his batteries for information, and this information enables him to recover some part of the heat that he dissipated in getting the information. Information is, therefore, proportional to free energy. This observation does not settle the mind-body problem, but it does give physical status to something that has traditionally been defined only in mentalistic language. *Any* ordering of elements, mental or other, is involved significantly in thermodynamic descriptions of nature.†

Information, Order, and Free Energy

The reader will recognize, in the discussion of the Maxwell Demon, its intimate connection with the problems of making measurements (Chap. 4) and, in particular, with the concept of information. In the present context the idea of information may be introduced in a more natural and general way.

After the work of Szilard, which directly involved the application of thermodynamic analysis, the next significant development was the analysis, by C. E. Shannon, of certain mathematical problems of communication connected with the coding of messages, their transmission over channels, the maximum rate of signal transmission over given channels, and the effects of noise.‡ In the nearly twenty years between Szilard's paper and Shannon's the former was almost entirely ignored. The term "information theory" was introduced in Shannon's paper as a natural colloquial label for a mathematical theory of communication. As applied to problems of measurement and communication the label seems appropriate. Since Shannon's work, however, information theory has been extended to many areas in which the term "information" has no obvious relevance except as a kind of metaphor. Even in the context of communication a transmission of meaningless nonsense is just as much information as an intelligible message. What is always involved in applications of the theory is some kind of physical coupling in virtue of which a duplication of pattern occurs.

It is a nice coincidence, however, that we can eliminate the apparent inappropriateness of the term "information," not by changing the term, but merely

---

† The belief that life, and especially conscious intelligence, give rise to violations of thermodynamic principles dies hard; see Chap. 10. For a complete outline of the discussion by Szilard, and for more recent history, see Léon Brillouin, *Science and Information Theory* (New York, 1956), Chap. 13.

‡ C. E. Shannon, *A Mathematical Theory of Communication*, Bell Telephone System Technical Publications, Monograph B-1598. See also Brillouin, *op. cit.* Shannon's work built upon earlier work of R. V. L. Hartley, "Transmission of Information," *Bell System Technical Journal*, vol. 27, pp. 379–423.

by reversing linguistic history, by renovating an original broad meaning that has almost disappeared. The meaning of "information" in current colloquial English is a degenerate specialization of the original *in* plus *formatio*—literally, the transference of form or, alternatively, form as transferred. The term is from medieval philosophy, and it was actively used in the intellectual context of efficient and final causation. In Shakespeare one hears of spirit informed with courage, and Pope speaks of Nature as "informer of the poet's art." The term is sometimes rendered today as "inspire," but that is wrong; it loses the technical meaning.

We return here to a theme developed in the last chapter: that twentieth-century science is recovering a concept of causality against which centuries of Newtonian imagery have conditioned us, which flourished in certain Hellenistic and medieval traditions and was kept alive in modern times outside the scientific culture. The imagery of information—in our revived sense—is that of *poiesis,* of artisanship. A cause is not merely what is abstractly necessary, or sufficient, to an effect; a cause is what shapes, informs, the effect. It is the sort of cause of which it is self-evident to say, "Like causes like," long regarded as superstition. The tradition is the tradition of Anaxagoras, in whose cosmology Cosmos is born of Chaos by the sorting action of Mind; and it is the tradition of the Great Chain, the graded hierarchy of Being. It is the tradition in which Anselm of Canterbury, echoed by Descartes and Spinoza, said that the cause can not be less perfect than the effect, so that every essence entails an antecedent and not less perfect existent; and "that than which nothing more perfect can be conceived, cannot exist in the mind alone."

The underlying presupposition, from Anaxagoras to Spinoza, is the association of cause with reason, of the order of nature with the order of thought. We may also see this presupposition as an elaboration of conceptions abstracted from workaday knowledge, to which science has given, until recently, no adequate place. In some important sense the tradition of the Great Chain is the prehistory of thermodynamics. Alternatively we may say that in the framework of twentieth-century categories "causality" in the old sense is a thermodynamical rather than a dynamical term.†

To support these remarks, we must extend the definition of information, given in Chapter 4, as the least number of binary discriminations sufficient to distinguish one object from among a set of N, and in value approximately $\log_2 N$. This result is achieved, as we observed before, if each binary discrimination is designed to split the set in half, each pair to split it in quarters, etc. If we

---

† See pp. 290–91.

do not restrict ourselves to this particular sort of efficiency, however, we may set ourselves the task of exploring all *possible* ways of discriminating one out of a set of N alternatives by means of a sequence of binary discriminations, which ends when the correct alternative has been found.

The familiar model to study here is the game of Twenty Questions, with the slightly artificial initial restriction that the person who chooses the object that the other player is to discover must choose from among a specified set of N objects to begin with. If the player who asks the questions plays by the strategy of Chapter 4, each question he asks will be designed so that half of the objects not yet eliminated will require "yes" for an answer, the other half "no." All possible ways of playing can be defined as follows: There are, in a set of N objects, 2^N distinct subsets if we include the limiting cases of the subset that contains all N and the subset that is empty. Then there are 2^N binary questions that the questioner may choose from: for each distinct subset X he can ask, "Is it in X?" (We assume that answers are honest and that there are no errors.) Then it is pointless to ask about the full or the empty subset, for the answer to the first is certainly "yes" and the answer to the second is certainly "no." It is also pointless to ask any question the answer to which is entailed by answers to previous questions. Subject to these trivial restrictions, the questioner is now free to choose any sequence among the possible questions and to continue asking the questions in order until identification is achieved. In the equally splitting procedure discussed in Chapter 5 the number of questions one needs in order to achieve identification is (within a unit) $\log_2 N$, whichever is the correct alternative. In other procedures the length of the sequence of questions and answers will vary, depending on the correct alternative. An extreme case is to ask only questions, one after another, about the unit subsets. If one is very lucky, a single question suffices, but with the worst possible luck $N-1$ questions will be needed.

In general, then, the length of the sequence of questions and answers will depend on which alternative is, in fact, the right one. Between the two extreme types of procedure are many intermediate types, and in a moment I shall suggest a fairly simple way of characterizing any one of them. First it is useful, however, to shift to a different model. If "yes" is written as "1" and "no" as "0," the sequence of answers is a sequence of 1's and 0's. The meaning of these answers, however, depends on the questions. As we noted before, if a sequence of questions becomes socially standardized, it also becomes what, in another context, we call a *code,* and a sequence of answers becomes a *message.* For discriminating among N alternatives, or N messages, the number of possible codes, or sequences of questions, is very large for large N. If at each stage the remaining subset is nearly halved by the next question, we obtain a code in which all messages are of the same minimal length. If some different principle of division is adopted, we get messages of different length, and in the extreme case referred to above there is one message of each length, from 1 to $N - 2$, and two of length $N - 1$. The last-named procedure, used as a way of presenting or transmitting *numbers,* for example, merely exemplifies each number (as a string of zeros terminated by a 1) in the manner of our primitive fisherman (of Chap. 1); and the representation by strings of uniform length is the essential principle of our positional number notation. The use of Roman numerals is a mixed case.

A socially standardized sequence of questions becomes a code, and answers so standardized become code messages. In the context of measurement, likewise, an operation leading to sensory discrimination is a question, and the answer is a measurement. In the extrahuman informational processes of nature—in biology, for example, but elsewhere as well—none of these terms seems appropriate, but in the sense now intended all of them are.

Clearly the length distribution of the messages in a code is an important property. It is, in fact, a measure of the relative importance of alternatives, as is obvious in the Twenty Questions model. A uniform way of representing the length of the coded message associated with each of N alternatives is to assign to it a power of $1/2$, subject to the restriction that the sum of such numbers, for all the alternatives, be less than or equal to 1; that is, to each i ($i = 1, 2, 3, \ldots N$) we assign a number $q_i = (1/2)^n$ with $n = 0, 1, 2, \ldots$, and with the condition that

$$\sum_{i=1}^{n} q_i \leq 1$$

This last condition expresses compactly the fact that we cannot always shorten some messages without lengthening others to compensate. The assignment $n = 0$ is a special case; it means that only one alternative is of any importance, and we make no effort to test it but merely adopt it as true. The sum condition cannot be strictly met, now, except by the convention that all other alternatives have $n = \infty$. A dramatic illustration of this attitude toward logical alternatives is Pascal's Great Wager: To seek Heaven has infinite value if Heaven exists; to seek it if it does not exist is, at most, a finite loss. One need not, therefore, attempt to settle first the question whether Heaven exists; one needs only to seek Heaven.

The inequality in the sum condition may be removed by the following consideration: if we replace a sum of powers of $1/2$ less than 1 by a sum equal to 1, we can define a code or a questioning procedure that *dominates* the one re-placed, that gives a set of messages in which none is longer and some are shorter than in the procedure dominated.

Finally, the restriction to integral powers of $1/2$ can be eliminated by the same idealization that we used in Chapter 4 with reference to sets of alternatives in which N is not a power of 2: by aggregating many problems of discrimination into one we can represent the importance of an alternative by the *average* number of binary discriminations imputed to that alternative along with many others being simultaneously established. Thus, in the limit, we represent the relative importance of each alternative by a number in the unit interval $q_1 = (1/2)^{\bar{n}}$, in which $\bar{n}$ is a positive *real* number. Evidently the set of numbers q_i, with sum equal to 1, assigned to the alternatives

$$A_1 \ A_2 \ A_3 \ . \ . \ . \ . \ . \ . \ . \ A_N$$
$$q_1 \ q_2 \ q_3 \ . \ . \ . \ . \ . \ . \ q_n$$

represents a scheme of discrimination, a way of playing Twenty Questions within the set A. It is remarkable that the numbers q_i have exactly the formal properties of probabilities, for they are not probabilities in any sense in which the term was defined in Chapter 6 or in which it is usually defined. They have, however, a perfectly defined meaning, and because of this meaning I shall call them *priorities*. An alternative A_i with a priority q_i is thereby assigned a high or low rank with respect to the other alternatives in a scheme of discrimination, and this means that its isolation as the correct alternative (if it is the correct one) requires a procedure of average length $\bar{n}_i$, in which $q_i = (1/2)^{\bar{n}_i}$ or $\bar{n}_i = \log_2 (1/q_i)$.

One assignment is

$$A_1 \quad A_2 \quad A_3 \ . \ . \ . \ . \ . \ . \ . \ A_N$$
$$1/N \ 1/N \ 1/N \ . \ . \ . \ . \ . \ . \ 1/N$$

in which all alternatives are treated with equal priority, the first scheme discussed before. Another is

$$A_1 \ A_2 \ A_3 \ . \ . \ . \ . \ . \ . \ . \ A_{N-1} \quad A_N$$
$$1/2 \ 1/4 \ 1/8 \ . \ . \ . \ . \ . \ . \ (1/2)^{N-1} \ (1/2)^{N-1}$$

which is the second scheme referred to.

Armed with this general logical equipment, schemes of priority, we may now take a further step. This becomes possible when the alternatives in a set A can be assigned probabilities. If A_i requires $\bar{n}_i$ steps to isolate it when it is the correct alternative, and if p_i is the probability that A_i is the correct alternative, then the *expected* number of discriminations, averaged over A, is

$$\sum_{i=1}^{N} p_i \bar{n}_i = \sum_{i=1}^{N} p_i \log_2 (1/q_i) = - \sum_{i=1}^{N} p_i \log_2 q_i$$

for the given scheme

$$
\begin{aligned}
&\text{alternative:} \quad A_1 \ A_2 \ A_3 \ \ldots \ A_N \\
&\text{priority:} \qquad q_1 \ q_2 \ q_3 \ \ldots \ q_N \\
&\text{probability:} \ p_1 \ p_2 \ p_3 \ \ldots \ p_N
\end{aligned}
$$

Having defined the expected value of the number of discriminations in this way, we now consider how this quantity varies for different choices of the q_i. It is not hard to prove that it is *minimum* when the q_i are chosen as numerically equal to the p_i. This is plausible if one thinks of the problems of efficient coding of information. If we shorten frequent messages at the cost of lengthening infrequent ones, we gain as long as the process is not pushed too far. The optimum is obtained when the message lengths are proportional to the logarithms of their frequencies.

In order to compress the notation, let us represent the second and third lines in the table above by Q^A and P^A, respectively, and the expected number of discriminations by

$$G(P^A, Q^A) = \sum_{i=1}^{N} p_i \log_2 (1/q_i)$$

Since this quantity is minimized by choice of Q^A as equal to P^A, we may then write

$$H(P^A) = \operatorname*{Min}_{Q} G(P^A, Q^A) = \sum_{i=1}^{N} p_i \log_2 (1/p_i)$$

And this is the same quantity referred to before as Boltzmann's statistical explication of the entropy concept. Now, however, we have the reason why it can be understood as a measure of *disorder*. It is the expected number of binary discriminations that we *need*, at the very minimum, in order to fix the correct description of a system that *may* be in a variety of states and about which we have only probabilistic knowledge. To say that a system is orderly is to say that there is some standard relative to which its state is highly predictable; to say that it is disorderly is to say that such a standard is non-existent.

When the molecules of a gas, for example, are in a collective state of maximum entropy, or disorder, all the alternatives consistent with the given total energy are equally probable, and therefore, by the most efficient method of measurement possible, the precise determination of the exact state of the gas will require the maximum amount of information. In effect, we divide phase space into equally probable volume elements and then play Twenty Questions with nature, to find which of these the gas is in. In classical theory there is a trouble here, for the size of the cells can be decreased without limit, their number increased without limit, and the entropy also therefore increased without limit. In classical theory this did no harm, for one was interested in comparing entropies under alternative macroscopic conditions, and one could show that *differences* in entropy were constant in the limit of small cell size. In quantum mechanics an elegant definition of a natural cell size appears; for the volume measure in phase space has just the dimensions of the quantum of action; the minimum physically meaningful cell size is defined by the quantum constant.

The number of binary discriminations—of *binits* or *bits*—is an obvious and wholly non-statistical measure of information. The elementary discriminations that it tallies are perfectly sure discriminations, by dichotomous division repeated as long as necessary. By introducing my G-measure for calculating expected values, and then choosing priorities so as to minimize that measure, I show that knowledge of probabilities over a set of alternatives reduces, in general, the number of discriminations over what would be necessary in the absence of that knowledge. Ergo, the knowledge of probability has a certain measurable value as information; it is *equivalent* to a certain number of sure discriminations.

In the absence of probabilistic knowledge the optimal strategy of discrimination is to give all priorities equal value, and the information measure is therefore $\log N$. With a probability law P^A over the alternatives, this reduces to $H(P^A)$, and the difference is the information value of P^A, which varies from zero when all probabilities are equal to $\log N$ when one of the p_i equals 1.

I have introduced the concept of information in an unorthodox way, possibly in a novel way, by showing that the Boltzmann-Shannon measure is operationally defined as the expected value of the number of sure discriminations one needs, as an absolute minimum, in order to define the correct alternative out of a set of alternatives with given probabilities. In the usual presentation of the subject the Boltzmann-Shannon measure is introduced axiomatically, with a series of justifications. These justifications are extremely plausible and are, indeed, correct. My argument constitutes a formal proof of their correctness. It is implicit in much of the discussion of coding theory, but, so far as I know, has not been pointed out before.

In physical problems of the classical thermodynamic variety the probabilities belong to collocations whose designating conditions are merely macroscopic conditions of pressure, temperature, and volume, applied to a whole system or to macroscopically distinguished parts (phases). If two gases, for example, are separated initially by a membrane, which is then broken, the amount of information one needs in order to define the detailed state of the system begins to increase, interdiffusion of the gases making necessary a lengthier chain of "questions" to locate each particle.

Suppose next that there are two sets A and B of alternatives A_i and B_j, with $i = 1, 2, \ldots N$ and $j = 1, 2, \ldots M$. The product set $A \otimes B$, representing all NM compound alternatives, has the probability law $P^{A \otimes B} = (p_{11}, p_{12}, \ldots p_{NM})$. Application of the Shannon definition gives

$$H(P^{A \otimes B}) = H(P^A) + \sum_{i=1}^{N} a_i H(P_i^B)$$

in which $P^A = (a_1, a_2, \ldots a_N)$ are the unconditional probabilities over A alone, and P_i^B, the probabilities over B, are conditional on the realization of the ith alternative in A. This formula says that the information we need in order to define the compound system $A \otimes B$ is the information we need in order to define one of them (say A) plus the expected value of the information we need in order to define the second (B), the latter information being conditional upon a knowledge of the former. If the two sets are completely independent, this becomes

$$H(P^{A \otimes B}) = H(P^A) + H(P^B)$$

which leads to the obvious conclusion that, if two sets of alternatives are completely independent, a knowledge of the correct alternative in one of them does not reduce at all the labor of finding the correct alternative in the other. Let us now abbreviate

$$\sum_{i=1}^{N} a_i H(P_i^B) = H_A(P^B)$$

calling it the conditional information for defining B when A is known. The difference

$$H(P^B) - H_A(P^B)$$

is the reduction of information for defining B when A is known and is thus the information of or about B in A. This quantity is non-negative and, for A and B correlated in any way, is positive. The standard application in communication theory is to let A be a set of alternative transmitted messages and let B be the messages received over a noisy (in the technical sense) channel. Then the quantity $H(P^B) - H_A(P^B)$ measures the received information. Since $H(P^B)$

$-H_A(P^B) = H(P^A) - H_B(P^A)$, this is also equal to the transmitted information.

The following is a simple thermodynamic illustration of conditional entropy. Suppose there are two molecular species A and B, which can exist either as a mixture of separate molecules or as a compound AB. The information needed for defining the system when the two are separate is obviously greater than that needed when they are combined; for in the latter case a knowledge of the position and motion of the A components would reduce the information needed for defining the position and motion of the B components.

The Maxwell Demon is another example. In ordinary thermodynamic problems the probabilities are calculated for collocations involving only the macroscopic parameters of the system. But the Demon could do better: he could measure the motions and positions of individual molecules. Thus the set of alternative recordings on the Demon's tape memory would be correlated with the micro-state of the gas. Collocations defined by reference to these recordings would have unequal probabilities; the conditional entropy of the gas defined in this way would be reduced; and a part of the erstwhile unavailable energy of the gas would become, for the Demon, free. But, as we saw before, the Demon must have paid for this free energy by expending an amount at least as great in order to put the relevant information on his recording tapes. What is now present in the correlation between gas and tape was present before, in the total system, in the Demon's storage batteries. One part of the system has become better defined only because the definition of another part is impoverished to compensate. We on the outside, without access to the Demon's tape, would continue to say that the entropy of the gas was maximum; but that, once we had determined the state of the gas, this would give us, in turn, information about the tape. The fact that there are different entropy measures of a specific system, relative to different given conditions, exactly parallels (and indeed follows from) the fact that probabilities characterize *collocations*, whereas *events*, as defined in Chapter 6, will have different probabilities, dependent on how they are designated.

A more fanciful illustration of the relation between information and free energy will emphasize the continuity with problems of communication. Suppose that there are, in aqueous suspension, molecular chains built of units shaped like letters of the alphabet. Suppose that on one side of a membrane the chains are formed of units strung together at random, but that on the other side they are all shaped like SESAME. Then a barrier with openings of that same shape admits molecules from the one side but impedes the passage of all but a few of the random ones. When the system is finally in equilibrium, the amount of osmotic work that has been done is proportional to the amount of information provided by the abnormality of the probability distribution of "words" in suspension.

In closing this preliminary discussion of information theory, we must realize that the physical concept of work, as distinguished from energy, has itself an informational aspect. The performance of "useful work" (symbolized traditionally by the raising of a weight) is to produce a situation having a certain order.† It is to inform a physical system in some way, to transfer order or information to it. To say that free energy is energy available for external work is to say that order cannot come into existence *ex nihilo,* but only by transfer.

If information theory recovers something of an old tradition, it does so unwittingly and without metaphysics aforethought. What information theory recovers is not the metaphysics but the source of that metaphysics within ordinary experience. But the tradition is not only recovered; it is extended. Surely we will not return to the ideas of Anaxagoras. Mind will no longer serve as the primary symbol of what organizes or informs. Such a symbol may have been appropriate for an age whose metaphors were drawn from handicraft technology. It would not do even for the age of the steam engine, in which the machine had a prime mover, a source independent of the artisan, for its free energy. Still less will such metaphors do for the clever machinery of an age of automation.

But there is a counter-development. As the newer interests of science shift attention away from the mere lawfulness of nature to the extraordinary complexities of organization within nature, from the laws *governing* a system to the boundary conditions *informing* it, technology evolves in a direction that is likely to subvert the classical modern notion of a *machine* no less than the ancient notion of *mind*. And, if that occurs, the scientific task of describing life and mind may be transposed to a more fruitful context than that in which the modern world has so far understood it.‡ It is to these subjects that the following chapters are devoted. In the meantime there remains, as the unfinished business of the present chapter, a set of questions about the second law of thermodynamics and the arrow of time.

---

† If we want to preserve the parallel, we may say that a heat engine is a kind of dynamical dictionary, which translates the free energy of the boiler-condenser system into the informed motion of the drive-shaft.

‡ See David Hawkins, "Design for a Mind," *Daedalus,* issued as vol. 91, No. 3, of the Proceedings of the American Academy of the Arts and Sciences (Summer 1962), pp. 560–77.

The Arrow of Time

The directionality of time appears to lie, not in the abstract dynamical laws of nature, but in the actual distribution of matter and energy. In this sense the second law of thermodynamics is not a law at all, not an unconditional generalization about physical processes in general. The temporal asymmetry of physical processes is not dynamical, we have seen, but statistical. But the converse statement, that stochastic processes are temporally asymmetric, is not at all necessarily true.

Let us return for illustration to the card-shuffling example. If the order of the deck is initially well defined, it is true that the degree of definition decreases thereafter. But the decay of order, at first rapid, slows as the state of maximum disorder is approached. After a long time there is no measurable correlation between the initial order and the order that has arisen from shuffling, except as a matter of chance. The system has reached statistical equilibrium. In this phase the arrow of time has simply disappeared. By chance, fluctuations will occasionally bring the order of the deck measurably closer to the initial order and even—for a finite deck—to an exact repetition of it. But here one can easily see that the statistical description of the process preserves temporal symmetry: approaches to a given degree of order are just as common as recessions from it. If the direction of time is defined as that of decreasing order, of increasing entropy, then, on the average, there is no direction at all. Applied cosmologically, such a model means that, by going far enough into our past or our future, we should reach a time when the direction was reversed; in our future there might be beings for whom the direction was the opposite of ours, so that they also would say that our world lay in their future.

Dynamical laws now formulated are invariant with respect to the direction of time. Statistical laws, in general, are the same. What has to be explored, therefore, is the difference between the model of a system initially in a well-defined state—the deck of cards in the manufacturer's order or the metal disk into which a hot plug has just been inserted—and the model in which there is no initial state, only a past and a future indefinitely extended and symmetrically interchangeable.

In the ordinary uses of thermodynamics the direction of time is already specified independently of the particular application, and it is only this fact that permits the meaningful use of the term "initial." In the first place, therefore, we need at least two systems, and we can now say whether the direction of entropy increase is the same in the two or different. In statistical equilibrium it is the same half the time and opposite half the time. But the context in which the second law is meaningful is one in which there are indefinitely many systems, independent of one another at any given time, not in equilibrium, and having the same temporal direction of increase in entropy. If these systems do interact, moreover, there is a characteristic difference between their joint states before and after the interaction. Before their interaction two systems have been isolated from each other, and by examining one of them it is impossible to find out anything about the other. Technically speaking, they are statistically independent, and the entropy of one of them, conditional upon the state of the other, is the same as its unconditional entropy. The entropy of the combined systems is the sum of their separate entropies. During the interaction, the total energy of the two systems decreases by the amount degraded as heat and directly or indirectly radiated into space. One system does some work on the other, so that, characteristically, there has been a transfer of information, and the sum of the unconditional entropies of the two is greater than the entropy of the combined system. Thus a photographic plate exposed for a moment at the focus of a telescope contains thereafter information about the configuration of the sun spots, and the silty riverbank is informed by the dinosaur that has walked over it. The banded metamorphic rocks in the high peaks were informed by ancient rivers and floods, and the mass of expanding gas in the Crab nebula was informed by interactions in an exploding star, as were certain marks in ancient Chinese and Japanese astronomical records.†

The obvious conclusion from these generalities is that the equilibrium model

---

† These statements, like those I made earlier about the free energy of information in an ordered deck of playing cards, will trouble my critics. When two systems A and B with independent histories are considered as a single system AB, their entropies are additive:

$$H(P^{AB}) = H(P^A) + H(P^B)$$

or

$$H_A(P^B) = H(P^B) \text{ and } H_B(P^A) = H(P^A)$$

But now let the systems interact. Because of their spatial separation, their difference in temperature, etc., the joint system AB contains a certain free energy. If the gases are on the two sides of a piston permeable by one of them but not by the other, the piston will be displaced and can raise a weight. Or, if a barrier between them is punctured, the free energy will be rendered unavailable as each gas expands to fill the volume available to both. Quite generally, in nature, there is some loss and some work that conserves free energy. One variety of such work imprints on one system the spatio-temporal patterns characteristic of the other. Let A^*, B^*, and A^*B^* be the separate and joint systems after interaction. The transfer of information means that

$$H(P^{A^*B^*}) < H(P^{A^*}) + H(P^{B^*})$$

In the transition the total entropy of the joint system increases. But it is less than the maximum by the amount of information the systems have deposited with each other in the process. Time-reversal would mean that systems came together for the first time mutually informed and parted in mutual ignorance.

of statistical reversibility is inappropriate except for very simple systems that stay isolated for relatively long times, the time depending upon the complexity of the system and the rates of change characteristic of it. If the metal plug had been inserted into the disk long before, and if a series of measurements had shown a flow of heat from the plug to the disk, we should not be justified in inferring, still further in the past, a still hotter plug and colder disk; the most probable inference, indeed, would be that of a slightly more uniform distribution of temperature just before the first measurement.

The arrow of time is, we see, a consequence, not of statistical lawfulness in nature, but of the prevalence of non-equilibrium boundary conditions over the operation of statistical laws. If there were some process that removed the metal plug from the disk whenever there was a sufficient accidental flow of heat from the disk to the plug, then, dating our thought processes by the time when this happened, we should make exactly the same inference about the earlier state of the system that we now make about the later, and we should be debarred from making thermodynamic inferences about the later state just as we are now debarred from making such inferences about the earlier state. For thermodynamic inferences depend upon an assumed condition of isolation, which we know, in each case, to be violated.

Much of the confusion that has existed in discussions of the arrow of time has come from the long-established habit—unavoidable in classical thermodynamics—of thinking only of systems in equilibrium. But the statistical behavior of a system, like its exact dynamical behavior, is relative to boundary conditions. When the hot plug is placed in the disk, the system approaches the equilibrium of an isolated system, that of uniform temperature throughout. This is the most probable state of affairs. But with respect to the situation a *short* time after the plug has been inserted, this is not the most probable state of affairs, which is very far from the final equilibrium. And, if the plug is supplied with a heating coil, the temperature distribution in the disk, cooled at its outer edge, approaches a limiting form, which does not change thereafter and is also far from the equilibrium of uniform temperature. In arguments directed against the possibility of life's arising without supernatural intervention, the improbability of such complex systems, according to purely natural causes, is sometimes alleged.† But such probabilities can be calculated only in relation to assumed boundary conditions, and usually the conditions assumed are those of equilibrium in isolation. The scientific investigation of the origins of life, on the contrary, requires the formulation of hypotheses about the bound-

---

† See Chap. 10.

ary conditions, a search for such conditions as would have made the appearance of living organisms highly probable. But hypotheses about boundary conditions are not themselves necessarily matters of probability; the testing of them fits the pattern described in Chapter 9.

Every system that we isolate statistically is part of some more inclusive system, and for this reason the general characterization of non-equilibrium interactions and time's arrow leads directly or indirectly to problems of cosmology. In particular, the characterization of temporally asymmetric interactions that was given above involves the throwing away of degraded energy as electromagnetic radiation. This is possible, however, only because matter and radiation, in the large, are not in equilibrium. On the contrary, radiation characteristically leaves material bodies and is not absorbed by them at anywhere near the same rate. This is symbolized by the blackness of the night sky. If our cosmic situation were like that of the Maxwell Demon in the box, or if the energy of matter were increasing at the expense of the radiation field, the temporally asymmetrical interactions of our world would be impossible. On the other hand, the condition that permits space to remain permanently a sink for radiation is evidently the expansion of the galactic universe, which constantly makes room for more radiant energy. The Doppler shift degrades the radiation from very remote galaxies so that the total of such radiation received by the earth, for example, is less than that from one nearby star, the sun.

Gold † has pointed out that a shrinking universe would imply that radiation was generally being absorbed by matter rather than radiated. In this case, he argues, the applicable solution of the Maxwell equations would be that of the advanced, rather than the retarded, electromagnetic potentials; *everything* would be reversed, and to an *observer* in such a world—himself reversed—the sky would be black and the galaxies traveling apart. By such an account there are two possible universes, but they are indistinguishable from each other, and therefore, according to Leibniz's principle, there are not really two possibilities at all, but only one.

Gold's suggestion really amounts to a conclusive underlining of the proposition that a cosmic direction of time is *not* a thermodynamical, statistical affair. Unless it is somehow going to be done with mirrors, there is nothing in space to send the radiation back "by chance." A bubble of gas released in the center of a very large evacuated container will *certainly,* not just probably, expand for a while. After the particles have reached the walls of the container, there is

---

† See Tom Gold, "The Arrow of Time," Onzième Conseil de Physique, Institut de Physique Solvay (Brussels, 1958).

a *chance* that they might bounce back and reassemble; if the container is infinite, there is not even a chance. The same is true of the non-equilibrium expansion of radiation into the blackness of space. The thermodynamic irreversibility of physical processes is the statistical image of non-statistical boundary conditions.

If we suppose that there might be a negative acceleration of the expanding universe, so that in some future epoch it would begin to contract, it is conceivable that there might be, literally, a reversal of time. The sky would wax whiter, and at some point history itself would begin to unhappen! But it is not clear that the contracting phase would simply undo the expanding one. I believe that one simply does not know how to think about such a pervasive transformation. As inherently cosmological, the question cannot be investigated in the context of man-made experiments; for a purely local reversal of the balance between radiation and matter would have to employ systems of various kinds whose own operation would be constrained by the existing cosmological boundary conditions, and these would render any local time-reversal, in a complex system, almost infinitely improbable.

In the steady-state cosmology† there is a radical temporal asymmetry in that every hydrogen atom, by hypothesis, has a beginning in time but no ending except in its union with other hydrogen atoms to make heavier nuclei. Matter is created to fill the space left vacant by expansion. But along with it is created new free energy. In such a system, as in the disk and the plug with the heating coil, equilibrium never arrives. What obtains is the steady state in which, over large constant volumes of space, matter, energy, and entropy are constant. Galaxies, however, are not typical of the average state: in them matter condenses into small volumes, energy leaves them as radiation, and their entropy increases.

There remains the question whether the subjective sense of time's direction can be accounted for in thermodynamic terms. From a purely physiological point of view there is certainly no difficulty. Living organisms in general and animals in particular are distinguished among physical systems by the complexities of their thermodynamic interaction with the environment; time's arrow is better defined by them than by anything else we know of. But the awareness of time is an intuition so primitive that we cannot equate it, as defined introspectively, with the highly conceptualized account of thermodynamics. The possibility remains, and ought not to be excluded by fiat, that the phenomenological elaboration of time as an intuition, and the thermodynamic

---

† See Hermann Bondi, *Cosmology* (Cambridge, England, 1952). For a brief popular account see Bondi, *The Universe at Large* (Garden City, N.Y., 1960), an Anchor paperback.

account of time as a character of physical reality, fail, in some fundamental way, to square with each other.

Bergson, in a famous thesis,† attacked the physicist's conception of time as a falsification, which, although justifiable pragmatically by its role in the prediction and control of events, should not be taken seriously in any account of the nature of things. Bergson thus contributed to the intellectual denigration of science that has become fashionable in our century. If he had done only this, his analysis would be worth little consideration. It is, however, a striking analysis and may be considered on its merits. Bergson's thesis is a criticism of the Galilean geometry of motion, by which measurements and orderings of time are mapped into measurements and orderings of space. The resulting characterization of process imports into the physicist's thinking (Bergson believes) the image of past and future as co-existing and co-determining. That such a way of thought belongs to one phase of our experience Bergson does not deny: in the practical planning of our lives, *this* must be done before *that,* and the whole array of present conditions relevant to a desired future must be organized into a causal system. But in another phase of experience the sense of the past is the sense of what is done, what cannot be altered, whereas the future is the realm of potentiality. Our ignorance of the future is not a *de facto* ignorance, but a learned ignorance; *knowledge* of the future would be, for Bergson, a contradiction in terms. The falsification, the spatializing, of time is, in fact, incident to our realization of some future. We imagine the future as a system of co-ordinate actualities, but only that it may, in the fullness of time, become so (we treat children, in some measure, as adults in order that they may become such). But this is no part of its actual character as future. The present is "big with the future"; in his attack on the dynamical image of nature, Bergson relies often upon biological metaphor, and he sees in the reality of present process a vital *élan,* transcending the capacity of mechanical science to elucidate it.

Though Bergson may attack science as falsification, and the scientific-minded critic may with justice attack Bergson's analysis as mystification, it is more interesting to examine the altered context that any such controversy has today. The thermodynamic point of view is much more congenial to the Bergsonian *metaphor* than is the conceptual framework of dynamics, particularly eight-

---

† Henri Bergson, *Introduction to Metaphysics* (New York, 1912), and *Creative Evolution* (New York, 1944). For a careful discussion of the topic of this section, see Adolf Grünbaum, "Relativity and the Atomicity of Becoming," *The Review of Metaphysics,* vol. 4 (1950), 143–86, and "The Nature of Time," in *Frontiers of Science and Philosophy,* edited by R. G. Colodney (Pittsburgh, 1963).

eenth-century dynamics (where many philosophers have stopped). The arrow of time, defined physically, distinguishes past from future just as surely as our intuitions do. The dynamical image of time as quasi-spatial is not false but only incomplete in comparison with time's full character. The thermodynamic image is, if not complete, at any rate less incomplete. If we may say, in thermo-dynamic language, that the present informs the future, surely we may also use Bergson's more colorful imagery to say the same thing. There remains, how-ever, the question of actuality and potentiality, of the unreality of the future *qua* determinate actuality.

Reichenbach, in a posthumous work,† argued that modern physics implies the unreality of the future in this sense. If Reichenbach's argument were cor-rect, Bergson would be right about everything except his denigration of science! The argument from classical mechanics for the co-actuality of past and future is the argument that, since the future is predictable by dynamical laws, the determinacy of the past implies an equal determinacy of the future, and thus the contrast between the actual and the potential loses its meaning. So far as the *laws* of quantum mechanics are concerned, the situation is not altered. But the laws of quantum mechanics define wave functions whose meaning, at the level of collocations, is their prescription of probabilities for those collocations. Thus in quantum mechanics there is no iron bond between past and future; the *occurrence* of a collocation from among the set of alternatives specified by interacting wave functions is something extra, a new boundary condition over and above all antecedent ones. The absence of such a bond does not, of course, establish Reichenbach's thesis; it merely removes one of the classical arguments against such a thesis. Quantum mechanics would not, for example, imply the falsity of the Christian doctrine of God's foreknowledge of the future; it would only contradict the belief that God knows the future by predicting it. But God does not need to predict the future if he can be simply and directly aware of it. In the view of Bergson (and Reichenbach), however, even this possibility would be unthinkable.

Philosophers have diverted themselves with this problem for a long time. The most obvious difficulty is in stating the issue in such a way that it is an issue.‡ One way of trying to formulate it is to ask whether statements made

---

† Hans Reichenbach, *The Direction of Time* (Berkeley, 1956).

‡ To say that past, present, and future coexist is silly if "coexist" means exist at the same time, and unedifying if it means that what is past did exist and what is future will exist. But it is not silly to ask for new models of the temporal relation, nor to wrestle with angels; it is just not easy. For an analysis of the logic of grammatical tense see A. N. Prior, *Time and Modality* (Oxford, 1957).

now about future events can properly be said to be either true or false. There are science-fiction stories, and some more sober speculations, on the possibility that time "branches," giving us a world A in which the hero dies and a world B in which he recovers. In such a case statements about the future would be ambiguous in their reference and thus neither true nor false unqualifiedly, but true (of one branch) and false (of another). There can, however, be ambiguities of reference for less drastic reasons. If we can show that there are some such ambiguities *in principle,* we shall, in one sense, be in agreement with Bergson and Reichenbach.

The proper context in which to discuss further our ignorance of the future, and the degree to which it should be called a learned ignorance, is that of human affairs, for there the identification of science with prediction is already most dubious. In the present section I have tried to lay the groundwork for further discussion. Whatever its importance and its poignancy in human affairs, the arrow of time is no invention of the self-alienating human psyche, but part of the common order of nature.

9

PROBABILITY
AND CREDIBILITY

In the present chapter we turn our attention to a much-discussed question of scientific methodology, that of the nature and rules of probable reasoning and probable inference. As I have defined probability, it is what Kant would have called a category, a form within which we find it possible, and sometimes necessary, to organize the description of things.

Statements of probability, so described, are contingent, synthetic statements; they represent factual claims that can be substantiated or shown to be false. They belong to the subject matter of knowledge. But, like the category of causality, of which it is a generalization, that of probability sustains inferences and therefore belongs to the methodology of science. For philosophers who want to make the division between scientific knowledge and scientific method an absolute one, this poses a serious problem. The characterization of good methods of inquiry ought, they think, to be worked out independently of the results of inquiry. We cannot investigate until we have a method of investigation. The rules of probable inference must therefore guide us even as we make inferences about physical probabilities.

These beliefs are half-true, but so are beliefs that contradict them. Methods of investigation are defined by abstraction from actual investigations, and to know that methods are good is to know something about subject matter. All method, moreover, is the *use* of knowledge to gain knowledge, and the kind

225

of knowledge that is used sets bounds to the kind of knowledge that can be gained.

In the following sections we shall be concerned with the kind of inductive use to which a knowledge of probabilities can be put. We can explicate this use by showing how the formalism of probability theory can function as an inductive logic, a logic in which conclusions can be justified without being deductively justified. The explication leads us back into information theory, for we are describing ways in which the human mind can inform itself, can be informed, by the order of nature. Thus even our concern for probability theory as inductive logic is descriptive. It is not merely descriptive, however, for there are alternative ways in which information can be sought; these are subject to comparison and choice. At the point where we advance reasons for preferring one procedure to another the investigation becomes normative or prescriptive.

In the first sections I develop the outlines of a theory of inductive logic; in the following sections I describe a sort of model of the evolution of knowledge under the sway of inductive procedures; and, finally, I explore one of the most important and least thoroughly understood aspects of inquiry—analogy. As in previous sections, so in those to follow, my approach is expository and dogmatic. Once again the justification is the complex and controversial nature of the topic, which could easily be expanded into a volume. And once again I beg the informed reader to postpone final judgment until I am finished.

The Probable and the Non-probable

To infer that a collocation known to have a probability near 1 will occur is a highly credible inference. It may turn out to be a false one, but this does not diminish its credibility *ex ante*. Such inferences, clearly, are of a special and narrow kind. They deal only with what I have called collocations, "possible events," and, perforce, only with the subclass of collocations for which we have adequate knowledge of probabilities.

The range of inferences that are, in *some* sense, probable is, however, very wide. The whole vast structure of knowledge is a complex that depends, quite crucially, upon inferences that are less than deductively compelling although better than blind guesses. Our very narrow and restricted meaning of "probability," as I have set it forth, is obviously inadequate to provide a framework for all the kinds of inference that we intuitively call probable—or so it appears.

In order to argue that this is not so, I begin with a classification of propositions into the probable and the non-probable. If a proposition is probable, if we can write $P(p) = k$, then what p proposes is a collocation, and what "$P(p) = k$" proposes is that this collocation occurs or fails under boundary conditions that define the measure. Let us say that p is a probable, or Class I, proposition. All others we put in the class of non-probable propositions, or propositions of Class II. What about the probability proposition itself, "$P(p) = k$"? It may, but certainly it need not, belong to Class I. The probabilities connected with the six faces of a die depend on the distribution of its mass, and this may, in turn, be determined by other chance collocations. Thus we could speak of the probability that such a probability lay in a certain range. A probability may, however, depend upon an unknown law or constant of nature; but a hypothesis about such a probability would be neither probable nor improbable.

The example shows that a probable proposition can be embedded in a non-probable proposition. But the non-probable proposition must be known to be true, or must, at any rate, be supported by good evidence, for otherwise we could not make inferences, justified by probabilities, about the probable proposition. Non-probable propositions can, indeed, be embedded in probable propositions, and this is how we can know that they are true or, more generally, are supported by good evidence.

A proposition can be defined as an equivalence class of statements, the term "statement" implying here that statements are stat*ings,* events, like lightning flashes or battles. *What* is stated on one occasion may be, or might have been, stated on other occasions; it is invariant under transformation from one stating to another. It is thus of the nature of a universal. This universality—one of the most remarkable achievements of human thought and speech—we may call subjective to distinguish it from the universality of content that generalizations have and singular statements lack.

The subjective universality of propositions permits us to think of even momentary and particular items of fact as having a kind of eternal status. An ant I was watching today fell off a pine-needle bridge. The mark of this passage was no doubt there, for a sufficiently discerning perception, like a human footprint in the sand. But, like the footprint, it will be gone the day after, or later. The fact I tell is not gone; it is frozen in the being of history; it is a fact, and a fact it will henceforth have been. The theological image of subjective universality is God's mind, unknown to which not a single sparrow falls. This image is the delineation as actual of the possibility that human language exploits.

Propositions are the semantic counterparts of facts conceived in this way; they are placeless, timeless, impersonal, and true or false *sub specie aeternitatis*. But a proposition can be *designated* by any element of the equivalence class, by a particular stating of it. Statements are the concrete particulars that we exhibit; the proposition is defined by abstraction. There are all the same puzzlements as in the case of number. Naive semantics avoids the distinction, as naive arithmetic does.

What we need here is only the fact that what is stated on a particular occasion may be true or may be false. In the human sphere, for example, there are collocations of the form $\phi \, x \, T$, in which ϕ designates what will be stated on a certain kind of occasion, and truth is predicated of what is stated. "$P(\phi \, x \, T) = k$" says that with probability k the statement so occasioned or selected is a true statement. If some of the marbles in a box are black, it is a good inference that one drawn by an appropriate black-seeking selection procedure will be black. If some of the statements in a set are true, it is a good inference that one selected by an appropriate truth-seeking procedure will be true.

There are, we see, two quite distinct senses in which a proposition can be probable: (1) that what it affirms, *qua* equivalence class of statements, is a probable collocation; (2) that it can be designated as what a suitable truth-seeking procedure has proposed, in which case it is possible that the same proposition, happening to be selected by different procedures, would have different probabilities in sense 2. In the first sense the procedure by which the proposition is arrived at, or the way in which it comes to be asserted, is inessential; the probability characterizes the collocation, however and whenever proposed. In the second sense this is not true; for the collocation to which the probability belongs is the collocation of a specific procedure for making statements with the semantic truth of the statements thus made.

With the greatest possible brevity: sometimes we infer what is probably true; sometimes we probably infer what is true. In both cases probability characterizes a collocation of designating and predicated characteristics; in the second case this collocation *is* the selecting or inferring of a proposition of which truth (or falsity) is predicated. It is a semantic collocation, a collocation the description of which involves us in talking about procedures of inference, propositions, and truth.

Semantic collocations are a small subclass in nature; but through this small subclass, this doorway, propositions of any kind, of Class I or Class II, may enter the domain of probability theory and inductive logic. Just how this occurs we shall now investigate.

Decisions and Information Theory

In recent years there has been an extensive development of the theory of statistical inference, called statistical decision theory.† It has come on top of a long history of controversy. Today there begins to emerge a broad general framework within which the old controversies are resolved or, at any rate, pursued more fruitfully than before.

Statistical decision theory is a direct generalization of the Twenty Questions theory that I developed in Chapter 8. In the earlier context I assumed that sure discriminations are always possible, but I showed that we can reduce the expected average number of them—the quantity of information—by exploiting probabilities to guide the questioning.

Twenty Questions theory is the theory of how to design a sequence of questions, or discriminations, taking advantage of probabilities and of collateral evidence in order to minimize the expected length of the game. If we wish to discriminate among the alternatives of a set A, collateral evidence is provided by collateral discrimination among the alternatives of a set B, connected to those of A by probabilities $P(B_j/A_i)$. Statistical decision theory is the same except that it takes for granted that *all* possible discriminations are collateral. The A_i are not accessible to direct, sure discrimination at all; the whole weight of the final decision among the A's must rest upon discrimination of the B's. The actual playing of the game, among the A_i, is therefore replaced by an inference, a decision. The pattern of Twenty Questions without collateral evidence is to proceed by a sequence of sure discriminations, a randomly variable number of these being required before one reaches the goal with certainty. A pattern of Twenty Questions with collateral evidence is to discriminate in that fashion the correct alternative in a collateral set B, and then to extend the process to the set of interest A, using conditional priorities dependent on the correct B_j. The pattern of statistical decision theory is to stop at the point where the correct B_j is discriminated, and then to make a jump, a probable inference, so that the goal is not reached with certainty but only with probability.

One characteristic of decision theory is that the set B, of evidential alternatives, is conceived as indefinitely extensible. A decision procedure involves a sequence of collateral discriminations, after each of which one decides by some agreed rule either to make an inference to one of the A_i or else to make another collateral discrimination. These additional steps may be thought of as repeti-

---

† Actually the label is used more broadly, to include alternative actions that are not necessarily acts of inference. I restrict it to the latter.

tions of experiments, the making of new experiments or observations, the refinement of measurement, etc. The number of alternatives at each step may be large
or small, but theory suffers no loss of generality if we assume them to be all
binary. Whatever the results of observation, the decision rule will dictate that the
process terminate after a finite number of discriminations, the number depending, in general, upon the results of previous discriminations. Thus the collection of evidence may be regarded as a Twenty Questions game, with sure
discriminations, over a finite set B. Hence the theory of this part of the process
is one we have already covered.

The second step of decision theory is to show how to construct rules of probable inference. If all probabilities $P(B_j/A_i)$ are known, as well as $P(A_i)$, the
multiplication theorem of probabilities gives us the $P(B_j)$ and $P(A_i/B_j)$. The
former will define, by the Boltzmann-Shannon principle, the priorities for discriminating among the B's. The latter will enable us to determine which of
the A_i to infer from the given B_j—namely, the most probable; and it will tell
us the probability that this A_i is true relative to B_j. In the more general formulations of decision theory the $P(A_i/B_j)$ may be weighted by utility measures,
and then the rule of inference will be to infer the alternative of greatest expected utility. My purpose, however, is to develop the theory of probable inference, and the generalization is inessential for this purpose. A good decision
procedure will be one that gives a small probability of error in going from the
B_j observed to the appropriate A_i indicated by the decision rule.

So far the outline of decision theory is simply a repetition of material we
have already covered. Up to this point we have assumed that all alternatives
are covered by known probabilities $P(A_iB_j)$. In the most interesting case,
however, this is not true. In general, the $P(A_iB_j)$ are incompletely known,
either for practical reasons or in principle—namely, because the alternatives A_i
are Class II propositions and cannot meaningfully be said to have probability
in the sense by which I have defined the term. At this point we return to a
neglected aspect of Twenty Questions theory.

Twenty Questions is a game of strategy, whether played against a human
opponent or a computing machine or nature at large. At this point, therefore,
I enlarge the scope of our discussion to consider the strategic aspects. For this
purpose I introduce ideas of game theory.†

---

† The best presentation of the ideas and spirit of game theory is still John von Neumann and
Oskar Morgenstern, *The Theory of Games and Economic Behavior* (Princeton, 1944). The mathe-
matical development has been simplified by J. C. C. McKinsey in his *Introduction to the Theory of
Games* (New York, 1952). The application of game theory to statistical theory was initiated by
Abraham Wald in his *Statistical Decision Functions* (New York, 1950).

In the game of statistical decision certain facts are assumed as given—specifically, the conditional probabilities $P(B_j/A_i)$. The A_i are formulated by the investigator as alternative *hypotheses*. Nature's play is to choose one of the A_i—that is, to make it the true one. The investigator's play is to choose a decision procedure—that is, to lay down a set of rules as to how he will behave after each discrimination within the set B; that means that, according to what he has found to date, he will either infer one of the A_i or decide to get more evidence—that is, to make a further discrimination.

Both nature and the investigator may choose to employ *mixed strategies*. For nature this means to choose the true A_i indirectly by assigning to each A_i a probability $P(A_i)$. For the investigator it means likewise that he may introduce chance decisions. We may express this by saying that, if S_1, S_2, ... are different decision strategies, he may assign to the use of each a probability $P(S_k)$. If nature's probabilistic strategy is known to the investigator, this corresponds to the case already discussed. If not, or if the A_i belong to Class II and have no probability, we still use the idea as a fiction.

In the general theory of statistical decision the investigator wishes to choose the strategy that maximizes his utility: counting each discrimination in B as a cost and each decision as a gain when correct and a loss when in error, he chooses the decision procedure that maximizes his expected profit in relation to nature's strategy, assumed to be known. Nature, in turn, tries to minimize this maximum. The fundamental theorem of game theory implies that a stable equilibrium results. Each player has a way of playing, which he cannot improve against all the strategies of the other and which cannot be worsened by any strategy of the other. To the investigator this means that he has a guaranteed minimum profit invariant to nature's choice. He does not have to impute malevolence to nature to seek this strategy; he simply does not want to leave any loopholes.

The investigator's strategy—the definition of the set B and the inference to be made from each B_j—is determined by economic considerations, but for the moment I wish to avoid these. I therefore assume that the decisive alternatives B_j are defined, and I concentrate on another aspect of the problem. Complementary to the investigator's desire to minimize the probability of error in his inferences is the criterion of minimizing the informational cost of the procedure. He therefore goes back to the viewpoint of information theory and imagines that he is going to play the game all the way, to a sure discrimination of the correct A_i. By the Bolzmann-Shannon criterion, then, he chooses priorities: $Q(A_iB_j) = P(A_iB_j) = P(A_i)P(B_j/A_i)$. The second factor in the last expression is fixed and belongs to the rules of the game. Nature can choose the $P(A_i)$, however, and does so in order to maximize the investigator's minimum needed information. If we carry through nature's analysis, we find that she chooses the $P(A_i)$ proportional to the corresponding quantities $2^{H(P_i^B)}$. It will be recalled that $H(P_i^B)$ is the information that one needs in order to discriminate among the B's if A_i is correct. The more relevance A_i has to the B's, in effect, the less likely nature is to choose that alternative. If the investigator imputes this strategy to nature and calculates his informational requirements on this basis, he cannot possibly be disappointed. The expected total amount of information that he needs in order to discriminate among $A \otimes B$ need not exceed what he thus calculates, and he cannot guarantee the result in less. Of this total information a certain amount will, in fact, be accounted for in discrimination among the B's; the rest is what he would have yet to spend if he could make sure discriminations among the A's. This quantity, the unattained information, is small for a good decision procedure. It is necessarily greater than the probability of error in replacing the final discrimination among the A_i by a direct guess. Thus, if the unattained information is a very small fraction of one bit, the probability of error is very small.

It should be clear that this procedure does not depend on the existence of probabilities $P(A_i)$, but only on the conditional probabilities $P(B_j/A_i)$ and the investigator's choice of priorities: he sets $Q(B_j/A_i)$ equal to $P(B_j/A_i)$ and then chooses $Q(A_i)$ equal to the probabilities that nature *would* employ *if* she were malevolent.

I have carried the account of statistical decision theory far enough to show that it is equivalent to a truncated game of Twenty Questions in which sure discriminations are terminated short of the final goal but near enough to it, in an informational sense, so that the final inference has a practically advantageous probability of success. The result is an inference that selects one of the A_i as true. This A_i may be a proposition of Class I or of Class II; it may or may not have a parametrically defined probability. The probability that justifies this inference is not the probability of a collocation that A_i describes, but the probability of a semantic collocation—namely, of the proposition that the decision procedure selects the A_i that is, in fact, true. As I said before, probability characterizes the inferring rather than the thing inferred.†

---

† The most cogent and vivid statement of the general point of view adopted here is that of C. S. Peirce in "The Probability of Induction," *Popular Science Monthly*, 1878, now available in his *Collected Writings*, Vol. II, Chap. 7, and in *Philosophical Writings of Peirce* (New York, 1955). See also David Hawkins, "Existential and Epistemic Probability," *Philosophy of Science*, vol. 10, 4 (Oct. 1943), pp. 255–61.

Credibility and Priority

In spite of my animadversions on other interpretations of probability than that which sees it as a parametrically definable trait of physical systems, there is still something to be accounted for in the common-sense meaning of "probability." The abstract noun is less suggestive here than the adjective "probable" and the adverb "probably" together with their synonyms and equivalents in other languages. The probability of an inference does not necessarily qualify the thing inferred; but one *somehow* qualifies the thing inferred as probable in *some* sense, even if the proposition is of Class II.

The history of science shows many examples of common-sense concepts evolving into technical ones, sometimes into more than one technical concept. The general idea of quantity of motion, for example, evolved into three: velocity, momentum, and energy. There is no reason to believe that the particular technical concept of probability that I have been discussing exhausts the latent technicalities of common thought and speech. Many writers have espoused alternative explications of probability, either in psychological terms as referring to intensity of belief, in logical-psychological terms as referring to reasonable intensity of belief, or as *credibility*. Many have argued, indeed, that the kind of probability here involved is epistemologically prior to probability as long-run relative frequency (for which I have substituted the notion of physical parametrization testable in terms of relative frequency). As I stated at the beginning of this chapter, I accept this order of precedence as half-truth, as not excluding the equally true statement of the reverse dependency.†

---

† Rudolf Carnap, *Logical Foundations of Probability* (Chicago, 1950), is a meticulous and cogent pursuit of the concept of credibility as distinguished from the frequency interpretation. Carnap attempts to build up the foundations within a formal language, according to which the measure of credibility is an additive function. This work is continued in *The Continuum of Inductive Methods* (Chicago, 1953). In this system statements of credibility are intended to be logically true rather than contingently true.

The scheme that Carnap starts with in the first work, and then generalizes in the second, is easily understood by means of a model. In the universe under consideration there are n attributes. An object may therefore be any one of 2^n in kind, defined by the presence or absence of each attribute. We imagine a box containing 2^n marbles, one for each *possible* kind. We sample from the actual universe, but we use the box to determine the credibility of a predicted sample. Thus initially all possibilities are equally credible. But, whenever an object is sampled in the actual universe, a new surrogate for it is added to the box. The theory of this model was developed by György Polya. See William Feller, *An Introduction to Probability and Its Applications* (New York, 1950), pp. 83, 101.

It is an unfortunate characteristic of the Carnap model that it leads to the following theorem: the relative frequency of any elementary property lies within an interval $1/2 \pm 2^{-n}$, with probability (credibility) $1 - 2^{-n}$; and this is true for a sequence of samples of any length. Thus, if $n = 100$, the statement "the relative frequency of the property A, as the number of samples examined ap-

I believe that I have already introduced an adequate technical explication of credibility as distinct from probability. It is related to, but not identical in meaning with, the probability of a probable inference. The explication in question is simply the concept of *priority* associated, as we have seen it to be, with a statistical decision procedure.

There are several ways in which this claim can be tested. One is that, if a proposition has a probability p, the admission of this fact in evidence gives to the proposition a credibility p also. Now all efficient decision procedures identify priorities with known probabilities. An inefficient decision procedure is one that can be improved for some of nature's possible choices without being worsened for any. The efficiency condition is really nothing other than the Boltzmann-Shannon condition on minimizing the expected length of a discrimination procedure.

But credibilities can be defined in the absence of known probabilities. In the case we discussed priorities were chosen to be equal to the probabilities nature would assign to her alternatives if she were out to maximize the needed information that the investigator is trying to minimize. We should like to interpret such priorities as being proper measures of degree of belief, of credibility.

Another test that the proposed explication must meet is that, when it is reasonable to assign a very high degree of credibility to a proposition, it is reasonable also to infer that the proposition is true. This requirement is the analogue, for probable reasoning, of the rule of inference, or detachment, in deductive reasoning.† We saw that this was so with good decision procedures: when the probability of error in the procedure is small, the unattained information is small also, and this is possible only when some one of the hypotheses A_i has a conditional priority near 1. The reverse is also true: in such a scheme a priority near 1 implies a small unattained information and a small probability of error in the indicated probable inference.

At the other extreme is a test of our interpretation that is familiar from the

---

proaches infinity, will be $1/2 \pm 10^{-30}$" has an *initial* credibility, in advance of all empirical evidence, of $1 - 10^{-30}$. To change this appreciably, one would have to add to the contents of the box (initially 2^{100} in number) some 2^{100} surrogates. At the rate of one a second, the examination would take about 10^{13} times the age of the Galaxy.

The natural way out of this excessive conservatism is to add to the box, not one surrogate, but several, for each empirical observation. If we add each time 2^{n-1} identical surrogates, the model will not give any very high *initial* credibility to long-run relative frequencies. But the model now has a very strong bias in favor of analogy. If the first object sampled has many surrogates of itself put into the box, this very rare combination of properties becomes thereby a very common one.

† See Lewis Carroll, "What the Tortoise Said to Achilles," *Mind,* N.S., 4 (1895), pp. 287 ff.; reprinted in Ralph M. Eaton, *General Logic* (New York, 1931), and in James R. Newman, *The World of Mathematics* (New York, 1956), pp. 2402–05.

history of controversies about probability. Laplace took it as a rule that, if we have no evidence relevant to a decision between two or more alternative hypotheses, we should assign them equal probabilities. Clearly this makes no sense when probability is interpreted statistically, but it makes precise sense in terms of information theory: if nature is presumed to maximize the unattained information that an investigator tries to minimize when he has no collateral evidence, she will make all alternatives equally probable. This is a picturesque way of saying that, if our ignorance is total, there is no reason for our putting one alternative ahead of another in a Twenty Questions routine. This is the logical form† of the principle of insufficient reason. More emphatically, there *is* a reason for not putting one alternative ahead of another—namely, that this symmetry surely minimizes the maximum needed information.

But it is doubtful whether we are ever in total ignorance. The very formulation of propositions borrows from past experience and present knowledge. Analogy is of the essence of language, and what leads to a question may also be evidence for or against an answer. Because we have been concerned with formalism, with logic, we have ignored what can never, in practice, be ignored: the relevance of that part of the collateral evidence that is already in before we start an inquiry.

A good way of taking account of past experience and present knowledge would be this: to *formulate* alternatives to be tested in such a way that, in relation to the evidence already attained, the decision from the next discrimination is as likely to be "yes" as "no." In the discussion up to this point I have not raised this vital question: how we get the alternatives for discrimination in the first place. But the limitation has some virtue. Within a formal model of inquiry, which ignores prior evidence, we can show its relevance. Suppose that within a decision procedure of the sort I have been discussing we stop halfway, and imagine that this is a new beginning. At this new beginning our procedure is, and ought to be, *biased* by the prior information. We might bias it either by weighting the alternative hypotheses or by reformulating them to be of equal weight. We weight by starting with the *conditional* priorities that are relative to previously accumulated evidence. We reformulate by subdividing some alternatives or collapsing others previously distinguished.

What holds within the interrupted artificial model holds in life as well, in what John Dewey called the continuum of inquiry. In science, conspicuously, we try to mobilize the resources of past experience for maximum relevance to

---

† Promised in Chap. 6, where insufficient reason was interpreted in terms of a physically defined probability metric.

the formulation of hypotheses. To look only for new data, to throw out the past, to start afresh in the belief that the traditions are worthless, may in some very restricted context be an appropriate if desperate remedy. Taken very seriously, it would be a kind of folly. New beginnings have often been proclaimed against apathy and dogma, but there the point is wrongly stated. Tradition may be a bad substitute for new inquiry, but without tradition new inquiry is unguided. The question is not whether tradition should be relied upon, but for what purpose. The proper use of tradition also has its counterpart within the artificial model of inquiry. An efficient decision procedure is one in which priorities are defined at each stage by reference to evidence accrued from previous discriminations, defined in such a way as to maximize the relevance of future discriminations. The technical rule is to ask questions, as nearly as possible, for which the "yes" and the "no" have equal priority. But they also must be good questions, and that means as far toward the goal as prior evidence allows.

It seems reasonable that the psychological sense of "degree of belief" could be a kind of residue of the collective relevance of experience of which, because of its sheer mass, only a small portion can be articulated and stated as definite evidence. It would represent an assignment of priorities roughly in the manner in which our model, interrupted halfway along, would assign them, but not always with a good recall of the justifying discriminations. Called up for justification in such situations, we do what we can by way of argument and then fill the remaining gap by lame appeals to common sense, to insight, or to hunch.

Here the question will not easily be removed. Past evidence is a weight, a moral responsibility to acknowledge. But what is the weight? "What is evidence?" jesting Pilate might have asked. We do not have the past, but only a synopsis, itself selective. Disagreement is inevitable. Mankind has had a vast experience with extrasensory perception and the lack of it. What are the prior weights, pro and con? By consensus there is a low initial priority, and enough favorable evidence pushes it toward the high end of the scale. To acknowledge that it is mainly subliminal, not obviously useful to gamblers, etc., is then to invite alternative explanations of some data, even if these explanations also have a low initial priority. Fraud? Sometimes, no doubt. Correlations by common cause rather than by information transfer? Has anyone tried to transmit "Mary had a little lamb" with suitable random coding over a thousand repetitions? This would eliminate the common cause, with one set of variables antecedently anchored in literature.

Another example, much discussed, is mathematical discovery. How is it that a conjecture seems probable to a mathematician before he proves it? How does one mathematician go on a much shorter path to new discovery than another, and thus get there first? Not all the reasons can be articulated, perhaps not even many of them.† I only suggest that the right way to think about the problem is to formulate it in terms of the variability of informational distance as a function of relevant prior evidence. The mathematician tests a different conjecture by looking to other propositions that resemble the given one or are related to it as antecedents or consequents. Propositions of mathematics belong to Class II, but probability is relevant because in doing mathematical research one samples, one casts about. To disprove a randomly chosen consequent would disprove the conjecture; to prove the consequent gives the conjecture a higher priority than it had before. But much depends upon the choice of evidence, since false conjectures may lead to trivially true consequents, and true conjectures may have trivially false antecedents. For this reason the procedure is not routine, and the distance to the goal depends strongly on the relevance of the evidence. Analogy presents even greater difficulties, on which I shall comment later.

By whatever heuristic procedures it is accomplished, mathematical discovery is properly so called. The process is a creative one, but the creation must, in the end, satisfy the constraints of logical syntax and deducibility that predetermine the truth or falsity of mathematical propositions in consistent systems of axioms. In relation to information theory, therefore, mathematical knowledge is a discrimination of the properties of an antecedently given reality. In every step of a proof one is called upon to discriminate, for the next line to be written down, one or a limited number out of all the logical formulas that could be written. The criterion of deducibility from earlier lines is the basis of discrimination, and the whole process possesses a definite informational value. Some writers have wanted to say that deductive discriminations of this sort should be given no information measure. It is true that the process of proof requires no information source *external* to the given things from which the process starts. But that does not mean that no information source is required. The interesting thing about mathematical proof is that the needed information is generated from the process itself, recursively. Routine operations, however, are not enough, for many deductions are usually permissible at every step, whereas we wish to make just the one that is going to lead toward a given final formula. This process is guided by an algorithm if one exists—which also is an information source. But in many cases—indeed, usually—proof is guided by heuristic devices

---

† The classic in this field—and a recent one—is György Polya, *Mathematics and Plausible Reasoning,* 2 vols. (Princeton, 1954). Polya shows—very plausibly—that credibility fits the pattern of the additive measure of probability.

that increase the probability of selecting the right pathway of argument and that therefore fall within the general scheme of statistical decision theory.

Statistical decision theory sometimes provides a practically usable logic of inductive inference. In some cases, such as that of mathematical discovery, it is not practically usable in the precise quantitative sense because of the inaccessibility of relevant quantitative statistical information. This is true in many other kinds of plausible reasoning, and perhaps in almost all of the subtler kind. My claim in these cases is that statistical decision theory provides a scheme, a model, for the procedures that we do, in fact, tend to follow. Whether it gives any practical guidance is another question, which we cannot pursue at this point.

One must grant—one must even insist—that many actual procedures of inference will not yield to explicit and detailed analysis based on our model. Human beings are influenced by a wider range of perception and knowledge than they can, in fact, bring to sharp formulation. The capacity to learn, derived from biological evolution and supplemented by the long history of culture and by individual experience, represents an extremely complex accommodation, only a small part of which appears above the surface as well-constructed argument. But this small part is an extremely important part, both historically and philosophically; it gives us a way in which our less analytical and more intuitive procedures can be tested and criticized, even if it can never replace them. In science, where procedures are most self-consciously scrutinized, it is still necessary to have a good character and not just good methods. Intuitive judgments have to be respected because they may be influenced by subtleties of evidence that escape conscious attention and articulation. They have to be tested as far as possible because, as we know from the statistics of experience, subliminal evidence is at times grossly misleading.

A final comment is in order on the thermodynamic significance of the quantities we have been considering. We have seen that the entropy of a physical system is defined in a way that depends upon the enumeration of its alternative possible states and upon the probabilities of those states. The conditional entropy of a system A, conditional upon a system B, is the entropy of $A \otimes B$ less the entropy of B. If the probabilities of alternatives in A are undefined, this entropy does not exist. We have seen, however, that in terms of the conditional probabilities $P(B_j/A_i)$ there is minimax—minimum of maxima—information measure, information we need in order to define the correct alternative in A with the help of collateral discriminations in B. If this information is less than what would be needed in the absence of information from B, there must be a free energy associated with it and paid for in our discriminating the correct alternative in *B*. Since no entropy is defined for *A*, no free energy can be either. The free energy we have to account for therefore belongs to the system *B*.

For imagery we can imagine a piece of hardware—a computing machine with suitable inputs, discriminations, and responses—that plays the game of decision theory against nature. If no probabilities are defined for nature's choice, the thermodynamic analysis of the process will show that the entropy decrease occurs through measurements performed by the hardware. Speaking more humanely, we do not in any sense reduce the statistical variety of nature when we are engaged in learning the fixed patterns, the constancies, of nature. Rather, it is nature that reduces the statistical variety in us. In learning, we reduce the statistical variety in ourselves. Our subsequent behavior becomes more predictable to an outside observer who knows the order of nature because it comes to be more closely coupled to, and defined by, that order. We have acquired, in Spinoza's phrase, more "aptness of the body" because our ideas are less "mutilated and confused."

The Inductive Maze and a Theorem on Progress

I have shown how probable inference is possible in the isolated case, and have shown that its evidential basis constitutes information. But is it possible to accumulate that information in a series of steps tending toward an indefinite growth of knowledge? This is the ultimate question in the old problem of induction. Is it possible to achieve an arbitrary refinement of discrimination without resorting, in part, to a succession of perfectly sure, binary discriminations? Is it possible to achieve long-run assurance by a procedure of steps in which each step is fallible?

A very simple example is found in lengthy numerical computations, in which error in any one step is improbable but the over-all probability of error is great because so many steps are involved. With large computing machines this problem can be serious. When the problem is not that of an isolated investigation, however lengthy, but the career of science itself, we are dealing with a chain of practically infinite length, non-terminating. The problem is not to make scientific investigation error-free, which is impossible, but rather to make it error-correcting and thus to find some assurance of progress. In order to examine this question, I propose to extend and generalize the statistical decision procedure in such a way that it becomes non-terminating. And this carries us back to information theory.

Clearly, any sequence of decision procedures can be represented as a single compound decision procedure. But the probability of error increases with the number of procedures compounded. Conversely, any decision procedure can be represented as a sequence of decision procedures of the simplest kind—namely, binary choices between two alternatives. A choice among N alternative hypotheses is made, that is, by the binary partitioning procedure of Twenty Questions. Only now the discriminations that answer the binary questions are unsure. If the probability of error per binary discrimination is $p < 1/2$, the information lost is $H(p, 1-p)$, and the information gained is $1 - H(p, 1-p)$. If one sure discrimination of the collateral evidence can convey the amount of information given above, we have a measure of efficiency in bits attained per bit expended. A fundamental theorem of information theory, due to Shannon, shows that it is always possible to approximate this degree of efficiency.† If the information we need in order to discriminate one alternative in a set is N sure bits, the number of unsure discriminations needed is $N/[1 - H(p, 1-p)]$. We achieve this by a deliberate use of question sequences that are inefficient or, in the language of Chapter 8, dominated. We then introduce additional questions, whose answers are entailed by the answers to the original questions. Because of this redundancy, otherwise undesirable, error reveals itself as inconsistency. If Twenty Questions were modified to allow, at most, k lies to be told by the answerer, the questioner could still infallibly get the right final answer by a number of questions in the neighborhood of the number given by the formula above, with p equal to the proportion of permitted false answers.‡

In this form the theory of Twenty Questions with unsure answers is equivalent to the problem of transmitting information over a noisy channel, in which each binary symbol transmitted is equivalent to nature's choice in a binary decision game, and each symbol received is equivalent to the collateral evidence on which an investigator bases his decision. The additional symbols used in the transmitted message to provide checks on transmission errors are equivalent to an appropriate retesting of hypotheses already decided.

In order to visualize more clearly what is involved, I represent the decision sequence of a game of Twenty Questions by a dichotomous maze, in which

---

† C. E. Shannon, in *Bell System Technical Journal*, 27 (1948), pp. 379, 623, presents a clear discussion. These fundamental papers are also in Shannon and Weaver, *The Mathematical Theory of Communication* (Urbana, Ill., 1949).

‡ There is a literature, mathematically interesting, on error-correcting codes. See D. Slepian, "A Class of Binary Signalling Alphabets," *Bureau of Standards Technical Journal*, 35 (1956), pp. 203–34. The subject of coding theory is a current one; see W. W. Peterson, *Error Correcting Codes* (New York, 1961).

each branching represents a "yes" or "no" answer to one binary question. If the maze is seen as one through which an experimental animal has to move, he will have to decide, at each point of choice, whether to go to the left (L) or to the right (R). A sequence of L's and R's will thus be a binary word that encodes one of the alternative hypotheses A_i. As the experimental animal runs the maze, we record his path in the same way, using the same symbols in quotation marks. The word that defines the correct path is then to be compared with the word that defines the actual path, and any differences of spelling are errors. To represent the whole career of inquiry, we make the maze endless. It need have no blind alleys, and no cage where the hard-working animal will be given, for his success in getting there, the final rewarding mush. Words get extended to sentences, sentences to paragraphs, paragraphs to chapters, . . . , and the reward is intrinsic to the process, to stay on or near the right path.

We suppose, finally, that at every point of choice information of some kind is available, and that the choice is based on this. If L and R are propositions indicating that left and right are, respectively, the correct choice, and if "L" and "R" represent alternative data on which a choice is to be based, the relevant probabilities are $P(\text{"}L\text{"}/L)$ and $P(\text{"}R\text{"}/R)$.

It is obvious at once that, even though $P(\text{"}L\text{"}/L)$ and $P(\text{"}R\text{"}/R)$ are, on the average, very close to 1, the probability of eventual error is 1. Once one is off the correct path, moreover, there is no short way to get back to it; so subse-

Fig. 25. Rat Entering Maze

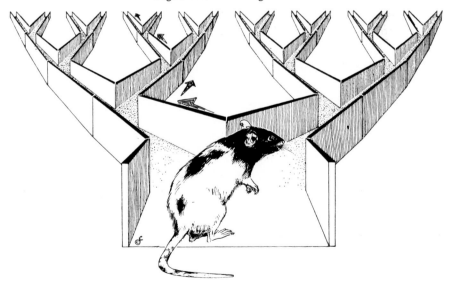

quent choices, however made, may diverge more and more from the correct path. The only means for the correction of error is, in one way or another, to retrace one's steps. Thus, in general, the choice at each point of choice must be *three*-fold: the correct decision is either *L, R,* or *V* (backward).

Under these circumstances it is possible to state simple necessary and sufficient conditions that guarantee, in a statistical sense, indefinite progress along the correct path in the maze. That is, every position in the maze can be classified according to two parameters; we reach it by going *n* steps along the correct path and *r* further steps along some incorrect path. By "indefinite progress" I mean that, whatever *r* may be, *n* will, with probability 1, increase without limit. The conditions are the following:

$$P(``L"/L) > P(``V"/L)$$
$$P(``R"/R) > P(``V"/R)$$
$$P(``V"/V) > 1/2$$

That is, the random walk in the maze must be more likely to go forward along the correct path than backward, and more likely to go backward along an incorrect path than forward along an incorrect path. The theorem is an extension of standard random-walk theorems.[†]

In error-correcting codes there is a redundancy, deliberately introduced, which, as we saw, provides the means of turning error into logical inconsistency. In seriate statistical decisions the same role is taken by logical constraints among the hypotheses examined. In general, such constraints must have the effect that any hypothesis antecedently accepted is eventually retested, and repeatedly retested, in the acquisition of subsequent information.

The introduction of redundancy, of logical constraints, as necessary to the indefinite progress of knowledge, throws a new light on the old philosophical problem of the uniformity of nature. The achievement of unexceptionable gen-

---

[†] See the discussions of random-walk problems in William Feller, *op. cit.* The theorem: If the inequalities above are satisfied, there is, for every *n* and every $t > 0$, an *N*, depending on *n, t,* and the given probabilities, such that, with probability $1 - t$, *N* decisions will be sufficient to leave no uncorrected error among any of the first *n* choice points along the correct path. Moreover, if

$$P(``L"/L) = P(``R"/R) = t$$
$$P(``R"/L) = P(``L"/R) = u$$
$$P(``V"/L) = P(``V"/R) = v$$
$$P(``L"/V) + P(``R"/V) = w$$
$$P(``V"/V) = x$$

the average rate of progress, in the long run, will almost certainly be

$$\frac{n}{N} = \frac{(t - v)(x - w)}{(x - w + u)}$$

eralizations in the description of nature implies, trivially, that nature *can* be characterized by unexceptionable generalizations. Under this heading we include the parametric description of suitably isolated systems in terms of probabilities. But more is implied than that. For the achievement of such knowledge implies the existence of thermodynamically accessible pathways along which knowledge can lead to discovery and to correction of error. Hypotheses to be tested must be surely or probabilistically related to new experience in the context of knowledge already achieved, and errors incorporated not only must be retestable in principle, but must be retested in fact, directly or indirectly, in the continuing application to which they are put. I shall pursue this question further in the following section. Here I wish only to notice that there is a sort of scale in the degree to which sequential decision procedure is hemmed in by logical constraints. At one extreme we have a sequence of hypotheses, wholly independent of one another, to be tested and decided on. Here the condition of error-free testing must be that each step is error-free as first taken. At the other extreme we have the limit of mathematical deduction, which is such that, after some number of initial steps, all further steps are determined by logical constraints without additional experiential, external discriminations to guide the process. In line with my previous statement about mathematical proof as a decision procedure, we may describe logical constraints as providing internal, recursively generated information; the distinction between "information" and "redundancy" is thus a distinction between two kinds or sources of information. Reliable empirical generalizations, once achieved, serve as internal information-generators and increase redundancy or, putting it another way, reduce the external information needed for further discriminations.

The complexities of the inductive pathways that may be defined are so great that I can make no pretense of defining a single, unique "scientific method" except in the barest sense. The inductive maze is intended as a model at this rather high level of abstraction. The permissible variety of pattern, which may still satisfy the conditions of the progress theorem, suggests the variety of the procedures actually applied between the more formally and deductively organized patterns of inquiry, on the one hand, and the more open-textured, naturalistic kind of inquiry, on the other. And none of this analysis touches upon the more creative side of inquiry except by implication. The formation of new concepts and hypotheses, the art of using old knowledge to bring order to investigation—all this is left aside. What I have concentrated on is the logical skeleton of the process and the formulation of conditions by which creativity in science must discipline itself.

The inductive maze illustrates what may be called the elementary thermo-dynamics of learning. In the next chapter I shall discuss the contemporary understanding of biological reproduction and shall, in the process, exploit the analogy of evolution and learning. Since any discrimination has a minimum possible energy cost of about kT, Boltzmann's constant times the absolute temperature, the high probability that the maze animal, after many branchings of the maze, is still somewhere on or near the correct path, corresponds to a certain expenditure of free energy. Knowledge is paid for by the sequential discriminations made in the elimination of alternatives. The description of molecular copying, self-reproduction, involves parallel arguments.

In illustrating the solution of one problem the inductive maze gives rise to another. If we interpret the inductive process (as represented by the maze) in a purely behavioral way, the probabilities of making correct choices may be known to one standing outside the maze, but not to the experimental animal, the inquirer, who has to labor in it. If the relevant probabilities satisfy our three conditions, his rules of behavior are, in fact, good, and we can predict for him a career of indefinite progress. But in reality *we* are the experimental animal; and, whether in fact our rules of procedure satisfy the three conditions, the procedures must somehow be justified *for us*, within the maze.

Historically, philosophers have taken two rather divergent positions on the issue thus raised. One group (the rationalists) have held that we in the maze must have a kind of knowledge not gained by exploration within the maze, a supra-maze knowledge vouchsafed somehow from without. The other group (the empiricists) have held that the very knowledge by which we can justify our inductive procedures must itself be a product of those procedures, and that there is no supra-maze knowledge. Since my analysis of probability leads to the conclusion that statements of probability are themselves empirically testable, I am committed to the view that the justification of our inductions is based on the results of other inductions. Thus my position is that of empiricism rather than of rationalism. But it is not *any* kind of empiricism, as will be shown in the following section.

The System of Knowledge

There is an obvious paradox in the conjunction of the two statements: (1) inductive arguments are justified only by empirical probabilities; (2) empirical probabilities are known only through inductive arguments. The sense of para-dox is diminished, however, if one notices that the situation is not unlike that of the famous dispute over the chicken and the egg: the probabilities that justify an empirical argument are not the same as those that the argument justifies. Induction is the use of knowledge to gain more knowledge, and what we can learn on any occasion is limited by what we already know; there is a continuity in the development of knowledge, just as the tools we can make are limited by the tools we already have, the tools to make them with. In neither case can we make arbitrary innovations, and in neither case are we limited to a mere replication of what we already have.

Thus every justifiable induction presupposes some relevant antecedent knowledge. It may now be objected that there must be one or more initial inductions, which, being initial, cannot be justified, and, if other inductions depend upon these, they in turn are not justified, etc. In this way we might try to prove either (1) that no inductions are ultimately justified or (2) that there is some non-empirical knowledge that justifies at least some of our inductions without itself having to be justified.†

This argument has to be met by the observation that the process of induction begins, not in a vacuum of ignorance, but in a plenum of knowledge and of opinion, some of the last true and some of it false. Our starting point in the maze is never at the beginning but somewhere well along. The problem that faces us is not getting some knowledge, but getting more knowledge. The belief that there *must* be some sort of primary induction, which rests only on direct empirical evidence and not on any prior knowledge serving to channel the relevance of that evidence, is a plausible one.‡ It rests, however, upon a confusion of the temporal order of discovery with the logical order of relevancy. The latter order can be cyclical, but the former cannot. The latter order does not lead backward, to a beginning of ignorant inductions, but in many directions simultaneously, from any one belief that we might wish to test to other accepted beliefs. When I say that a belief is tested within the *system of knowledge,* I mean that a belief that is in doubt is confirmed or rejected by new empirical evidence when taken in the logical context provided by other beliefs within the system. Again we must put ourselves into the spaceship, and look for structures, not foundations.

This conception of the system of knowledge deserves some analysis. Not every statement made and believed in a society is part of the system. For, in the first place, many statements are so particular, so contextual or colloquial

---

† See Spinoza's comments on method in *The Improvement of the Understanding.*

‡ It is stated classically by Jean Nicod, *Foundations of Geometry and Induction* (New York, 1930).

in their form, that they cannot, without modification, become socially current or preserved through time. A certain measure of abstractness and formality is required for that linguistic standardization without which the conception of knowledge as a social precipitate and possession would be meaningless. Knowledge in this social sense has, moreover, a certain universality of relevance, so that one is tempted to say that the system of knowledge consists only of generalizations. But this is really not necessary, for statements can be singular in reference, like descriptions of the earth and other planets, or like historical statements, and still have social currency and endless relevance.

Aside from generality of relevance, the other implied characteristic of propositions in the system of knowledge is that they do form a system, that they are, in some measure, interconnected logically. An isolated statement may well be true, but it is not a part of the system of knowledge if it is truly isolated, having no relevance to other propositions in the system. In some cases the logical relations among beliefs within the system of knowledge are those of inter-deducibility. In other cases the logical relations are too loose to permit this kind of deducibility except by the introduction of new subordinate premises describing experiment and observation. In still other cases the logical relations among beliefs justify *probable* inference of the sort discussed in the present chapter. Finally, of course, the logical relations within the system of knowledge as a whole may be loose enough to justify our describing it as partially decomposable into sub-systems.

In view of this analysis, my previous account of the inductive maze may be modified. Its utility is that of an intuitive presentation of the theorem on progress in knowledge. Let us now conceive of the sector of the maze already traversed as defining the system of knowledge, with the proviso that the elements in it may be reformulated, combined, analyzed, and rearranged, and that such operations are justified, without any new empirical evidence, so long as they conform to the canons of logic. It is obvious that what we call the logical order in any branch of knowledge is different, in greater or lesser degree, from the temporal order of its historical development; this very reordering, moreover, is part of the history.

The Justification of Probable Inference

We are now ready to consider the problem left unsolved at the end of the section on the inductive maze. In what way, known to a participant in the inductive maze, can his decisions be justified? The most general possible answer, in my opinion, is the following: The participant can follow rules of decision, concerning which there is, within the system of knowledge accumulated up to that point, a basis for knowing the probabilities that they will lead him to make the correct decisions, and these probabilities show that the conditions of the progress theorem are satisfied. If this answer is not available in a specific case, a decision made on other grounds may be the correct one or may be made in such a way that it does, in reality, satisfy the conditions of the progress theorem; but this fact will not be known to the participant, and the decision will not, then and there, be justified. No doubt people very often *feel* justified in their inductive decisions, even though they are not able, consciously or explicitly, to give the justification; all they can consciously say is that a certain inductive step seems justified, or probable. But we are concerned with the logical discipline of inquiry, not with its practice on all occasions.

If the problem is stated in this way, it is obvious at once that the first two conditions of the progress theorem can generally be met and involve only the kind of probable inference discussed before. In my discussion of probable inference, however, I left a sharp division between *antecedent knowledge* and *hypothesis*. This division cannot now be maintained in an absolute way, for I am allowing that the system of knowledge may contain errors, and these errors may invalidate our probable inferences.

The crucial question, therefore, concerns the means of discovering error, of satisfying the third condition of the progress theorem. The simplest inductive procedure that provides for this is testing a hypothesis more than once or in more than one way. Usually one thinks of this as a way of reducing the probability of errors; but it is a way of discovering them as well. Suppose that, according to accepted belief, there are *two* good rules of inference about the same hypothesis, and that they lead, according to the data, to contradictory inferences. The situation provides us with an analogy, in the sphere of probable inference, to the *reductio ad absurdum* of deductive reasoning. Unless the sufficiently improbable has, in fact, happened, there must be some error in the antecedent knowledge that we brought to the inferences. If we call such a result a statistical contradiction, we may say, generally, that the signal for re-examination of propositions previously accepted into the system of knowledge is the occurrence of statistical contradiction. The progress theorem includes the condition, however, that the probability of going backward along an incorrect path (of seeking error in what has previously been wrongly accepted) must be greater than that of going forward—that is, greater than 1/2. Since our very beliefs about such probabilities may be infected with error, it is obvious that the third condition of the theorem cannot, in any particular case, be absolutely assured. Here we are forced back upon the viewpoint of an external observer of the process; it may be that the third condition is, in fact, satisfied, but this fact is not assured, at least not wholly assured, to the participant.

The logical organization of the system of knowledge is relevant at this point. The backward path taken in the search for error need not be, and in general is not, the same as the forward path of previous development. At any particular point the propositions relevant to the interpretation of experience are organized in a more or less coherent fashion, so that the occurrence of contradiction leads back, not along the path of history, but along a path of logical relevancy. The effect is to shorten the backward path and to provide guidance in the search for error. This may weaken considerably the statement of the third condition. Still, the third condition requires some positive probability of contradiction resulting from errors in the system, and this cannot be guaranteed.

The difficulty is not so serious as it may at first appear. In the first place, the system of knowledge has some generality of relevance, and the continuing practical experience of a society, relying upon it for guidance, spontaneously retests, in effect, the beliefs relied upon. An increasing total experience is a potential source of refinement in discrimination among alternative formulations. But social experience notoriously becomes canalized, and errors that can be made obvious only by exploration of the byways may go for long unrecognized. The spontaneous evolution of orderly knowledge is a slow process compared with the advances of science deliberately pursued. In the second place, when we classify errors according to the degree of probability that they will lead to statistical contradictions, this classification turns out, in the end, to be the same as a classification according to orders of approximation.

There will, first of all, be errors such that the probability of contradictions in later testing increases. If it becomes greater than $1/2$ for a sufficient number of steps, so that the average probability of going forward from the given error is less than $1/2$, the progress theorem will still hold. If not, then we shall be able to say that the errors thus incorporated are nearly irrelevant within the system. A characteristic error of this sort is of the kind that we call an idealization. The Ptolemaic astronomy, the phlogiston theory, and Newtonian mechanics are examples of theories that, although ultimately incorrect, proved perfectly adequate within a certain range of empirical tests and led to difficulties only in the context of additional knowledge from other sources and of further refinement of observation. We may therefore conclude that the system of knowledge is self-correcting up to the given level of refinement in the means of empirical testing to which it can be subjected. We find no absolute guarantee of progress available to us the maze-runners. In order to be relevant to new situations, our knowledge must extend beyond the range of previous tests of it. A world sufficiently complex and capriciously variable would frustrate the inductive method. Our knowledge and its progress are guaranteed only on sufferance of nature and of our own creative and imaginative capacities. A theory of induction that gave stronger guarantees than this would be suspect; for the uncertainties to which our analysis leads us are just the ones that are obviously there.

Analogy and Category

In a work referred to before, Carnap says, "Neither the classical theory nor modern theories of probability have been able to give a satisfactory account of and justification for the inference by analogy." † The statement is fair enough. Carnap's viewpoint is similar, apart from quantitative features, to that of John Maynard Keynes.‡ Here I shall not "justify" the inference by analogy, but only try to indicate how the subject may be discussed from a point of view essentially at variance with Carnap's.

In my treatment of probable inference there is a wide scope that has not been exploited in the present chapter. I have explicitly limited myself, in particular, to the probability of collocations as arrows that hit or miss propositional targets, and to a particular class of such arrows—those that are themselves inferences or guesses that hit or miss factual targets. My examples of the latter class have been choices among alternative hypotheses, already formulated and enumerated, the choices being justified by known conditional probabilities. The potential range includes, however, not only the choices among formulated alternatives but also the formulation of hypotheses, hypotheses *in statu nascendi*. My discussion of the inductive maze left this side of the scientific process, the creative side, out of account. Here the failure will be remedied, if only in a tentative way.

The suggestion to be considered is that the creative side of hypothesis-formation is essentially analogical. Most discussions of thinking or arguing by analogy start with the analogy as already given and go on to discuss its validity. This is parallel to the fact, already emphasized in this chapter, that most discussions of probability start with the proposition as already given. But the analogy is

---

† Rudolf Carnap, *Logical Foundations of Probability* (Chicago, 1950), p. 569.
‡ J. M. Keynes, *A Treatise on Probability* (London, 1921).

found before it is given, and the finding is a chancy process. Just as it is true that some propositions, as given, are probable, so it is true that some analogies, as given, confer an added, conditional probability on a proposition as given. But some propositions are probable, are credible, only in the sense that they are asserted under conditions such that what is true is likely to be asserted. And some analogies add to the credibility of what is asserted because they make it more likely that what is true will be asserted.

A field for illustration is mathematical discovery, mentioned above. Clearly, some procedures of conjecture are more likely to produce theorems than others, and conjectures produced by good procedures are more probable, more credible, than those produced by bad procedures. An essential stock-in-trade of the creative mathematician is a fund of analogies. He uses them in conjecturing what is likely to be true and in trying what may turn out to be a proof or a disproof. Everything depends, we feel, on finding the right analogy. We talk about the grounds of analogy, wide or narrow. We call one analogy deep, one superficial. As logicians use the term, an *argument* is the same as a sequence of deductive inferences. But, as we often use the term in practice, an argument is also partly an essay in persuasion, designed to get an auditor or reader to see an analogy and then to accept it. Deductions may then, but only then, follow. A mathematician might say, "Perhaps we should see this as a problem of iterated substitution" or "Perhaps this follows by a kind of Tauberian argument" or "It seems reasonable that this function should behave like log x."

One does not rely on such analogies. But then, again, one does. Reliance is a matter of stages. Creative mathematics relies on such analogies; otherwise it would not be creative. In the end a proof is found, and the sense of walking over a bridge has disappeared. But it would not have been found if someone had not "seen the problem in the right way," and that means finding a fruitful analogy. The analogy as first suggested is a hunch, a guess. It leads us to redescribe the problem; what fits the analogy is, for the moment, of the essence; what does not fit is accidental, to be put in the background. We try it out, but it does not work. We look for some other analogy.

Analogies that are frequently successful become wider paths, more often trod. Their patterns become familiar, described and labeled, formalized. After a while one says, not "A is like B and perhaps also has property X," but "A is a B' and therefore has property X." B' is now not the original analogy but an abstract of it, an essence from which incidental features have dropped away, and it involves X. The essence came to definition because it was the ground of many successful analogies. What was once reasoning by analogy was reconstructed and became subsumption under a general rule.

The pathway beaten through a good analogy becomes, in the end, an element in a formal deductive system. The terms in such a system, when applied to specific cases, are theory-loaded. Not all kinds of killing are to be punished, but murder is fraught with consequences—the logical consequences of its function within a system of criminal law. But the legally pre-formal, descriptive concept of killing had to be fraught with real and generally *similar* consequences before the legal concept could be elaborated.

The simile of the pathway is useful. The question how to organize, to formalize, is like the question how to keep people off the grass. The right method is to have no pathways at first, only grass. Then the paths will develop, and after a time one paves them. The figure is better if one supposes an ancient college campus, with walks already paved. Functions are moved, and new buildings are built for new functions. How are the paths to be modified?

Another limited analogy for the function of analogy is the evolution of a filing system. Routine items get filed routinely, or there is no system at all. But such a system is, in part, arbitrary. Items get filed together that could be apart, and apart that could be together. Difficult items accumulate, and cross-references become necessary. To put "earth" under "physical object" was once a new analogical surmise; then it was followed by a period of confusion when it was suggested that *the* earth (*qua* physical object) must fall toward Earth (*qua* cosmographic domain), and finally the older category of cosmographic domain had to be reconstituted or abolished.

Nuclei are found to split, and a liquid-drop analogy guides the theory. Quantum restrictions support the analogy: the drop must vibrate as a whole. Nuclear forces play the role of surface tension, and many quantitative or semi-quantitative conclusions are verified. The grounds of the analogy are good. Or again, particles interact with nuclei in a manner analogous to the optics of a clouded crystal ball.

Like the earth as a physical object is the analogy that underlies quantum mechanics, but here the trouble is still fresh and vivid. Such phenomena as particle diffraction and interference, and wave quanta, create first a logical repugnancy, a conflation of two different schemes of classification. Under these conditions the "essential" wave properties and particle properties get re-examined, and similarities are looked for. Similarities emerge and are elaborated. In wave physics the integral of an inverse phase velocity over a path is an extremum. In particle physics the integral of a momentum over a path is an extremum. When we find some way of relating the two sorts of integrand that have physical meaning, we are inventing quantum mechanics. There will still be a duality, but the old distinctions will be relegated to a subordinate place, like "down" or, for the modern astronomer, "sunrise."

Another new analogy is that of information and entropy, a major preoccupation of this book. Not only does the unification of these concepts extend the range of classical thermodynamics and statistical mechanics, but it extends it in such a way—as I shall argue in the following chapters—as to recast the whole conceptual structure of the scientific description of nature. The next chapter is an outline of the contemporary ideas about the origins of life, but it is also, obliquely, an argument designed to weaken the dichotomy of the mechanical and the teleological. The concept of information-transfer cuts across all the old boundaries; we shall follow its possible implications in psychology and in ethics, and in the social sciences.

The image of the filing system and the mode of its evolution will support one further suggestion. Taken broadly enough, the categories of knowledge, the major structural divisions of the filing system, suggest the role of philosophy in the division of labor that has traditionally been called metaphysics. The metaphysician seeks to understand the nature of things, the language of nature. It is my view, as it was Aristotle's, that the nature of things becomes accessible to human understanding only by reflection and not by any sort of direct confrontation with the universe. What we call knowledge in a positivistic sense, *Erkenntnis,* is constructed and tested out of cumulative experience. But it is constructed, it is an artifact; its mode of construction is human, and it bears the mark of style. Hence at any point in time it contains elements of the arbitrary, of cultural relativity, of ideology. But the system of knowledge is not an arbitrary collection of little facts, of *Erkenntnisse.* The system of knowledge, considered over and above its cash value of factual assertion, is the kind of mirror, of *speculum,* that gives the phrase "philosophical speculation" its old meaning. The categories of the filing system, according to which knowledge is organized, are the guide we have to the categories of Being.

In Chapter 2 we examined Kant's doctrine that the forms of spatial perception are *a priori,* independent of something called the sense manifold, which I likened to the direct input of a communications receiver. I argued against the belief that such sensory input can, in any intelligible sense, be said to receive form solely from some synthetic capacity of intuition, in accordance with *a priori* organizing principles. This belief implies that sensation is, *per se,* form-

Fig. 26. "Hand with Reflecting Globe" [*From* The Graphic Work of M.C.E. (*Oldbourne Press, London*) *with the permission of the artist, M. C. Escher*]

less. But the only sensory input that is formless is sheer random noise, and with such an input nothing is perceived at all. I would make here the same general criticism of the Kantian account of the categories of discursive knowledge. My argument is, very simply, that categories in this sense—ways of organizing knowledge in terms of causality, substance, magnitude, etc.—are evolved: we have these categories and not others because these facilitate flows of information as others would not; we evolve the channels to match the characteristics of the signal source, of nature.

Kant regarded the categories as mind-dependent and fixed, once for all. They were the constant organizing principles of variable experience. They were not learned by experience; they were prior to experience and facilitated the organization of experience into knowledge. Hence for Kant there was a proper skepticism about the metaphysical reach of the categories; metaphysics was a pursuit of an illusion. If the theory of knowledge is to limit itself to the short term, to an analysis of the static cross-section of experience, Kant was right. But what is constant and what is variable are functions of the time scale. The theory of knowledge does not have to be limited in this way; that is only a philosophical fashion. And on the longer time scale the articulation of categories, of basic analogies, is a variable that accommodates itself to massive experience, to the better recording and control of phenomena. But to say this is to return to Aristotle. The categories of knowledge reflect, however imperfectly, the nature of things.

These remarks are a sort of credo and not a close argument. But there is an argument, based on our probabilistic account of credibility. We return to the point that, though the refinement of analogy does not, in general, make what we believe more probably true, it does make it more probable that we shall believe what is true. If in this way there is an evolution of analogies into categories and of categories into altered categories, they make true belief more probable and are selected and survive by this merit; they do so because their articulation has been informed by man's environment. The patterns of thought and discovery may be relative to culture, but this fact loses its skeptical implications if we remember that they are part of culture and that culture evolves with them; culture is relative, in turn, to the universe.

10

THREE EVOLUTIONARY
STAGES

From the viewpoint of the physicist the order of nature falls into two great categories, the order of dynamical law and the order of contingent fact, of boundary conditions. Laws in the abstract do not describe nature except incompletely. They are complete in the sense already explained, in their own way; but this is not the only way. In the classical picture the rest was rather simply defined. Laplace's predicting intelligence, armed with a knowledge of dynamical law, had to know, in addition, only the positions and motions of the particles of matter in order to determine the behavior of the whole of nature.

The Demons

Against the background of relativity and quantum mechanics Laplace's notion seems incredibly naive. Because of the limiting velocity of light, information-bearing signals can be received by his Demon only after an appropriate lapse of time. If distant events initiate electromagnetic disturbances that will affect the Demon's predictions, he cannot know about those events *ex ante*. No information channel can be faster than the disturbances themselves. According to quantum mechanics, moreover, he cannot make the measurements that would be classically required without introducing new and irreducibly significant disturbances into the course of events.

But the Laplacean predicting Demon raises an interesting question when we put him in the context that Maxwell put him in: if the Demon himself is counted as part of nature, his effective functioning involves a violation of the second law of thermodynamics. The multiple initial conditions that the Demon must measure can be measured only at a cost in free energy that is proportional to the number of discriminations he has to make. If the Demon is to measure everything with perfect accuracy, the number of discriminations will be infinite. We must therefore restrict him to a finite accuracy of measurement in a finite world. Given enough free energy to begin with, the Demon can make his measurements and produce a map of the initial conditions. But the expenditure of this energy in gathering information will produce heat. If this heat is retained, it will distribute itself by equipartition among all the Demon's degrees of freedom and will decrease the reliability of the map. The Demon will melt! If the heat is radiated into the rest of the universe, it will change the boundary conditions, and the predictions will fail anyway. In short, a material Laplace Demon is impossible.

But there are demons with more modest ambitions; they can acquire information about some parts of their environment, using other parts of the environment as a system for disposing of wasted energy, of heat. These demons are what we call living things. Their heat dump is, ultimately, the blackness of space.

The question then arises whether the existence of such demons, of life, can itself be deduced from the dynamical laws. And the answer is clearly "no." Whether there is life or not does not depend on the laws, but on the boundary conditions. This is why, in the deistic theology, God arranged the initial conditions so that the particles would come together in such a way as to make living things. If he had arranged them differently enough, but under the same laws, there might be no life.

According to an outmoded philosophy of science, the study of dynamical law is fundamental, and biology is just fussing with detail, with boundary conditions. This is the same sort of fundamentalism that I discussed in connection with measurement. But, clearly, we have here a test of the adequacy of the "fundamental" laws; they must not exclude the *possibility* of life. Now, in point of fact, the classical laws exclude not only life but even simpler things, such as stable identical atomic and molecular species and crystals. We must therefore start with the quantum laws and with the new *scala naturae,* the quantum ladder. If the quantum laws are adequate, we must be able to find the possibility of life within the framework they provide. Whether the history of nature is such that life actually comes about is another matter.

Within the framework of quantum mechanics one does find the possibility of stable atomic and molecular species, of crystals. They are on the quantum ladder. Is life? It would be presumptuous to answer with textbook dogmatism, but so far the hypothesis is convincing and fruitful. What about the higher complexities of life, of perception, knowledge? For biology the presumptuous affirmative has a great deal of supporting evidence, which we shall review in this chapter. For psychology there are so far only clues, which we shall look at in the following chapter. If the progress of psychology in the next fifty years parallels that of biology in the last fifty, there will be some answers. It is in this sense that biology and psychology are more, rather than less, fundamental than *today's* physics. For in their progress they will test the adequacy of the present propositions of physics and may one day lead to the need for a revision of those propositions. But by that time there will be no invidious distinctions, no academic rivalries, and no pecking order among the sciences. Or, if there are still such diversions, they will be new ones.

Self-reproduction

In the last decade a revolution in biology has occurred. It is not the work of one man or the consequence of one idea. A number of lines of investigation have converged, and in their convergence a new pattern of thought has appeared. To explain it, we start outside the world of biology. The contrast between the living and the inert is so profound that it needs to be taken by stages.

The first stage might be to fabricate a cube of metal and give it to a physicist to investigate. "Here is a curious piece of metal," we say. "What can you find out about it in the physics laboratory?"

The cube is a sort of trick, a practical joke. Using standard evaporating techniques, we deposit a layer of some metal, ten atoms thick, on a smooth surface. Three metals are used to build up successive layers in this way, say copper, aluminum, and lead. After every ten atoms of thickness the metal being deposited is changed, but can then be either of the remaining two metals. The deposit is built up to a thickness of a centimeter, detached, and machined to a cubic shape.

There are about 32 essential typographic symbols in our fonts of type if we

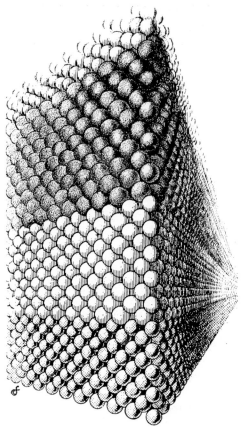

Fig. 27. Coded Cube of Metal

disregard capitals and a few other luxuries. In five layers of the cube, with two choices per layer, we have a total of $2^5 = 32$ choices. We make a code by assigning each of these choices to a typographic symbol. Building the metal to a thickness of one centimeter gives us room for about 3,000,000 layers or, at six letters per word and five layers per letter, 100,000 words. The physicist does not know it, but the cube we give him is a copy of *Huckleberry Finn*.

What would the physicist do with our cube to investigate its nature? Good and useful things, but not quite relevant. First there would be simple determinations, of density, of thermal and electrical conductivity, and a microsample for the chemist. Then there would be micrographs, showing some curious crystalline features, and X-ray diffraction studies, likewise a bit hard to interpret. But there would be nothing really extraordinary about the cube. When he was through, the physicist might use it as a paperweight—but he would not have read *Huckleberry Finn*.

To compound the trick, imagine the cube built not of uniform layers but of tiny cubelets, each ten atoms on an edge. Three million volumes could now be encoded in a single layer, and all the world's literature in a few layers. The whole cube could probably incorporate the literature of the Galaxy.

But let us keep to the point of view of the physicist and insist on asking what, from a purely physical point of view, is remarkable about this cube. What differentiates it physically from an ordinary metal cube? Well, of course, it is literature, which the latter is not. What then—still from a physical point of view—is literature? Because we keep things in compartments, the question seems a strange one, which neither physicists nor literary critics are likely to think proper; and this is the point of raising it: it is the sort of question that suggests something of the new way of thought in biology. Living cells contain vast molecular structures whose nature is rather like that of a book and whose complexity is of the same order, or greater. The characters of type are certain species of molecules, which, like the type or like the metal layers of our cube, can be put together in arbitrary sequences and thus provide a sort of biological code.†

This code governs the chemical activity of the cell and, as a culmination, the final act of mitosis, of self-reproduction. But, before becoming involved in the biology of reproduction, we should examine a simpler and more general question: how can *anything*, living or non-living, reproduce itself? The question takes us into the theory of computing machines and logical automata. It is discussed in a now classical paper by the late John von Neumann, who showed that a crucial part involved in the design of such a machine was, in a sense, rather like a book: not the metal cube or a printed volume, but a roll of punched paper or magnetic tape. He considered an automatic machine that was capable of assembling machine parts in a great variety of ways. Since this machine itself consisted of machine parts connected in a particular way, the self-duplicating machine seemed possible, so that the race of such machines might perpetuate itself.

But there are objections. One might reason that it would take a machine of moderate complexity to build even a rather simple machine, and a very complicated one to build another only moderately complicated. Perhaps, in general, a machine can be built only by one more complicated, and in that case the machine race is doomed to extinction. Neumann's analysis shows, however, that the essential trick is turned as soon as a machine is complex enough to use a punched tape on which is recorded an adequate description of itself.

First there must be a universe of machine parts, from which, by selection of the proper parts, any machine of a certain kind can be built. The self-duplicating machine will consist of three recognizable components: (1) a universal assembly machine capable of selecting parts from storage bins and putting them together in arbitrary combinations; (2) a punched tape, which contains the description of two particular machines and which, when fed into component 1, causes the latter to select the proper parts in the proper sequence and join them properly; (3) a second machine, which, when fed a punched tape, duplicates it.

There exists, at the outset, component 2, a punched tape that has the proper

† The analogy of the cube I owe to Philip Morrison.

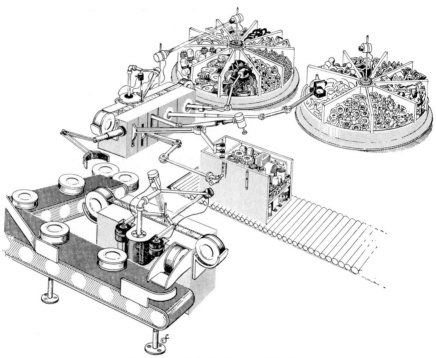

Fig. 28. A Self-duplicating Machine

instructions for producing machines 1 and 3. When it is fed into machine 1, a new machine 1 is produced and then a new machine 3. The tape is then fed into the initial machine 3, and a new tape, identical with the initial tape, is produced. The cycle is completed.

It is my contention that such a self-duplicating machine, though in no sense a living thing, indicates *something* essential about living things. Whatever else may be said about a living thing, this much may be said truly: a living thing is a system that contains within itself encoded information that will guide its own reproduction, including the reproduction of that very information.

I shall be criticized for treating life mechanistically, in spite of the cautionary words above, or for describing machines animistically. Indeed, I have already been talking animistically about machines. If the term "information" has been adequately generalized in previous chapters, it will cause no accusations. Information is a transfer of pattern, or a pattern transferred. In the Neumann machine there is transfer of pattern via a language or at least via a code. The description has no metaphysical depth in the present context, and I propose to continue it. There is never a settled language for novelties; and, if there is metaphysics in these analogies, the discussion of it must wait.

One confusion, however, must be avoided. In saying that the Neumann machine contains a complete description of itself, one means only that it contains a complete set of directions for reproducing itself. If self-reproduction requires 3,000,000 positions on the tape, each punched or not punched, the number of *possible* sequences of that length would be $2^{3,000,000}$. The taped description would cause the machine to select the right sequence out of this number. It could be read by a human being properly equipped and would be about as long as *Huckleberry Finn*.

It might take much more information than this to describe the Neumann machine in another sense—for the human designer of it in the first place or for the historian who discussed its subsequent career. But only one volume—3 million bits—of this more complete description would be needed by the machine itself to reproduce itself. Such information may be called *differential information*,† needed if one is to distinguish one out of a large number of assembly sequences, and no more.

The analogy of the Neumann machine with the living cell is straightforward, although the style of architecture and the mode of operation are profoundly different. The punched tape corresponds to the chromosomes in the cell nucleus. The assembly machine and the tape-duplicator correspond to phases, fairly distinct, in the performance of the rest of the cell, the cytoplasm. The bin of parts is the surrounding nutrient of the cell, whose wall is engineered to accept certain molecules from the ambient fluid. In the cytoplasm at any time are molecules of many kinds, which can interact to form new molecules. Among them are energy-rich structures capable of driving reactions, to the products of which they transfer some of their energy. Among them also are rate-controlling molecules, enzymes whose variety and concentrations determine which reactions, of the enormous number possible, will predominate. These catalysts are like little assembly machines that bring things together in specific orientations, facilitating associations and dissociations that would otherwise go much more slowly. And catalysts are catalyzed; the original catalyst is the set of chromosomes themselves. Like the tape of the Neumann machine, moreover, the chromosomes catalyze the production of molecular machinery that duplicates them, in the end, and starts a new cell on its career.

The genetic material, the catalyst of catalysts, exhibits one of the most characteristic architectural themes of biochemistry. Whereas most inorganic molecules and crystals are essentially three-dimensional structures, the characteristic

---

† The total information, if it can be defined at all, is transferred through the environment of the tape—that is, the machine itself and the rest of the universe.

biochemical big molecule is a linear chain, a string when stretched out, but often coiled as a helix: such is the material of which chromosomes are built, desoxy-ribose nucleic acid (DNA). Each molecule is a very long double chain with cross-links, like a twisted rope ladder with rungs close together. Each cross-link consists of two links, one of a type called purine and the other called pyrimidine. In DNA there are two purines, A and G, and two pyrimidines, T and C. Purine A forms a cross-link only with T, and G only with C; we have, there-fore, four distinct cross-links: AT, TA, GC, and CG.

At this point the analogy of the metal cube and the punched tape comes into its own: the cross-links are code symbols in a four-letter code, and in n successive rungs of the ladder 4^n messages can be coded. With the rungs spaced as closely as they are, a few hundred-millionths of a centimeter apart, there are a billion or so loci to be filled in the chromosomes of a single animal cell. Within these loci is written the book of life. In some way still not understood in detail, the sequence of cross-links in the DNA helix acts through a sequence of stages as a guide or template for the fabrication of myriad enzymes. And here the sense of analogy is very strong; for the detailed problem is to crack the code, and the chief statistical technique for doing so is, in essence, cryptanalysis.

The enzymes are linear arrays composed of the twenty essential amino acids of which proteins are built. They are abstracts from the parent catalyst, and they direct the chemistry of the cell. Their number is currently estimated at about a hundred thousand for human cells, slightly less for other animal species. The number may be much greater. Each is informed by, and in that sense is the translation of, some corresponding section along the chromosome fibers, and it is these sections that are called genes. If the chromosomes are comparable to volumes of a great encyclopedia or formulary, the genes are the separate articles.

The structure of DNA is of recent discovery.† Still more recent investigations support the conjecture that the all-important reproduction of the chromosome is a process in which it comes unzipped down the middle between the two halves of each purine-pyrimidine pair. Each half chromosome is the unique comple-ment of the other; each attracts, from the ambient fluid, the complementary purines and pyrimidines, and a new side chain forms. After chromosome divi-sion, cell division takes place.

Many of the small steps and some of the big ones in this process of cell-reproduction are only partly understood, and there may still be big surprises. The general outline seems, however, to be secure. In terms of this outline it is

---

† See the report of the discoverers, J. D. Watson and F. H. C. Crick, in *Nature*, 171 (1953), p. 964. See also Proc. Royal Soc., A, 223 (1954), p. 80.

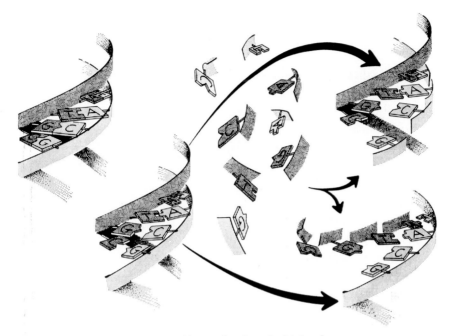

Fig. 29. Self-reproduction of a Molecule

possible to give a general and very abstract characterization of life. And this characterization brings us back to information theory, to the Maxwell Demon, and to the thermodynamic relations between information, entropy, and free energy.

The thermodynamic concept of equilibrium—the state, characterized by maximum entropy, toward which any isolated system tends in the long run—implies the equipartition of the total energy of the system among all possible modes of energy, potential and kinetic. In a system consisting of many chemical species equilibrium implies, in particular, statistical abundance for each compound—that is, the abundance in which the rate of formation of the compound's molecules is just equal, statistically, to the rate of their dissociation. Under conditions of equilibrium the typical organic big molecules are exceedingly rare, often so rare that, in a vat of the size of the ocean, the existence of even a single molecule is extremely improbable. It is this thermodynamic rarity, raised to a high power for any single living thing, that makes life appear to be a miracle.

It is one of the classical austerities of thermodynamics, moreover, that abundances in equilibrium are unaffected by catalysts of any kind, which merely alter the rate at which a system approaches equilibrium. But the atmosphere and the vat of ocean are not in thermodynamic equilibrium; the earth is a way-station between the sun and the blackness of space, and there is a constant source of free energy in the temperature differences between incoming and outgoing radiation.

A kind of equilibrium results, but it is not the equilibrium of an isolated system. The term commonly used for it is *steady state*. The metal plug with a heating coil transfers heat to the surrounding disk (see p. 191), and after a time there is a stationary temperature distribution that is characteristic of this system. Such states may, like that of true thermodynamic equilibrium, be characterized by extremal principles like that of maximum entropy. The translational motion of the air behind a rotating propeller sets up large turbulent cells of swirling air. These interact with one another and with the surrounding air to make more, and smaller, cells, and so on down through a hierarchy of cell sizes. Finally the cells are so small that they cannot break up into smaller cells, and the energy is transferred to Brownian motion. The many way-stations of turbulent motion constitute a path of flow between ordered motion of air and heat. A river cuts straight, but, when cutting has done its work and gradients decrease, the river fills its own channel. Then meandering begins, leaving no depression unexplored. In the approach to steady-state equilibrium there is a principle of maximum deviousness analogous to the meandering river. For suggestiveness, with an eye to the traditions of metaphysics, it might be called a principle of plenitude.

The steady state involves a thermodynamically unidirectional flow, and its steadiness is the steadiness of pattern, like that of the waterfall or the candle flame, a kind of frozen history. The concept is applicable approximately to many kinds of systems. Component processes go on at very different rates, and the quasi-stationary patterns that appear change slowly and give way to new patterns. Every relatively stable part that appears is a catalyst of new processes. There is cumulative change, an evolution of nature, a history. Under these conditions the whole problem of abundance in different component phases becomes vastly more complicated than in thermodynamic equilibrium. The classical austerities of thermodynamics are lost, but in place of them we have the familiar world, not only the biologist's book of nature but also the geologist's and the astronomer's.

At terrestrial temperatures some of the species that form are supramolecular in any ordinary sense—macroscopic crystals knit together in the crust, not in perfect equilibrium but evolving on a geologic time scale. Under these circumstances macroscopic as well as microscopic configurations become significant, as in the record of old sediments that have never been completely metamorphosed. It is at this level that order and arrangement have informed men's thinking first of all, and only gradually have we realized the historicity of things on the ultra-microscopic scale. Under steady-state conditions new niches in the ecology of molecular species are first created and then filled. Whether or not this means an over-all change for the entropy of the earth system is a difficult question; all the second law requires is that, if the entropy decreases, it decrease at a rate limited by the power supply of solar energy.† This is not a question that can be dealt with, so far at least, on a high plane of abstraction. For some sub-phases of the system, clearly, a decrease of entropy is implied. If in the earliest history of the earth the biogenic elements existed mainly in simple compounds, then, by their being locked into place in the great organic molecules of living matter, vanishingly few in kind compared with what is chemically possible, their entropy is vastly decreased. Some favored few configurations have their probabilities increased, and the great majority are pushed near zero. Nature is informed by its own development.

The component of entropy we are interested in here is that associated with spatial configuration, the entropy of arrangement. It applies to things that have some sort of structure and refers to order in this spatial sense. A diamond crystal has a lower entropy of arrangement than an equal mass of diamond dust. A piece of iron magnetized has a lower entropy of arrangement than the same iron with its atoms randomly disoriented.

In a living cell some part of the total arrangement at a given moment is simply random, thermal ordering. But a large part is genetically determined and would be different with a different genetic code and even more radically different with no code at all.

The negative entropy of a cell is the abstract measure of the planfulness of its molecules and the orderliness of its functioning. Patterns of molecular arrangement, encoded in the DNA, are transferred repeatedly to constituents of the cell. Being formed to a pattern rather than assembled at random, the molecules of each species within the cell have a very low entropy of arrangement. When the supply of them has increased sufficiently and the DNA duplicates itself as well,

---

† As we noticed in the discussion of temporal irreversibility, radiation leaving a star expands spherically without appreciable interactions in space. The energy density is inversely proportional to the square of the radius of this sphere, but the individual photons are characteristic of the higher temperature at the surface of the star. In the degradation to earth temperature, the radiation entropy increases. This initial negative entropy may be lost, or it may pay for a decrease in the entropy of photocatalyzed molecules in photosynthesis by green leaves. See Erwin Schrödinger, *What is Life?* (New York, 1944). For calculations of the income, in coin of the realm, see Wesley Brittin and George Gamow, "Negative Entropy and Photosynthesis," Proceedings of the National Academy of Sciences, 47, No. 5 (May, 1961), pp. 724–27.

the two daughter cells resulting from fission are, in essence, identical twins; bar-ring accidental variations or mutations, their DNA and their other constituents are replicas. But this means that the genetic entropy of arrangement, in the two cells considered together, is no greater than that of either one alone; and the specific genetic entropy, the entropy per cell, is half as great as it was before.

The lowering of entropy in such systems corresponds, however, to a greater free energy, a greater capacity to do work. The second law of thermodynamics asserts that such an increase of free energy cannot come about spontaneously; it can come about only if there has been a loss, at least as great, of some other kind of free energy. The free energy that is lost is chemical energy, constantly re-newed from the food supply and constantly expended in the work of self-duplica-tion. It is lost only in a relative sense. Part of it is stored in the chemical bonds of the cell's constituents; part of it is truly lost, converted to heat without any compensating reduction of entropy; the part we are interested in is not lost. For by the ordering it has brought about it can be recovered again to do work.

The quantities involved in this thermodynamic bookkeeping have not all been well measured, but the upshot of rough estimations, according to Philip Morri-son, is that a sizable part of the power input of living matter is accounted for by the work necessary in the duplication of structure and in the reduction of entropy that this duplication involves.

It might be found, indeed, that the total power supply of the cell is *less* than what is needed to produce this increment of order. We should then be faced with the possibility, sometimes entertained by vitalists, that life is a standing violation of the second law of thermodynamics. Probably, however, the free energy of reproduction is more like a tenth or a hundredth of the total available. Whatever the fraction, it is a large proportion of the total and enormous com-pared with the corresponding energy in any non-living system that can split or in some other way increase the number of its parts. For most such systems the free energy involved is even negative; the increase in the number of parts goes along with an increase of entropy.

Even for the Neumann machine the free energy of reproduction, though posi-tive, would be utterly negligible against what was needed for the gross oper-ation. For this free energy is proportional only to the amount of order created. If a Neumann machine weighing tons and consuming kilowatts of power man-aged to be anywhere nearly as complex as a cell, if its tape had to be as many words long as the DNA, its free energy of reproduction would be no greater than that of the tiny cell. It seems, therefore, that life has to be chemical in its operation and microscopic in its organization. Only in such a structure is it possible to operate without the creak and grind of energy-wasting macroscopic processes.

A living system is a system that contains a complete differential description of itself and in which the free energy of reproduction is comparable to the total free energy. Only in living matter, so far as we know, is this proportion large; elsewhere in nature it is utterly trivial.

Stage One: From Molecule to Cell

The distinction between the living and the non-living is still incomplete. It is sufficient, however, to reveal a separation, a gap, in nature. On the scale labeled "specific free energy of reproduction" living things cluster in the region of one-tenth, 10^{-1}. Non-living things range from near zero—perhaps 10^{-20}—into the negative region of the scale. And there is nothing in between. The theory of evolution implies, however, that the gap diminishes toward the past. Until recently the theory of evolution started with the hypothesis of single-cell life and left its antecedents to speculation. But a single cell is already so complex that colonies, organisms, and even man are only slightly more so, on the thermodynamic scale. To close the gap, if we can, we must go into the pre-Cambrian era. In that era, unfortunately, the fossil record is very dim.

Let us start, instead, with a second look at the Neumann machine. Its self-reproduction is completely controlled, so that the daughter machine is a replica of the parent. If the generations are not infinite, there must have been a first, and the first must have come about differently. One is faced with the problem of creation. Neumann suggested that, in the process of copying tapes, little errors might occur, the analogues of genetic mutations. These might be gross, so that the daughter machine could not reproduce; or the mutant machine might still be fertile, and natural selection could operate.

Clearly, however, such a process of mutation and selection will not account for the origin of *Machina Neumannensis*. For *any* self-reproducing machine must have a considerable minimum complexity; this gap must be jumped in some other way. It was in a similar condition that Darwin, apart from suggestive remarks, left the origin of life. Like the simplest Neumann machine, a living cell cannot evolve and become differentiated into species until it is already complicated enough to be capable of self-reproduction.

The answer in the case of the Neumann machine is evident. On every such machine there is a small brass plate, reproduced along with everything else and saying: *Neumann me fieri fecit.* This machine is an offshoot of a new kind from the previous evolutionary tree, a twig from the branch of Man and symbiotic with him. Its pedigree does not begin in the twentieth century, but billions of years ago, in the tide pools of the pre-Cambrian. It is not alive; but it is complex enough, in the sense in which life is complex, so that it can hardly exist against a less ancient and distinguished background.

Aristotle was right: order can come only from order. *Machina Neumannensis* can be explained only as the product of an external cause, as Aristotle explained the bed and the house. Perhaps man's earliest living ancestor cannot be explained except similarly, as a miracle.

There are two kinds of miracles, according as they violate the first law of thermodynamics—the principle of the conservation of energy—or the second law. The origin of life may seem to be in violation of the second law, for the chance assembly of matter into a self-reproducing cell appears so improbable that no sober scientific logic could distinguish it from the impossible. The second law says (just as Aristotle did) that the entropy of an isolated system will not spontaneously decrease, and that is just what the appearance of life seems to involve.

The argument against a spontaneous appearance of the Neumann machine seems to hold, in fact, of life *a fortiori;* for, as we have seen, the free energy of reproduction is much greater per pound of living matter than per pound of the Neumann machine: life is more highly organized than the machine.

But the argument works both ways. The Neumann machine is a probable sort of thing in the industrial world of the twentieth century. Do we know that life was not a probable sort of thing in the conditions that existed on the earth two or three billion years ago? At temperatures probably not very different from those that prevail today, in an atmosphere containing things like ammonia and methane but no oxygen, sunlight and its subsidiaries, such as lightning, would produce energy-rich carbon compounds of considerable complexity—for example, the amino acids. This has been demonstrated repeatedly.† In such a milieu a complex carbon-dominated molecular evolution would occur. Oparin and others have argued that the main error in most previous discussion of the origin of life was the unconscious assumption that the environment was similar to the present inorganic environment.‡ One must, on the contrary, assume a previous chemical evolution of great length, some of whose molecular products are the basic chemicals of life today. Applied to that early period, the term "non-

---

† See S. L. Miller, "A Production of Amino Acids under Possible Primitive Earth Conditions," *Science,* 117 (1953), pp. 528–29.

‡ A. I. Oparin, *The Origin of Life,* a translation from the Russian (New York, 1952).

living" is as inappropriate as the term "living," for by the former we tend to mean the simple environment of today. Life and its environment have evolved together; the old environment was, quite literally, eaten up.

Under such conditions of chemical environment, moreover, one may postulate a fairly simple mechanism that is self-reproducing, a double chain structurally like the genetic material of life, DNA. Random DNA, in which the enzyme code has been scrambled, has been made in the laboratory. We may take this as a model for the first self-reproducing molecules. They come apart, and each part picks up its complement, bit by bit, from the environment; in place of one such molecule, there now are two. And soon there will be four, eight, and so on until the "food" supply becomes a limiting factor.

This self-reproducing molecule is, thermodynamically, the absolutely basic turn of events. Here is a molecule of two parts bracketed, [AB]. Each part uniquely defines the other, and therefore their total entropy of arrangement is no greater than that of either one considered by itself. They come apart, and each, in a process with many individual steps, rebuilds a complement. As this process is repeated, the orderliness of a region of the universe increases, its entropy of arrangement decreases. Free energy flows in, heat flows out, and an increment of order is left behind. The principle of the self-reproducing molecule is a new law of thermodynamics, one whose formulation marks the confluence of two great nineteenth-century traditions, the traditions of thermodynamics and evolution, of Maxwell and Darwin.

The self-reproducing molecule removes one thorny problem about origins. Living things did not come first and later acquire the capacity to reproduce. This would indeed have been miraculous, for biological learning—spontaneous variation and natural selection—presuppose reproduction. Living things did not learn to reproduce themselves; rather, things that reproduced themselves learned to live.

A self-reproducing molecule, even though internally inert and externally naked, is subject to the Darwinian principles of variation and selection. At the stage when such reproduction became limited by a scarcity of raw materials, some DNA-like molecule suffered a chance mutation of order among the cross-links of the chain, and this region of its structure became the first gene; the molecule catalyzed the formation of the new molecules needed for its own reproduction. The molecule tapped a previously untapped reservoir, and its descendants flourished.

But I should not call such a system "life." Like the modern virus, it was internally inert. If the term "life" is to be applied to this stage, it should be applied

to the whole tide pool or perhaps to the whole ocean. There was still no differentiation between organism and environment. Life appeared, I should say,
when the self-reproducing molecule and the reactions that it catalyzed—by then
a whole system of them—became encapsulated in a membrane that gave its
possessor a new advantage. The membrane increased the concentration of materials and therefore raised the reaction rates of the processes involved in reproduction.

The description of such membranes involves us in a new application of
thermodynamic ideas. The semipermeable membrane, which admits one
molecule and excludes another, is an informed membrane; it exists in a specific
relation to the environment: its entropy is lower. The cell is discriminating,
selective; it sets itself over against its environment, is not merely an inert element in an ensemble. It is a microcosm that maintains commerce with the
world and is not just kicked around. It is alive.

In modern organisms there are some very long reaction chains, from simple
raw materials to complex "consumer goods." In the new framework of thought
these chains evolved backward, from final product to present-day raw materials. At first everything was provided from the previous stage of purely
chemical development, in a sort of aquatic Garden of Eden. As in the social
evolution of economic systems, more steps of fabrication appeared, and raw
materials became simpler in structure. Man may, before long, learn to produce
his own food supply independently of the green plants. Life as a whole became
independent of the earlier chemical stage of evolution when these same green
plants, the photosynthesizers, appeared.

This conception of backward development takes care, in principle, of another
weighty argument against evolution. The long biochemical reaction chains
need many enzymes, which imply many evolutionary steps, before the useful
final product appears. Since the biological utility of the whole chain depends
upon the appearance of the last member, the intermediate steps would have
given no evolutionary advantage and would not have evolved. N. H. Horowitz
pointed out, however, that in backward biochemical evolution, from product to
raw material, every step has utility; for every step taps a new source of supply.†

Is this account of the origin of life science, or is it mere speculation? I give a
cautious answer and say that it is not *mere* speculation. Some of the guidelines
are well-established, but the historical account itself is not. A better question is:
Can this account be tested, and is it open to continuing research? The geological

† N. H. Horowitz, "On the Evolution of Biochemical Syntheses," Proc. Nat. Acad. Sci., 31 (1945),
pp. 153–57.

record, so far back, is pretty completely erased; but, as Aaron Novick suggested,† it is not inconceivable that ancient DNA may one day be found in rocks, and even revitalized.

But there is another source of evidence, still largely unanalyzed. The backward evolution of chemical reaction chains means that such a chain, and the genetic code that controls it, is itself a historical record. As gross comparative anatomy permits the reconstruction of recent evolution, so comparative biochemistry and the micro-anatomy of genes and enzymes will extend the range. We and our biological contemporaries are, all of us, history books. Naturalists have marveled at the inventiveness of life—the craftsmanship of the spider, the husbandry of the ant, the vector language of the bee. But here, surely, is a marvel beyond all others—that life has kept, through a billion years, the written chronicle of its own career.

The cell wall is the end of a chapter and the beginning of a new one. It is an incipient sense organ. Evolution constructs it to fit an environment—with, at first, a kind of average fit. For the environment is variable, and in a later evolution the cell gains advantage by mechanisms that react differentially to changes in what comes through the wall. The biochemical mechanisms of this responsiveness are encoded in the genetic record and passed on. One is tempted to use the word "learning" for such adaptations, but the word is not right. The genetically transmitted information by which a species is able to take account of its environment is not an achievement of that species; rather, the species is an achievement of the information. The learning is not in the life of the individual but in the transition to a new species. The individual, like the soul in Plato's account of it, may *know* but does not *learn*. If the species learns, it does so only by becoming a new species.

Stage Two: The Verb "to Learn"

Cells are perhaps automatically responsive to one of the crucial variables of the environment, the existence of other cells. If a cell wall traps some molecules and excludes others, the first effect is a competition for nutrients, and this limits the population per unit volume. But cells may affect one another by their excretions as well as by their depletion of the environment. Because they are all variations on the same few biochemical themes, the coexistence of cells is a potent factor in the evolution of each of them. Whether as symbionts, predators, or prey, they are coupled more and more strongly to one another in an ever-

---

† In a private communication.

changing ecology. Organisms appear, and within them specialized cells and tissues. Whether in the protozoans, the most complex forms still classified as cells, or in multicellular organisms, something that may be called learning appears. In the more complex forms the nervous system appears, and with it reinforcement and inhibition. It should not be supposed, however, that this is the only mechanism of its kind. Even at the purely chemical level we find mechanisms that store acquired information, notably in the phenomena of immunology. The watchdog mechanisms of the body distinguish between proper and alien proteins, attacking the latter and tolerating the former. In his discussion of the recently discovered phenomenon of experimentally induced tolerance Sir Macfarlane Burnet has introduced the concept of immunological self-recognition. Antibody-producing mechanisms are informed, at an early stage, by the ensemble of proper proteins. Like a system of passwords, this information protects them from antibody reaction later on. Investigations of this order are typical of contemporary discoveries in the new microbiology and demonstrate its essentially information-theoretic character.†

To recur to the Neumann machine for analogy, let us suppose that it not only was self-reproducing but had to function in a complex and variable environment. The equipment with which to face this environment could be incorporated in it, but only at the cost of a longer tape, and at some point the tape could no longer be extended. At this point a new possibility would appear, however. We could encode on the original tape, instead of all the detail of response to environmental contingencies, the construction of a new component with a new tape of its own, a *learning* machine, and make provision, perhaps, for a sheltered infancy.‡ The point of the innovation is that the code description of a machine that learns, that acquires information from and about the environment, can be small compared with what the machine learns. Subtleties of behavior that exceed the capacity of the original tape can be learned, can be recorded; and they can be learned within the life-span of the original machine rather than at the slow pace of natural selection.

When such a step occurred in the evolution of animal species, an essential limitation upon all previous evolution was removed: the self-reproducing molecule was no longer burdened with the organism's entire stock of vital informa-

---

† See the Nobel Lectures of Peter Brian Medawar and F. M. Burnet in *Science,* vol. 133 (Feb. 3, 1961), 3449.

‡ Some part of the detailed circuitry, as well as the gross anatomy of the nervous system, is genetically determined. In terms of our analogy some part of the new tape is transcribed from the old. The development of embryological science is not yet sufficient for us to say where and how genetic control leaves off and learned control takes over.

tion. The importance of such a step is comparable to that of the beginning of life itself, and the step deserves to be called the second main stage of evolution. It has little or no significance in the plant world; but, tied to the sensory-motor equipment of multicellular animals, it became a dominant theme of evolution thereafter.†

The simplest learning mechanisms are of an obvious kind and are quite mechanical in their operation. In the conditioned reflex and in the switching mechanism that is the basis of the large digital computer, the essential thermodynamic condition is again the availability of free energy for the performance of entropy-reducing, order-increasing work. The switching mechanisms transmit flows of energy larger than the incoming signals that direct their behavior. Through reinforcement and inhibition, relatively simple stimuli come to release complex responses adapted to the character and behavior of the environment. The patterning of such responses represents, *vis-à-vis* the environment, a lowered entropy of arrangement.

Such a description of learning, of human learning or even of most animal learning, may be absurdly reductionistic. But, whatever else may be involved in such learning, its outcome is one of which this simple, reductionistic account will hold.

In spite of such learning's limited, mechanistic character, in spite of the images of relays and vacuum tubes that the comparison evokes, simple systems of this kind have features that ought not to be ignored. Being causally open systems, whose future functioning is contingent upon intervening signals received from the environment, the machines are unpredictable in their behavior except as we manage to anticipate what their experience will be. After it has been functioning, learning, for a time, the inner form of such a system is unknown to us; information has been written on the *tabula rasa* of its recording tape. It is more than the mechanism that was assembled. A part of its order is the order that was designed into it; but a part is the order, not of the drafting table, but of a universe, to which the machine responds and from which it gathers information. In this respect, one might suggest, the machine already has that aspect of *soul* that appears in Aristotle's system of ideas. To speak of life, especially of human life, in a machine language is commonly thought to deny it

---

† By estimates that are, of necessity, *very* crude one can conclude that the information-storage capacity of the animal nervous system is of the same order of magnitude as that of the genes. A crucial difference is, of course, in the rate of adaptation in the two cases. The genetic variety at any one time is limited to the size of the "pool" of alleles, of variant genes. The "cognitive" variety is limited, as J. S. Mill saw in his famous essay *On Liberty,* to the analogous pool of variant ideas.

the aspect of soul. It is more cogent to impute this very aspect to the machine that learns. In some ways, indeed, we are rather close to Aristotle, or at least we parallel him at a distance. The genetically informed organism has a "vegetative" soul; the mechanisms we are now speaking of, informed by learning, correspond to the Aristotelian soul that is "sensory" and "locomotive."

Here there are other issues at stake, of course, which it would be wrong to ignore. In the first section of this chapter the mechanistic description of life was defended, but so equally was the animistic description of the Neumann machine. In the Aristotelian tradition the soul is described as the form of the body, and by "form" is meant all the habitudes and capacities of that body. If one body can metabolize and another cannot, the former can be called a living thing and the latter not. If one body can sense and react, self-moving, it can be called an animal in contrast to one that cannot. If one body can possess and exercise principle, or reason, it can be called a person. Only equivocally is it, in each case, a body that has these capacities. In the first case it is a plant, in the second an animal, and in the third a man. These are just as different from one another as their capacities show them to be. It is because of this Aristotelian influence on Christianity—in part, at least—that there must be a literal reincarnation; the soul *functions* only as a body informed. One would have to visualize its interim state, it may be suggested, as that of being somewhere encoded; it is, *qua* soul, a potentiality, not a substance.

Popular Christianity has never elected this view, and has perhaps not been very strongly urged to elect it. The view that has prevailed has been the dualism of substances. In reaction to the metaphysics of seventeenth-century physics, the other substance, the soul, became even more the repository of all those capacities of which matter, it was alleged, was incapable. But, as Spinoza remarked, no one has been able to demonstrate that of which an automaton—it would be better to say, in our perspective, an informed body—is incapable.

In my earlier defense of the blurring of mechanistic-vitalistic categories I stated that the analogies appealed to were without metaphysical depth. But, if they flourish in science, and if metaphysics is a commentary on the nature of things via an analysis of the fundamental categories, then the scientific necessity to blur—more precisely, to dissolve and reconstruct—these categories will inevitably have metaphysical depth.

There is still another dualism, one that we have not yet faced and from which that of the mechanical and the vital undoubtedly draws much of its sustenance. For this reason metaphysics must again be postponed until we can consider the problem of human self-consciousness.

I have emphasized the separation, in the self-reproducing machine that also learns, between genetic information and information learned. In self-reproduction the tape that guides the process is copied, but the tape that records the biography of the individual machine is not. A new machine must first face the world in innocence, guided only by inherited reflexes. What is learned is lost and must be learned again in each generation. There results a steady state, an average level of sophistication. As in our hypothetical machine, so with the animal species. Sophistication is almost zero for the paramecium, low for the ant and the bee, higher but still bounded for doves and lions. Life in the first stage can transmit structure and variation of structure, but it cannot learn; life in the second stage can learn, but it cannot transmit what it learns.

It was remarked by August Weismann—and possibly first by Goethe—that death is a biological invention associated with sexual reproduction. Death provides damage insurance for the precious genetic record of multicellular life, while rendering that life more adaptive than the immortal cell. Death is, genetically, the servant of life. Only at the second stage of evolution does death become poignant. The accidental death of a cell loses nothing to the world; but the death of any learned organism is, in principle, a loss of something unique.

Stage Three: Culture

The capacity to learn is an externalization of function, the creation outside the cell nucleus of a new way of acquiring and storing vital information. The nucleus has its limitations, of information capacity and rate of evolution. The capacity to learn has its limitations too, of which the dominant one is death. The stage is set, at last, for a further externalizing of function, not only extra-nuclear but even extra-organic. This stage, the stage of culture, is dominated by *Homo sapiens* and his late ancestors. In this stage learned information is incorporated into the environment, and from that environment recovered and extended. If a sheltered environment merely protects the young animal in his first learning, this is not yet culture. If he learns in an environment altered by parental and social influence, learning shades over into education, and this is culture. Culture is information transmitted extra-organically through material artifacts and social influence. The bees can build a hive. To the extent that this ability is genetically transmitted, it is not culture. If any of it is learned in the context of a pre-existing hive, so much of the vital information of bees has been transmitted without benefit of DNA, and this is culture. It is the evolution of these capacities that removes the main limitation of the second stage. Cultures may die, as cells may; but death is not built into them, as it is into multicellular animals. And through cultures learning becomes cumulative, evolutionary.

Various animal societies may be characterized by the level of culture they achieve, may be defined by the ratio of culturally to genetically transmitted information. Bee culture at a low level, beaver culture at a higher level, chimpanzee culture at a still higher level—these reach a stage beyond which they do not go. Culture enhances the individual capacity to learn, but only to a degree. The parasitic culture of dogs, absorbing information from the host culture of man, may reach a higher level than the culture of dogs in the wild state. But, once reached, the equilibrium level of animal culture can change only at the slow pace of biological evolution.

In our own ancestry, nevertheless, this upper bound ceased to be effective. From some point on, the level of culture could rise at a rate determined by its own dynamism. The third great stage of evolution is marked, within a single genus, by the appearance of a new *mode* of evolution, non-biological and more rapid by orders of magnitude than the biological mode.

What are the distinctive characteristics of man that, considered biologically, remove the limitations upon cultural evolution? We all know the list: upright posture; coordination of hand and eye; coordination of voice and ear; increased capacity of the forebrain; changes of the sex impulsion. There are many other, minor ones. Some of these changes seem obvious necessary conditions. That they are sufficient is too strong a claim. Perhaps it is possible, however, to describe the change in some simple and meaningful way, even though we cannot define all the crucial conditions. The other animals learn, but man also transmits what he has learned: he teaches. The other animals modify their environment by living in it, but man also remakes his environment. The other animals copy the order of the world within themselves; they live, as the old phrase says, in accordance with nature. But the individual man has greater freedom from the immediate dictates of perception and desire. He likewise copies the order of the world, but he is productive, poetic; he makes artifacts, tools to make artifacts, and tools to make tools. Man likewise makes myths. And in all of these activities he is transferring order to a social and material environment. The storage of vital information is no longer solely in the cell nucleus, or in the brain, but in the environment. A new externalization of function has occurred, and in the measure of it nature lives in accordance with man. In the measure of this externalization, also, man learns what he has himself produced. A knowledge that is self-knowledge has become possible; a soul "is mirrored there where it may see itself." †

The complement of this externalization is a new sense of internalization. What is externalized must again be internalized. The human infant develops toward physiological maturity in an environment that transfers to him the distinctively cultural attributes, notably the use of language. This acculturation goes so deep that one is led to describe our primary biological nature as clay, humanly informed only after parturition. One is led to say that human nature is all second nature. But, if so, even if this is only a penetrating half-truth, we need to hold fast to the broadest meaning of "information." Another old word, less simplified in present popular usage, is "instruction." The genetic code instructs the cell, and the closest counterpart in human language is the imperative mood, not the indicative. The human infant and child is instructed in this etymological sense, and in being internalized the instruction does not lose its imperative mood. The human being sees himself reflected in the world but not as an object of detached contemplation. He sees himself in terms of love and hate, approval and disapproval, inculpation and exculpation—as standing in need of instruction. One may find the fragile rudiments of the superego formation among other mammals, notably dogs. But only in man is it crucial. In our time we have learned that this development is intimately linked with psychogenic illness, and this fact has tended to obscure its contribution to health, in the transmission of that essential part of culture called the moral.

The distinctive characteristics of man as a biological organism are connected, it seems, with the aptitude for culture. This aptitude has three phases, interconnected. The first is the aptitude to be taught, to be cultured, to be brought up. The second is the aptitude to appropriate, to use, to modify and even reject what has been learned from the culture. The third is the aptitude to produce and to teach, to give back what has been consumed, with those additions and alterations that are the mark of individuality. Someone has paraphrased the Freudian stages of development by three verbs: to get, to keep, and to give. The chief biological novelties in man, those listed and others almost certainly, are the instruments of this reproductive cycle.

The self-reproducing molecule, the brain, and finally the tool and the book— these mark the major transitions of evolution. Each is a way of accumulating the kind of thermodynamic order that has come to be called, by a curious return to the archaic original meaning, *informatio* or information. Evolution has been

---

† *Troilus and Cressida,* Act III, Scene 3.

the elaboration of three variations on a theme. The story of evolution is a history of nature, under the aegis of the second law of thermodynamics, in a sector of the universe low in temperature but rife with free energy. From one example, at least, we know something of what happens under these conditions over times comparable to the age of our planet and sun.

11

THE THEORY OF THE SOUL

The disciplines that go together under the label "psychology" no longer parallel Aristotle's three-fold division of vegetative soul, sensorimotor soul, and rational soul. But they do parallel the last two and also the distinctions I have made between stages two and three of terrestrial evolution. If the more primitive processes of animal learning were well understood, including neuro-anatomy and neurophysiology, we might have a neater articulation of subject matter. In the present state of knowledge it is difficult to disentangle specifically or predominantly human capacities from others more primitive but also equally unknown. If we emphasize our uniqueness in too peremptory a fashion, we are likely to underestimate our animal cousins; and, if we adopt the broader point of view of comparative psychology, we are apt to miss our uniqueness altogether.

Human Nature

Under these circumstances it seems wise to rely heavily on the viewpoint of the preceding chapter, beginning with the proposition that man's special characteristics, for the psychologist, ought to be those that permit man to be the vehicle of cultural evolution. This is a preliminary guide, but it is a guide.

It is a guide that introduces into psychology a certain bias, and it spells defeat for certain preconceptions of science, both those that require a rigid taxonomic ordering and those that aim at mechanistic predictability, so much admired in the modern classical sciences. It is of the nature of life to change its nature, its specific functional forms. And it is of the nature of life not to remain dynamically isolated (and thus predictable from well-defined boundary conditions) but rather to be informed by its environment and sometimes to be better described as predictor than as predicted.

Genetically, this means evolution. Neurophysiologically, it means adaptability and individuation. In man it means much more, and the conceptions of science that fail for life in general fail doubly for human psychology. It is a deep thing that custom—and, by continuation, the whole of culture—should be called "second nature." In the sense set forth previously, man, a single species when considered biologically, is as variable as the whole mammalian order when described in terms of cultures. In this sense human nature is a transient thing, and a general psychological theory that ignores this radical variability is defeated from the outset.

This is not to minimize the importance of subordinate studies of those culturally determined formations—using the word as a geologist might use it—that may from time to time be identified with human nature. For these need not be transient or, as achievements, likely to be set aside. Evolution, whether biological or cultural, implies selection as well as variation, and selection implies irreversibility. What was once an inessential and reversible novelty becomes irreversible and essential through use and accommodation. But the constants of human nature, those with which a general science of psychology must be concerned, are the specific modifications of man's prehuman nature that have equipped him to be the vector of cultural evolution.

Learning capacity *per se* is not one of these. This we share with the elephant, the porpoise, and even the bee. What is distinctive in man is, in our earlier summary formulation, not the ability to incorporate and copy but the ability to externalize, to build and to communicate. Nature—organic nature and the given environment—sets limits to variability and individuation through learning alone. Man's variability is greater because it extends to some of the constraining constants of animal existence. Like the other animals, man is always bound, in the short run, by these constants of character and environment. But on a somewhat longer time scale, still short by the measure of organic evolution, these erstwhile constants are dependent, culturally evolved. The present chapter is intended to explore the supporting evidence for, and some of the implications of, this view of human nature.

The first step is to characterize human variability, the aptitude for culture and cultural variety and evolution. This I do by an odd juxtapositon of two thinkers who are in many ways at variance with each other, but in whom I see an essential agreement of emphasis. These are the late V. Gordon Childe, archaeologist, and Jean-Paul Sartre, philosopher and playwright.

The second step is the discussion of self-consciousness. Nature-oriented philosophy, in the modern age, has had a hard time with the concept of consciousness. Subjectivity, an attribute of human and no doubt of animal existence, is a threat to materialisms and naturalisms because it is the starting point for a whole alternative philosophical tradition, that of idealism. A philosopher's arguments may be cogent within the framework he builds for them, but different frameworks are possible. One framework is built of the naturalistic categories of space and time, matter and motion, structure and disorder. This is the framework of the sciences. Life fits into it, but not without some tension between physical and biological concepts. Evolution fits into it as part of the plain story of the history of nature. At some point we get to the psyche, late in the text as it were. A philosophical idealist *starts* with the psyche, with consciousness, as his primitive datum. For him everything is transformed. Space and time are treated in terms of the cognition of space and time, as things that appear real to a consciousness rather than as realities that appear to a consciousness. The primary order in the idealistic framework is the order of experience or, rather, the order that some kind of epistemological analysis claims to reveal in experience. Experience and intuition expand, as it were, and take the place of the material universe. The material universe shrinks, in the same sense, and takes its place as a system of constructs, of "posits," within experience and alongside other things: the world of esthetic experience, the moral domain with its goods and bads and its oughts. The problem for the materialist or naturalist in all of this is that he first fixes his basic categories and later tries to fit the categories of personal experience into the naturalistic framework, in a subordinate position.

There is a minority tradition that steers clear of this sort of split. It is a tradition—containing Aristotle for one example and Spinoza for another—that perceives man as part of nature but does so without belittling man's proper character. Its proponents have not been anxious to trim the description of human nature to fit a particular set of naturalistic categories; they have welcomed idealistic insights without surrendering to the extravagancies of idealism. Man is a conscious being, indeed a self-conscious being, who feels, who wills, who perceives and discourses. Only a part of his experience relates directly to the common world of nature; a part is, as we say, personal, pertaining to the person, with personality itself a very special category. A part of this human character is the capacity to know and to philosophize, to produce idealisms and materialisms and much else besides. Man is *that* kind of being, and, if some naturalistic philosophy is unable to accredit him as such, so much the worse for the philosophy. That kind of being belongs to the order of nature: comprehends nature, in one sense, and is comprehended by it, in another. This duality is the deepest topic—not "problem"—of philosophy. It is currently unfashionable to acknowledge it. Wrestling with angels is tedious, and one may at times be well advised to practice on minor demons.

One of the tendencies of this expansive naturalism is to soften the sense of contrast between man and the rest of nature by blurring the lines. A crude attempt is *panpsychism,* which puts psyche everywhere and thus makes it no special trait of man. This remains one of the possibilities, but it has been so far unrewarding. Another is *gradation.* Men are self-conscious; the other animals are at least conscious. Perhaps the lower animals, or the plants, have no *con*sciousness, but they may have some odd sort of "sciousness." A. N. Whitehead, whom we include among the wrestlers with angels, wrestles by decorticating human *ap*prehension and finding a universal "prehension," of events by events. I have expressed this same concern by insisting upon the relevance of thermodynamic ideas to problems of biology and of learning, and by trying, in the process, to legitimate the ancient Aristotelian conception of natural teleology. But informational processes are not airy metaphysics; they are part of the common, and scientifically penetrable, aspect of nature.

I do not pretend, moreover, to bridge gaps, but only to deny them where we may reasonably suppose that none exist. "Sciousnesses" and "prehension" are useless. What is accessible to study, whatever its more modest beginnings in nature, is the fact of human self-consciousness. I take it as the kind of fact that is hard to study in its simpler and more primitive forms because these, in the nature of the case, are less accessible to the only kind of scrutiny available—self-conscious scrutiny, reflection, phenomenology. "Mere" consciousness I suppose to be somewhat more remote from easy study. Extensions lacking the prefix "con" or having the doubled prefix "uncon" or "subcon" we must recognize as hypothetical and as subject to tests of theoretical utility.

A part of phenomenology, and the third step supporting the views I hold on human nature, is the investigation of purposiveness as revealed in the self-conscious and memorable experience of purposing, planning, judging, and deeming. Here, however, we come back to the theme of the general teleology of nature, lacking consciousness or intent. What we find, indeed, is that consciousness is not a function or attribute of purpose as such, but is incidental to the creation or modification of purpose through learning. At the ideal limit, when purpose is well defined and settled, it has lapsed into the functional realm beyond consciousness, into the automatism of natural teleology.

My argument, up to this point, is one-sided and requires a fourth step, a confrontation with methodological problems of psychology. Because there is variety in our ways of knowing about human beings, there are issues that call for adjudication between these ways. The issues very often are issues that divide the schools of thought in psychology. The adjudication has a long history, and I do not even untangle the issues, but confine myself to a few suggestions related to the more general problem, appearing in other sciences as well, of describing observational methods in terms of the kinds of causal coupling, between observer and observed, that they entail. Descriptive concepts appropriate to one mode of observation may be inappropriate to another, and this is why psychology is, so far, irreducibly pluralistic.

A fifth step confronts my analysis of human nature with a problem of a different order, metaphysical rather than methodological. At the end of the chapter I discuss a topic that is relevant to what follows: the meaning of freedom as a human capacity, sometimes affirmed, sometimes denied, and long debated. It is suggested, again in anticipation of what is to follow, that this capacity, in its most eulogistic sense, is the capacity for a kind of learning that is distinctive of humankind.

Human Variability

V. Gordon Childe expressed the indeterminacy of human nature by the title of one of his books, *Man Makes Himself*.† By this he meant that, as men have explored their physical environment and achieved new kinds of mastery over it, they have developed new interests, new modes of association, and new complexities of character. These emerging characteristics have not been latent, preformed aspects of human nature but have evolved in a sense as literal as that in which the species has evolved.

Childe speaks from the historical-descriptive point of view of the modern archaeologist. From a quite different background, that of the high metaphysical tradition of Descartes, Kant, and Hegel, Jean-Paul Sartre urges upon us the statement that man has no essence antecedent to his existence, no nature except the one he chooses for himself.‡ The primitive fact of human existence

---

† V. Gordon Childe, *Man Makes Himself* (London, 1936; New York, 1951, a paperback).

‡ Jean-Paul Sartre, *Being and Nothingness*, translated and with an introduction by Hazel Barnes (New York, 1956).

is the freedom to choose, a freedom not merely to *do* this or that but to *be* this or that. Sartre does not deny the "facticity" of nature and history, including those culturally embodied formations or models of human nature with which we are always surrounded; but their significance is that they inform choice, not that they explain it. In spite of its dramatic and paradoxical use of the contrast between "essence" and "existence," existentialism is, first and foremost, a theory of human nature, an assertion about the human essence fulfilling the Aristotelian conditions of "essentialist" definition. Man may bury or otherwise conceal his autonomy but be rid of it only in "bad faith." The inescapability of freedom is, for Sartre, not a probable generalization about man but an *a priori* necessity, something following in virtue of the kind of being man is.

Sartre is, in fact, rejecting a conception of man's essence that it would never have occurred to Childe, reared in the evolutionary tradition, to accept in the first place. It is doubtful whether even Aristotle had in mind the notion of human nature that Sartre rejects. Capacity for choice is certainly one of the main aspects of the rationality that distinguishes man, in Aristotle's account of things, from the other animals. Aristotle talks of human capacities, not of unalterable patterns of human behavior. In Sartre's account, no doubt, man is more radically indeterminate than in Aristotle's. But, because he belongs to the high metaphysical tradition rather than to the historical and scientific tradition of Childe, Sartre is, in a sense, more of an essentialist than Childe. To discuss man apart from his working relations with his material and social environment and out of the context of the evolution of culture is to have nothing to talk about but human nature.

But, even if one is restricted to human nature, that is not quite nothing. Man's variability, his "aptness for culture," is the basic trait suggested, on the one hand, by the working categories of the anthropologist and supported, on the other, by the metaphysical tradition (in many ways antithetic to science), according to which there is a sort of radical indeterminacy about the human character. Sartre is only a recent rather vivid expression of this tradition, whose roots can probably be traced back to the earliest commentaries on the subject— to the story of the Garden of Eden, certainly.

The specific variability that fits man to be the bearer of cultural evolution is connected with elaborately evolved neurophysiological and psychic capacities, which impose their character upon the processes of individual human life and upon the very content and character of culture. The belief—widespread in the recent past—called cultural relativism from one point of view and cultural determinism from another fails to recognize adequately the biological and psychological constraints upon culture and the unequal viability of different cultures.

After the first glorious period of generalization about cultural evolution— as, for example, in the work of Lewis H. Morgan—cultural anthropologists settled down to the long labor of collecting detailed information about the world's societies, and in some periods generalization was almost taboo as "unscientific." Like biological evolution, cultural evolution is not a quite neat affair of stages. Like nature in the greater ensemble, man in his more restricted world has tried everything. But the old classifications are still important. Hunting, agricultural, and urban society still mark irreversible general shifts, and detailed differences in material and moral culture are meaningful only against a common background, which is taken for granted.†

Human cultures, moreover, have upon them the mark of a common mode of evolution, peculiar and quite specific sorts of variation and selection connected with tools and tool-making, language, and the human mental processes. Different cultures may predispose toward different areas of innovation and different rates of innovation, but cultures are the cumulative products of a common kind of innovation, which can be contrasted with genetic novelty.

Mutation, by itself, is merely dissipative of order and organization, for it produces a certain random dispersion of genetic type; variation without selection is always downhill, thermodynamically speaking. This is even true of those more complex secondary mutations, recently recognized as a broad general category, that are involved in the exchange of nucleic acid structures between cells. This kind of mutation includes sexual fertilization, conjugation among protozoans, and also the effects of so-called latent viruses. Convergent evolution, in which information-bearing components evolved in one species are taken over by another, might, under some conditions, greatly accelerate evolutionary change.‡ But for the biosphere as a whole it is still true that this sort of variability, considered of itself and apart from selection, is merely dissipative.

The variability of human behavior, on the other hand, is, in greater or lesser degree, the consequence of human mental capacity. To the extent that cultural evolution results from the normal, more or less random, unpremeditated variety of behavioral patterns, it is roughly analogous to primary genetic muta-

---

† See V. Gordon Childe, *Social Evolution* (New York, 1951); Leslie White, *The Evolution of Culture* (New York, 1959); M. P. Sahlins and E. R. Service (editors), *Evolution and Culture* (Ann Arbor, 1960); Julian H. Steward, *Theory of Culture Change* (Urbana, Ill., 1955).

‡ The idea of "macromutation" was advanced by R. B. Goldschmidt, *The Material Basis of Evolution* (New Haven, 1940).

tions. To the extent that it is learned by diffusion between cultures, it is roughly similar to the exchange of genetic information between cells. But variation through primary learning is without biological parallel, for it involves pre-selection. In at least some of its aspects it is not merely dissipative; it is already going uphill thermodynamically; it anticipates experience.

In the Marxian account of social evolution this primary innovation through learning is assumed to take place, or in the past to have taken place, primarily in the technological sphere. The relations between men have had to be accommodated to changes in their working relations with nature. A similar idea lies behind the concept of *cultural lag,* which implies that planned innovation in one sphere is followed by unanticipated disruption and eventual unplanned accommodation in other spheres. These are difficult matters, and it might be better to define a spectrum of planfulness in innovation, technical problems being continuous, in principle, with economic problems, and economic problems being continuous, in turn, with problems of social direction. A new tool, transferred or invented, may prove a cultural pathogen, just as extracellular DNA may. Conservatism in the face of threatened innovations, more characteristic of some cultures than of others, is a kind of automatic safeguard against the consequences of innovation. But all cultures safeguard themselves in this way in some areas, and this general fact suggests one of the fruitful ways of understanding the specific human phenomenon of morality. Unlike the natural behavioral patterns of the other animals, those of men are highly constructed, metastable; and even the barriers that more or less stabilize them, the barriers of morality and morally sanctioned custom, are likewise constructed.

Self-consciousness

The range of learning extends to the place where it modifies the concrete ends of human action and is no longer limited to changes and refinements of the instrumental scaffolding built around ends fixed independently of culture. When this happens, and when such ends get modified and redefined not only through accident plus adaptation but also through deliberate investigative activity, one is faced with the problems of describing choice and responsibility. But the natural language of that description raises, in its acutest form, the old philosophical dualism of human nature. A second reason for mentioning the metaphysical tradition to which Sartre belongs is that it raises this further question about human nature. Descartes, in his famous method of doubt, sought to evoke self-consciousness in order to denote it as a kind of reality radically different from the realities of the material world and the human body. Sartre is expert at this kind of evocation, and a grasp of what he is doing is made easier—but not easy—if one recognizes from the start that this is his approach.

The important philosophical duality in Sartre, as I have already suggested, is not the contrast between "essence" and "existence." It is, rather, the contrast between two aspects that Sartre labels with Hegelian phrases, the "in itself" and the "for itself."

To explain things in the Aristotelian way of thought is to explain them by their "natures," by what they are "in themselves." But men confront themselves, they are self-conscious, they are "for themselves." It is this contrast that Sartre conflates with that of "essence" and "existence," so that man "for himself" has existence but—in this odd sense—no essence. The obvious contrast, however, is not between "for itself" and "in itself," but between "for itself" and "for another." So interpreted, Sartre says that other things in nature seem to behave in determinate and predictable ways under given external conditions—that is, for an external observer. Man can describe himself in the same way and by the same conceptual expedients of dispositional properties, causality, etc.; man can also describe himself "self-consciously," as a singularity in relation to which other things are perceived and known. Sartre wants to give this second sort of description metaphysical priority over the first.

> "One must be conscious in order to choose, and one must choose in order to be conscious. Choice and consciousness are one and the same thing. This is what many psychologists have felt when they declared that consciousness was 'selection.' But because they have not traced this selection back to its ontological foundations, they have remained on a level in which selection appeared as a gratuitous function of a consciousness in other respects substantial; . . . to be conscious of ourselves and to choose ourselves are one and the same thing." †

And here the conceptualization is of a different kind: it is the language of personal experience and interpersonal communication, of desire, feeling, perception, cognition. It is, above all, the language of deliberation and choice. Self-consciousness is not a sort of passive observation of self but is a mode of experience in which there is, at the focus, something problematic, something in need of resolution or decision. Even when self-consciousness is not focused on problems of conduct—but, say, on the properties of a tool or the opacity of a mathematical puzzle—it involves the invention of a hypothesis the testing

---

† Sartre, *op. cit.,* p. 462.

of which one will subsequently be committed to, and the sense of choice is still there.

From this point of view, then, it makes sense to say that man for himself is an arena of choice, and through the history of his choices he can be said, for Sartre as for Childe, to make himself. Taking his departure thus from the phenomenology of self-conscious experience, Sartre can say that man is essentially indeterminate, elective, autonomous. And he can say it for the sole initial reason, in the end a very compelling reason, that a man cannot otherwise describe himself when it is his turn to be faced with indecision and choice.

I have brought Childe and Sartre together, not because they have a common viewpoint, but because they have antithetical viewpoints and nevertheless reach conclusions that are grist for my mill. The variability that Childe finds in man's evolutionary history is related to the variability of which individual men are aware in their individual experience, in their self-conscious doubts and perplexities. This means that general psychological theory, in attempting to describe the constants of this variability, must relate itself not only to the anthropologist's description of man's peculiar past but also to the phenomenologist's description of himself "for himself."

Purposive Behavior

During that period in the history of science when the dominant framework of ideas was organized round the laws of motion and the desire to establish the lawfulness of all kinds of phenomena, the impact on psychology was to foster a conception of mental processes involving simple sensations or ideas, the laws of association by which these were built into complexes, and the role of the complexes in determining conscious behavior. Later, but under what was essentially the same influence, the point of view shifted from the introspective to the behavioristic account of association. In present-day behaviorism the laws of psychology are conceived as functional relations in which response-variables are given as functions of physically defined stimulus-variables and other, "intervening" variables associated with the functioning of the organism.

The idea of purposiveness gets introduced into this framework as soon as the unit of behavior studied is complex enough to require the ideas of drive and drive-reduction (satisfaction) and the idea that overt activity continues until drive-reduction is achieved.† As exemplified in the behavior of well-motivated rats in mazes, this process is one in which a large variety of alternative pathways converge upon an antecedently defined focal state (encounter with the rewarding mush) and in which alternative pathways are differentially reinforced or inhibited as a result of trial-and-error learning.

At such a level of description, behavior is purposive in much the sense in which biological evolution is purposive. The term means that the mechanisms of information-transfer eliminate, in successive steps, all but certain initially improbable pathways—namely, those connected with survival under some complex of initial conditions. In the first case the survival is that of the altered species; in the second it is that of the informed organism.

In the posthumous work referred to in Chapter 8, Reichenbach observes that the phenomena we call, or are tempted to call, teleological have a superficial resemblance to phenomena explained by antecedent causes but seen in the reversed-time direction. This is a very old idea, implied in the contrast between *vis a tergo* and *vis a fronte*. In my discussion of the direction of time we saw that, when two systems interact transiently, they tend to be statistically independent *before,* with additive entropies, but that *after* the interaction one or both bear its mark, so that they are statistically interdependent and their joint entropy is less than the sum of their separate entropies.

But in teleological phenomena a mere reversal of time is not right. Living things become informed antecedently by other systems in their environment, living or non-living—antecedently, that is, to further interactions. Astronomers assemble on some small Pacific island *before* the eclipse occurs, then pour their concrete and assemble their instruments. Except for metaphysical anxieties it seems perfectly proper to say that the eclipse is the cause of their preparations. The biochemical clocks that cells maintain do the same sort of thing. As we can generally infer backward in time, from the footprint in the sand to the man whose passage left it there, so in some aspects of vital interactions we can infer forward in time to some interaction yet to come, for which the living thing is prepared or has prepared its environment. The thing to come can be read forward from the preparation for it, in much the sense in which the man Friday can be read backward from the footprint.

The point is, of course, that the resemblance between *vis a fronte* and *vis a*

---

† See Egon Brunswik, *The Conceptual Framework of Psychology,* International Encyclopedia of Unified Science, Vol. I, No. 10 (1952); Chap. V, section 20, gives a brief account of recent ideas on purposive behavior.

tergo, in the inverted-time direction, is incomplete and superficial. The astronomers packing up to go home *after* the eclipse are not like the situation on the beach *before* the footprint was made. The coupling of concrete piers and telescopes with the eclipse is just as remarkable in inverted as in normal time. The interactions between eclipses and astronomers are none of them like the massive dynamical interactions that leave glacial valleys or fossil beds as records of the past. Moreover, a literal *vis a fronte,* without antecedent interactions, would violate the second law of thermodynamics. The astronomers get to the place for observing the eclipse because of a long antecedent history of similar observations, of which the earliest ones were not prepared in the sense in which later ones are: the thermodynamic price has long since been paid.

In this connection I revert to a point made earlier about the informational thermodynamic character of causality conceived as a temporal and asymmetrical relation. Discussing this in connection with the force-acceleration concept of classical physics, I pointed out that in the context of local interactions, where the time lag of propagation is not involved, there is no essential asymmetry. The causal relation (as distinguished from the unconditional functional relation, as of gravitational and inertial mass) is an informational relation in the thermodynamic sense. The wind blowing makes the trees move. The statement cannot be converted or transposed. From "A causes B" we cannot deduce "B causes A," nor can we deduce "not-B causes not-A." Both statements would involve a violation of the second law!

The relevance of causality to *experimental* situations, and the difficulty of applying it to the description of the uncontrolled course of nature, are further confirmation of this analysis. A *prepared* system behaves in a way that is predictable from a knowledge of the preparation. In an unprepared system, on the other hand, we may be incapable of discriminating among conditions that would lead to alternative predictions. In quantum physics this comes to be crucially important. Because interactions are quantized, the discrimination among alternative pure states in a probabilistic mixture cannot be distinguished from an act of preparation, of putting the system in a pure state.

But reference to man-made, experimental situations is not of the essence. The foot of Robinson Crusoe's man Friday was the cause in this sense— the informative cause—of the footprint that Crusoe found. To repeat: it is characteristic of antecedently independent systems to interact so as to become interdependent, to increase the joint entropy but, at the same time, to decrease some component of the conditional entropy of each. Each informs the other.

Phases that are improbable in isolation become, in interaction, probable in each. By such standards man is the most extraordinary of catalysts: in the measure in which he is informed by the world around, he transforms that world. The connection between cause and purpose is not a philosophical error. In the description of the non-human world it is this connection that legitimates the natural teleology that I have defended in the account of evolution. In the description of the human world it goes to the essence of what man is.

Behavior becomes purposive, in a sense in which biological evolution is not purposive, when the animal organism has an antecedently defined model of the drive-reducing state and of the environment, of such a kind as to direct activity toward that state. Purpose, in this sense, is a kind of cause. We can call this model a *definition* of the future state; the definition informs activity leading toward the state it defines. We can also call this kind of activity a quest rather than a drive. But the existence of such models is not accessible to direct behavioristic verification unless we identify them with previously reinforced patterns that we can antecedently designate. Phenomenologically, of course, we are able to entertain and communicate such definitions independently of overt behavior.

The first meaning is the one we use when we try to define an end-state toward which an organism tends simply because it is drive-reducing. Activity is not *directed* toward the goal, and the goal is only called that because of a superimposed imputation of our own. A newly hatched chick runs around in the sunlight until it finds itself in the shade. If more or less random running is an inherited response to stimulation by light, and if the chick becomes quiescent when the stimulation is eliminated, we say that the phenomenon is purposive in the first sense: an inherited pattern, selected through evolution, has the biological utility of tending to get chicks under the maternal wing. In an informational sense it is economical. The light stimulates random motion, and this uses no detailed genetic code. The attainment of shade, plus reinforcements, increases the probability of paths toward shade, and after some repetition the chick seeks the shade. The biological information has been supplemented by a greater quantity of learned information. The whole mature seeking response could have been genetically spelled out, but it would have required much more of the limited genetic capacity.

In another sense of "purpose" there is no purpose here, only the imputation of one by a human observer. Purpose, as imputed in this sense, is something defined phenomenologically in the experience of that observer, and the more hard-boiled object to the notion of chick phenomenology as unscientific.

What is the difference between the human being and the chick? I shall maintain that it is the difference between *having* goals in the first sense (whether the code is innate or is built up, in part, by reinforcement and inhibition) and *constructing* goals, building models of goal-directed activity that may subsequently be switched into the circuitry of overt behavior. The human consciousness of purpose—of what stands out for naming as such—is incident to the human capacity, first to construct a description of purposive activity in the first sense, and then to initiate the activity thus described. The description informs the activity; the activity, a departure from previous habitual patterns, has the description, the model, as its informational cause.†

We find ourselves concerned with goals only as, in some way or other, *inadequately* defined. If a goal is well defined and only the means of attaining it uncertain, our attention shifts to these means. If the means available suggest a more or less different goal as attainable, if there are conflicting goals or at least temptations to stray from the goal-directed path—only then does the term "purpose" have its full phenomenological reference. The awareness of purpose is connected not so much with purposive behavior as with the *modifiability* of such behavior. The imputation of awareness of purpose to the chick running around in the sunlight or to the rat laboring in the maze is questionable, not mainly because it lacks hard-boiled certification, but because, under quite similar circumstances, human beings also are focally aware, *not* of purpose, but of means, barriers, etc.

It appears, for such reasons, that the phenomenological account of purpose is really an account of a certain kind of learning process—not the primitive learning of reinforcement and inhibition acting on overt behavior, but what we have called model-building. Our more self-conscious experience is a transient phase connected with the resolution of what is problematic.

The phenomenological account of self-consciousness as a kind of learning process should, perhaps, bear no simple relation to the behavioristic account of learning. It does, however, suggest a somewhat different emphasis from that usually given. It has commonly been supposed—for example, in John Dewey's classical description‡ of problem-solving—that self-consciousness replaces routine overt activity when the forward path is blocked in one way or another, and that it merges again into overt activity when the literal or figurative barrier

---

† An important analysis of teleology, too little read in this context, is Kant's *Critique of Judgment*. See especially the introductory essay, "On Philosophy in General," and the included "Critique of Teleological Judgment." Kant anticipated correctly the general framework of Darwinian theory.

‡ John Dewey, *Logic: the Theory of Inquiry* (New York, 1937), Chap. VI.

is overcome. By implication, at least, the problem-solving activity is both limited and motivated by the antecedent organic drive that was interrupted. Phenomenologically, however, the reinstatement of overt activity appears and is defined as an objective condition to be met in the process of inquiry. We become aware of our motivating desires and interests as objects to be described, analyzed, and even redefined. It does not follow, in the least, that these desires and interests are, at the same time, supplying the motive power for our activity of describing, analyzing, or redefining. The less urgent the task, the more artificial appears the hypothesis that motivation is supplied by the drive of interrupted activity. Even a man reaching for a stone to throw at some pursuing animal might momentarily register its peculiar color or heft and might return another day to look for it. And he might do this, not because he needed the stone, but because of some surplus interest, not trimmed to the requirements of the moment, in color or heft.

The suggestion that thus appears is the suggestion of a specifically cognitive interest, related in a rather complex way to other interests and to relatively fixed organic drives, capable itself of being reinforced, inhibited, or directed, but having some kind of organic basis independent of the other biologically determined drives. My phenomenological account of the means-ends complex and of all the cognitive activities derived from this complex thus represents the ascendancy of the cognitive interest at work.

If we emphasize the creative or constructive aspect of cognitive activity, the distinction between the object of knowledge and the object of desire appears as a distinction between two species of a common genus. Both objects will satisfy the given conditions and be tested by means of further information. This is not to blur the sharp distinction between the information of belief and the information of conduct, but to recognize them as two kinds of finality that self-conscious inquiry aims at. The sense of objectivity—which, of course, is no sense at all, comparable to sight or hearing or touch—is connected with the heightening and focusing of awareness, is affective rather than sensory. Perception and recognition, considered not for their content but as marking phases of self-consciousness, are the building up and the release of this cognitive tension.

Goals get recognized as such in self-conscious experience only when they are *not* stable determiners of behavior but, on the contrary, are objects of the cognitive interest and are, therefore, open to inquiry and modification. Throughout the history of modern thought there has been anxiety about the use of teleological language in descriptions of inorganic nature, plants, and animals, and even in the scientific description of man. Through information theory and the implied thermodynamics such teleological language acquires a perfectly respectable scientific meaning, and it becomes possible to say that evolution is teleological, that learning—even in its simplest and most mechanistic forms—is teleological. But, paradoxically and ironically, it appears that, when we start to explore the nature and consequences of man's peculiar variability of behavior, we find it connected with a capacity *not* to be governed entirely by predefined and organically fixed ends. Instead of being the only animal that can properly be described in terms of purposive behavior, man now appears as the only animal in which the adequacy of that description is open to question. Human learning, the kind of learning associated with self-conscious inquiry, still fits the description "purposive"; it is no doubt a trial-and-error process in which information transfers are effected by inhibition and reinforcement. But it has the peculiar effect of altering the patterns of human activity. To be aware of purposes is to destabilize them, to be unsure of them; and the resulting rhythm of thought and action marks the human career as different in kind from that of man's animal cousins.

If man is, in some measure, free from the enchainment of fixed organic drives as the source of reinforcement and inhibition, it is entirely possible that even his animal cousins are less dominated by them than the maze model would imply. Indeed, many phenomena of the rat laboratory suggest this. The learning of "unmotivated" rats was at one time the subject of controversy among American psychologists—controversy over learning that was called "latent" when the rat, in a sufficiently Platonic mood, did not feel called upon to exhibit the discriminatory skills he had acquired by wandering in the maze.[†]

Even at the level of hardware models of learning it is not difficult, in principle, to see the possibility and the importance of autonomous motivation of learning.[‡] A machine that copies its environment, that classifies and correlates various stimuli, may be designed on the general principle that tensions leading to random exploratory behavior are built up through sensory stimulation and released through information transfers from environment to machine or from one component of the machine to another. In the stereotype of behavioristic studies, the coupling between organism and environment is "torn," external stimuli being thought of as independent variables and responses as dependent. In the design of even simple learning machines, we may modify and partially invert the order of dependent and independent variables. A source of random-

---

[†] See R. C. Tolman, "Cognitive Maps in Rats and Men," *Psychological Review*, vol. 15 (1948).

[‡] For a review of current ideas see Karl H. Pribram, "A Review of Theory in Physiological Psychology," *Annual Review of Psychology*, Vol. II (Palo Alto, 1960), especially pp. 24–32.

ness can be built into the machine, so that its responses to a given stimulus are statistically variable and so that it can, in fact, "respond" without any transient stimulus from the outside. We can also describe the environment itself, in part, in a stimulus-response language; the machine can act in various ways to poke and prod the environment, and this will produce from the environment responses that transiently stimulate the sensory hardware of the machine. Thus both machine and environment can exhibit both dependent and autonomous variation.

As a final modification of simple stimulus-response design we can set up, within the machine, internal couplings that provide for the flow of signals from peripheral to central components and from central to peripheral; the latter may be keyed to sensory input in such a way that, if efferent signals match incoming sensory signals, the latter are extinguished. Such a machine—it could be called Epicurean, as seeking tranquility—will be capable of inattention to its environment as long as it can anticipate the environmental input, but will be shifted into a phase of exploratory activity when matching is not achieved. Thus the stimulus to learning activity is not sensory stimulation *per se,* but sensory novelty, information in the technical sense.

If an artificial environment of such a machine is finite and of not too great variability, the machine will tend asymptotically toward a state of completely habitual response. So long as autonomous or induced change in the environment is anticipated correctly, the machine will act like a system with no internal degrees of freedom, like an automaton. But novelty in the environment will awaken it to fresh exploratory activity.

More complex and interesting machines could be built by the coupling of many such unit machines, together with units of different kinds. If a system of this kind is considered as a single complex unit, a part of the sensory novelty stimulating a sub-unit may be internal, and the sub-unit thus gets involved in copying an internal as well as an external environment, and the interactions between them.†

The only reason for discussing such models here is to exemplify the partial uncoupling of animal drive from the learning process. It is, of course, quite clear that idle curiosity, "unmotivated" exploration of the environment, and

---

† An interesting prototype of the causally unenchained machine is the Perceptron designed by F. Rosenblatt. See "The Perceptron, a Probabilistic Model for Information Storage and Organization in the Brain," *Psychological Review,* vol. 65 (1958), pp. 386–408. The substantial part of the detailed circuitry of the Perceptron is by *random* connection. The effect of cumulative reinforcement and inhibition creates a uniformity of response that is initially lacking. This uniformity is of a kind that fits very well with Brunswik's lens analogy, mentioned on p. 298.

prodding to test its responses can have great biological utility. To the extent that such activity becomes important for the economy of animal life, it comes to represent a distinct system of needs, added to the more primitive needs connected with food and reproduction. No animal so endowed could, strictly speaking, be said to live by bread alone. A kind of learning motivation independent of other kinds would have biological utility, but it would also create a new component in the *definition* of that utility.

Observational Problems in Psychology

The classical metaphysical problems of psychology arise because of the multiplicity of standpoints from which human beings can be observed and described. In the present chapter I took my departure from the contrast between the phenomenological and the behavioristic, which is related to the old problem of free will and determinism and to the mind-body problem. But there are other contrasts: between the central and the peripheral, between the molar behavior of the organism and the molecular processes of its nervous system, between stimuli conceived proximally as they affect the sensory end-organs and stimuli conceived distally as objects of perception. And, finally, there is the contrast between organism and person, the latter term being understood in the context of self-conscious interpersonal communication. Cutting across all these polarities is the time scale on which investigations can be classified, from the phenomena of a fleeting moment to the developmental patterns of a lifetime.

Each mode of observation, moreover, carries with it a characteristic apparatus of concepts and characteristic commitments as to the type of organization of knowledge to be achieved. Starting from the microphysiological viewpoint, one is led to think in terms of the vast network of neural circuitry, of afferent sensory and efferent motor channels, complexly linked by the central system and interacting at the periphery. If the starting point is phenomenological, one is cut off from any direct neurophysiological reference; the field of self-conscious awareness is functionally related to the activity of the central nervous system, but its contents are not describable in neurophysiological language at all. Much of this reference, indeed, is to things spatially outside the organism—to the physical environment, to other persons; but the field of self-consciousness has other dimensions—of perception and recognition, of affective reaction, of memory and purpose. And, although we may refer to the former as outer and to the latter as inner, the sense of the contrast is not the same as that of the contrast between the extra-organic and the intra-organic. The contrast is functional rather than physiological.

One of the classical problems concerns the nature of perception. From a physical-physiological point of view, perception involves a copying of the environment, which copying, in visual perception, is mediated, in part, by the real image on the retina. We also use the term "image" in phenomenological language to cover a wide range of phenomena, some of which, such as after-images and hallucinatory images, are intimately related to sensory stimulation. Identification of the physical description and the phenomenological description leads to a curious and undoubtedly incorrect account of things, in which the direct object of perception is identified not as physical reality but as image, as sense datum. I do not hear the physical sound of a bell, but I have an auditory experience caused by the sound of the bell; I do not see the bell but a visual image of it. This account owes at least part of its persuasiveness to a confusion of the two modes of description. We trace the information transfer from physical object to sense organ and, with increasing uneasiness, to central nervous system. But we then superimpose the phenomenological description and identify the mental image with the physiological image, with the pattern of input signals from the sense organ. It thus appears that the object of perception is not the extra-organic object from which information has been transferred to the organism, but an intra-organic physical image or a mental image caused by or associated with it. This identification is quite gratuitous. The physiological information transfer is undoubtedly a causally necessary condition for the occurrence of perception, but the *object* of perception is normally *not* an intra-organic state *to* which information has been transferred; it is an extra-organic state *from* which information has been transferred. The fact that perception is causally mediated neither implies nor contradicts the phenomenologically grounded assertion that the direct or immediate object of perception is an extra-organic, physical reality. We are relying here on two modes of observation, and two corresponding modes of description, which simply do not fit together in any easy or obvious way.

The closest analogue of the object of perception that we can define from a physical-physiological point of view is, in fact, simply the physical object as defined by the investigator. The information transfer from this object to the subject's awareness and description of it is very complexly mediated, not only through myriad sensory clues but also through the subject's past experience and present state. Thus there is a simple relation between the object as described by the investigator and the subject's description of it, whereas the detailed mechanism of perception is very complex. Egon Brunswik described this situation by his lens analogy.† There is a simple correspondence between a physical object and the real image of it formed by a convex lens, but any attempt to define this correspondence by investigating what goes through the mid-plane of the lens is virtually impossible. Even this analogy would be misleading if it were taken to imply that the neurophysiological real image was, in any sense, the *object* of perception. The verbal reports of the subject may be statistically correlated with the measured properties of the object. But, considered as reports, as statements, they are not about the state of the percipient, but about the object.

Another source of difficulty arising from the observational problems of psychology is the propriety of *causal* description. The possibility of testing a causal hypothesis depends, in general, upon observational arrangements in which the system being described is isolated. Uncontrolled causes of variation are eliminated or accounted for in one way or another. Our ability to achieve this is always problematic, as I pointed out in Chapter 5, but causal description is certainly unreliable if there are uncontrolled couplings between a system and its environment. In any phenomenological description, however, there is always this possibility of coupling; the state of mind that is necessary if one is to describe one's experience cannot be wholly isolated from what is being described—a situation very different from that of an observer behind a one-way screen. Even the perception of one's physical environment, normally fairly stable and insensitive to what one is doing, may be radically disoriented by various kinds of positive feedback.

When two-way communication is employed as a means of psychological investigation, there are similar problems as to the appropriateness of causal description, and it clearly devolves on the clinical psychologist to prove that the causal coupling involved in communication does not significantly falsify his descriptions. The inter-subjective character of communication, which is a liability from the point of view of one interested in detailed causal description, is, of course, an extraordinary asset from other points of view. Speech may always be regarded as nothing more than "verbal behavior" and thus fitted within the conceptual framework of the stimulus-response categories of behavioristic description. But nothing except a behavioristic program of description requires that it be thought of in this way; it may equally well be considered as a phenomenological report. When a subject's speech is coupled, as it

---

† See Brunswik, *op. cit.*, Chap. II.

usually is, with that of another person cast in the role of investigator, the coupling involved is obviously that of two phenomenologically oriented observers. However great the asymmetry between the roles of investigator and subject, the spontaneity involved in communication blurs the boundary conditions under which the subject's behavior could be described as that of an isolated system. Or, putting it differently, it is, in principle, just as legitimate to apply this description in reverse, to see how things look with the roles of investigator and subject reversed. This is the source of most psychological jokes. The task of the participant-investigator is not to isolate the subject, to put him in the state he would be in if isolated from the observer, but to exercise control over the *kind* of coupling, to stabilize the subject, as it were, in a special and otherwise improbable state, and to avoid interactions that may, all too easily, result in disorientation of one or both participants.

Criticisms that say that clinical methods cannot be used for purposes of objective psychology are either trivially true, or false. They are trivially true if "objective psychology" means description under conditions of isolation, and they are false if "objective psychology" is a euphemism for "good psychology." That such methods are easy to use in a way that gives significant and reliable information no one would claim. The investigator must turn himself into a means of control and observation, whose operation is as complex and poorly understood, in principle, as that of the subject he investigates. In spite of these famous difficulties, psychological investigations that depend mainly upon communication or that fit, by continuation, into the same framework of descriptive concepts—the interpretation of spontaneous behavior as expressive or meaningful—tap a very rich source of information, which is available only because the investigator and the subject are similarly constituted and capable of those remarkably complex information transfers that biological and cultural evolution has made possible. The depth of our knowledge depends upon the richness of our interactions with the rest of things. Different kinds of interaction require different modalities of description, different conceptual expedients. There is very little reason, therefore, *a priori,* why the phenomenological mode of description, intrapersonal or interpersonal, should join neatly to that of the organism as a complex physical system. From this point of view the dualism of body and mind, or body and soul, is not initially a dualism of two kinds of entity somehow joined, but a dualism of mutually exclusive observational standpoints: in one case the strong coupling of self-observation and its interpersonal extension, in the other case the weak coupling implied in causal description. To say "strong" and "weak" here is, of course, a gross oversimplification. Observation and communication are not sharply distinct and the mix is richly variable. A clinician has access to a vast amount of information about his patient, only a part of which is described under our heading "strong coupling." Our doubts about the adequacy of causal description at some levels could be matched by affirmations of its importance at others. Psychoanalysis, as a general theory, has been strongly deterministic in its claims. As a developmental theory—either of personality in general or of psychopathology—it is obviously and properly committed to deterministic formulation. For quite unavoidable reasons it is extremely difficult to test the predictive implications.† The limitations of this sort of determinism become important if development depends significantly on interactions and transactions with the human ambient, including, but by no means limited to, articulate communication. But where these limitations will be found is not something that can be decided *a priori*.

My program is to emphasize the duality of the physical and the phenomenological description of the human being, of organism and person. But I want to present the former in something like the true framework of twentieth-century physics. Hence my continued emphasis on thermodynamics and information theory as ways of physical thought most likely to facilitate fruitful interaction between the two standpoints. In spite of the necessary crudity of all present efforts to discuss it, the machine that learns presents the possibility of a system —designed (or, it would be better to say, evolved) out of the kind of hardware known to present-day electronic technology—that would be of real value as an analogue to animal and human neurophysiology. Even the present machines are, indeed, not wholly negligible in this respect.

I know of no way to set absolute limits to what a machine can do. But "do" here is ambiguous. If it is restricted to overt functioning—moving around, engaging in exploratory activity, producing answers in human language to man-made questions, saying "ouch," producing statements or questions that, if produced by human beings, would be regarded by us as humor, mathematics, or metaphysics—then I do not know any principles that preclude such behavior. But, one hears the reply, such a machine—granting its possibility as a matter of argument—could not *feel* a pain, or *be* humorous, metaphysical, or mathematical; for this would impute to it some kind of self-consciousness. But what kind of impossibility is here alleged? The arguments are essentially similar to the behavioristic arguments against the possibility of verifying the existence of

---

† See John D. Benjamin, "Prediction and Psychopathological Theory," in *Dynamic Psychopathology in Childhood,* edited by Lucie Jessner, M.D., and Eleanor Pavenstedt, M.D. (New York, 1959).

another *person's* pain, or of verifying his state of mind as humorous, meta-physical, or mathematical. This is, simply, the assertion of the behavioristic viewpoint. If I use it against the self-consciousness of machines, I can also use it against the self-consciousness of other human beings.

There are, of course, excellent general reasons for being skeptical about the possibility of machines that are, in any real sense, equivalents of human beings or animals. The degree of organization required is so vast that one would probably need units of molecular dimensions and times like those of biological evolution to design them. It is quite possible, in short, that the only members of this species already exist, and in that case the argument goes by default. For *we* feel pain, are humorous, mathematical, and metaphysical.

Apart from the scientific questions as to the limitations of machines, there are metaphysical questions, specifically about body and mind, or body and soul. But it seems doubtful if these are relevant. People believe that a machine that thinks, feels, etc. somehow demonstrates the non-existence of mental or psychic exist-ence. But this does not follow; quite the opposite in fact: if the machine thinks, feels, etc., these psychic states *do* exist! The trouble comes from ambiguity in the term "machine," which normally means a highly degenerate assemblage of causally enchained components, but which has come also to mean an assemblage of mechanical *parts* capable of the sorts of information transfer I have discussed and *not* causally enchained in the sense of the classical image of the machine.

If a machine can think, feel, etc., it exists just as genuinely in the mental and psychic dimensions as man and the higher animals do. We might know a great deal about the essential circuitry of such a machine, the order designed into it as distinguished from the order transferred to it during its functional interactions with the world, but a knowledge of that circuitry would give us no more insight into the metaphysical questions concerning the physical and the psychical than we should gain by knowing an equivalent amount, for example, about the inherent structure of the human nervous system. And, if we were able to share a common phenomenological language with such a machine, we should, in communicating with it, be no nearer a metaphysical understanding of the psyche than we are now in our communications with one another. The mental and the psychic are basic organizing categories of our experience; they are dimensions of reality. This we *already* know. It is, however, a scientific question, not a metaphysical one, whether there are or can be material systems different from those with our complex, carbon-dominated chemistry, which nevertheless exist significantly in those dimensions.

What is in question, philosophically, is not the reality of the psychic dimension, but the right way of conceiving it in relation to the physical. Throughout the present work there have been suggestions of an altered perspective on mind-body problems, an alteration connected with the emphasis on information theory and thermodynamics. A summary is now in order. In the discussion of Kant's analysis of perception I used the image of the telecommunication system: nature encodes her patterns in the sense manifold, and mind decodes, constituting the decoded patterns as perception of an external reality. Thus what the mind grasps is not the external reality but the phenomenal construct. The external reality, the "thing in itself," is a pole of reference rather than an item of content. It is unperceived in the way the perceiving ego is unperceived. The field of perception exists in a kind of bipolar stress. The stress gives meaning to the idea of a transcendent reality and a transcendent ego, but neither belongs in the field. Kant's statement that the ultimate thing perceived and the ultimate perceiver are unknowable is not a confession of failure to know but an affirmation of learned ignorance: they are not in the category of perceivables, just as the earth is not in the category of things that fall to the earth.

Kant sought to avoid subjectivism by denying that self-knowledge has any priority over knowledge of nature. But his way of thought has not proved stable against subjectivistic interpretation. The easy and popular patchwork, discussed previously, has punned on the word "image," identifying physical image, which is causally related to the physical object of perception and knowledge, with mental image, which is directly intuited by the mind. The mind is, as it were, a hole inside the head, an inner room equipped with projection screens and a seeing I (or eye).

Since the problem is to relate two different languages of description, each appropriate to a different way of getting at the common subject matter of perception, the hollow-head, projection-room account is simply a naive error. The junction box we need is not to connect the mind with the brain; it is a logical box to contain and relate two complementary kinds of abstractions. For this reason I have said that the content of perception is the analogue, not of the message as received, but of the message as transmitted. What corresponds to the received message is the act of perception, not the content.

Now we are in a position to throw out the whole analogy, keeping only the fact of information transfer as key. For nature does not transmit articulated little messages, but a simultaneous variety in many dimensions. Perception achieves a selective inattention to all but a small part of this variety.† Much of

---

† See W. Pitts and W. S. McCulloch, "How We Know Universals," *Bulletin of Mathematical Biophysics*, vol. 9 (1947), pp. 127–47.

this selection is overtly and physically accomplished through our muscles and the technology we have evolved around them. Part of it is accomplished, more subtly, within the nervous system. At the periphery of the nervous system the communication analogy is still plausible. There are well-defined channels of signal flow. The signals go both ways, but afferent and efferent pathways are distinct. In the center the distinction must break down, but it dominated all the older thinking. Information from or about the world flows in through the senses. The commands of action flow out to the muscles, with a mystery in between. The post-Kantian idealist philosophers attacked this presupposition by showing that knowledge is not received, but constructed. By a metaphysical pun they concluded that the mind constructs the world around, including the brain: the brain doesn't house the mind, but the mind the brain. The Marxists and the pragmatists attacked the metaphor of one-way flow as ignoring the unity of thought and action. And they attacked the idealists for talking about action as though it were a kind of thought.

The account of the nervous system that is emerging today is bound to change the implicit metaphysics behind the whole discussion of mind and body. The physiological differentiation of paths in and paths out has been misinterpreted. From the central nervous system through the peripheral and into the environment there is a manifold interaction of a kind radically unsuited to the metaphor of message transmission. The relation of transmitted message to received message is one-to-one. The transfers of information between organism and environment are simply not of this kind. If we try to follow, in principle, all the small pulses of energy from the environment that are involved in the perception of an object, we shall find that this configuration of pulses does not define the object at all. The object is lost in it, rather, like the needle in the haystack. The object could equally well be represented by many other such configurations. The whole class of such configurations is what corresponds to the object, an equivalence of which the given configuration is only one element. Discrimination between elements of this class is inhibited, and this inhibition is learned (some small part of it could, of course, be innate). This is what I mean by saying that perception entails selective inattention to differences.

It follows that the task, in psychology, of defining a stimulus of a sort that that will provoke a unique response is of the same order of complexity as the perception itself. If we try to define "stimulus" in microphysical terms, we are swamped by complexity. If we try to define the term by grouping the microphysical complexities into equivalence classes of our own, the problem arises whether our groupings are the same as those of the organism we are studying.

This brings us back to the genre of anti-psychological jokes: the subject discriminates where the investigator does not, or he is taken to be stupid because he has learned not to discriminate what the psychologist regards as important differences. In the language of one investigator, stimuli, in the sense in which psychology talks about them, must be response-inferred.† If the variety within each stimulus class is large, moreover, this stabilizes perception against error. A much greater quantity of information is received than is needed to discriminate between meaningfully different objects of perception. The amount of information we get in recognizing a friend is much greater than the number of persons among whom we have to discriminate. Individual sensory clues may therefore be only weakly correlated with the response-inferred stimulus, and yet the mass of such clues gives rise to highly reliable perception.‡ On such an account, finally, the analogue of decoding in telecommunication is not error-free recovery of an univocal message transmitted from the periphery, but rather an error-correcting constitution of stable stimulus equivalence classes. It is this constitution that corresponds to Kant's transcendental framework, and response within this framework is the physiological counterpart of the act of perception. In such an account of perception there is no inner sensorium; the object of perception, only more or less attained, is the physical reality that the whole account of perception necessarily starts with.

Problems of Freedom

The phenomenological language of self-consciousness and of interpersonal communication gives rise to a way of describing behavior that is certainly different from the causal description adopted by an external observer. When the latter way gets refined into the conceptual apparatus of deterministic description, it appears to leave no room for the phenomenologically meaningful elements of choice. Over against the situation of A, a person making a choice, we imagine the situation of another person B, who is investigating the behavior of A. Into a sufficient set of deterministic laws B plugs enough information about the antecedent state of A and his environment to sustain a prediction about the details of A's choosing and his subsequent behavior.

According to the postulate of determinism, such a prediction is possible in principle. That it may be difficult or practically impossible in some cases is be-

---

† Richard Jessor, "Phenomenological Personality Theories and the Data Language of Psychology," *Psychological Review*, vol. 63 (1956), pp. 173–80.

‡ The lens analogy again. Cf. Jan Smedslund, *Multiple Probability Learning* (Oslo, 1955).

side the point. Many persons, including some called philosophers, believe that the deterministic postulate, applied to human choice, implies the falsity of another postulate involved in choosing or presupposed by it. This is the postulate of freedom. It is not easy to say just what this postulate means, but let us overlook that for a moment. The belief we have to examine is that A and B, both engaged in standard investigative pursuits, are committed to contradictory postulates applied to the same situation. This alleged contradiction gives rise to the problem of freedom and determinism.

But what is the postulate of freedom? It is rather clearly not *equivalent* to a denial of determinism. Purely chance decisions would be unpredictable, but they would also be uncontrolled by the person "making" them; they would be just as much beyond his logical control as the throw of dice. In view of what we have found to be the relation of chance and determinism, a decision that was predictable only from a multiplicity of independent antecedent conditions would be a chance decision. From this point of view, freedom of choice is absent, not because there is a set of antecedent conditions sufficient for prediction of the choice, but because essential conditions in that set are uncoordinated with one another. It appears that a free choice is one that *reduces* the number of independent determinants of action, not one that lacks them. In this sense it is more, not less, determined—more simply determined—than determinism requires.

On the other hand, the concept of freedom clearly suggests the absence of certain kinds of determinants of action, of what we call restraints and compulsions, and of any causal conditions that determine action independently of the procedures that we describe, phenomenologically, as deliberating, considering, calculating, etc. The irresistible impulse, the conscious compulsion, the unconscious compulsion that predetermines choice (as in post-hypnotic suggestion)— these are examples of determinants, in addition to externally imposed compulsions and restraints, that would be said to be incompatible with free choice. But suppose that action is genuinely the outcome of deliberating, calculating, etc., and that these psychological operations and their results are predictable from antecedent causal conditions. Then choice is free in any sense defined so far, and also predictable.†

The psychological operations of decision-making are hard to describe and

---

† The classic is Thomas Hobbes, *Of Liberty and Necessity* (1654). An extract appears in Woodbridge (editor), *Hobbes: Selections* (New York, 1930). A very careful analysis is that of Paul Marhenke, in *Knowledge and Society,* by the University of California Associates (New York, 1936), Chap. VI, which is reprinted in *Readings in Philosophical Analysis,* edited by Herbert Feigl and Wilfred Sellars (New York, 1949).

very inadequately understood, but they involve, as a common element, the making of discriminations of many sorts. The prediction of their outcome is therefore possible only in terms of an antecedent knowledge of the things discriminated. If the decision of a driver to stop at an intersection depends on the color of a traffic light, the color of the light is a necessary datum in predictions of his behavior. Free choice is a process that involves learning, information transfers, whose content is thus necessary to the prediction of the choice.

It follows at once that the successful predictor of a free choice must be at least as well informed as he who makes the choice. If this were not so, no information transfers would occur in the process of deliberation, or at least they would be causally inefficacious, not transfers to the system of determinants of action. Speaking colloquially, the predictor must manage to be smarter than his subject—a condition not always met in psychological experiments.

But there are further implications. A being capable of making measurements, discriminations, must exhibit, at some level, randomness, noise. The Maxwell Demon projects his radar beam outward, in a manner not coupled antecedently with the molecules he would observe. Probable inference involves sampling, variability. Our hardware model of a learning mechanism has a deliberately built-in source of noise, and at this level its behavior is not predictable—behavioristically. But here, as in evolution, variation is followed by selection, by some kind of differential reinforcement or inhibition. Behavior comes to satisfy some set of conditions that are initially *not* antecedent conditions and that become conditions only through information transfers. The degrees of variability are reduced at a certain cost of free energy; disorder is increased elsewhere.

While free choice is not random choice, therefore, it nevertheless involves random elements and can be predicted only teleologically, only in reference to a state toward which successive information transfers will inform it. We come back to something like the inductive maze, in which a sure result is eventually achieved through a repetition of individually unsure discriminations. To predict the successive steps by which a mathematician will tackle the proof of a theorem is very difficult, but another mathematician could do it more easily than a psychologist—unless, of course, the psychologist was a mathematician.

It will be objected that I have equated choice with cognitive learning, whereas, in fact, choice involves arbitrary, subjective elements that are missing from the cognitive sphere. It is quite true that these are two different ways of accepting and organizing information. To plan a system of actions is, from one point of view, utterly different from organizing a system of beliefs. From another point of view, however, they are species of a common genus and phases of a continuous process, for the investigation of which we reserve the term "ethics."

It will also be objected that the real meaning of "freedom" has been missed. This is the freedom of Adam and Eve, or perhaps the arbitrary elective capacity that Sartre celebrates. It is my view, however, that the eulogistic meaning of the term refers to informed action, action with knowledge. The initial phase of choice involves a kind of arbitrariness, an instability with respect to routine and habit, an accessibility to temptation, a waywardness. And this is a precondition of freedom in the eulogistic sense, but in and of itself it is not freedom; it is only a precondition and a promise.

There is one more step to the argument about freedom, a step that we have not yet considered. It has to do with the implicit connection between freedom and responsibility. A person is praised for his good deeds, inculpated or exculpated for his misdeeds. However much we may try to identify free choice as informed choice, and choosing as learning, our description is suspect if we cannot account for the fact that the complex informational processes involved are not anonymous but are imputed to the surveillance and guidance of an agent. This agent is conceived, not merely as the organism *within which* the informational processes go on, but as the person *by whom* they are carried on.

This sense of agency is lost in a physiological and behavioristic description of human behavior. But it is lost also in phenomenological description. For within the field of self-consciousness there is to be found nothing that can be described as the agent. Kant spoke of the " 'I think' that accompanies all our representations"; but this "I think" or "I choose" is not to be found among the representations that it accompanies. I discriminate means and obstacles, I bring knowledge to bear on the prediction of consequences, I define ends. But the referent of this pronoun "I" remains peculiarly a blank. Until we have some account of it, our analysis of freedom is incomplete.

CHAPTER

12

ETHICS

Human learning capacities have reached a level of development commensurate with man's capacity to be the vehicle of cultural evolution. But our knowledge of animal psychology is in so unsatisfactory a state that this contrast between ourselves and the other animals is hard to make out. It is rather obvious, however, that the cousinship of man and the higher mammals is close. The qualitative transition is an accumulation of quantitative changes that have reached a critical point. The new species in this case is not merely a new species of animal, but a new species of evolution.

New species of animal and new species of evolution are coupled. Cultural evolution implies developmental variability in the individuals of the species that supports it. This variability itself gains recognition within the culture, in the language and viewpoint of phenomenology. We chose a vivid if rather pathetic expression of it, the Sartrean account of man-for-himself. In the strong interaction between man the self-observer and man the self-observed, animal determinateness of character and behavior is weakened, and at the core of human self-consciousness is always an uncertainty, a figment of "non-Being," a "worm at the heart of the apple." This is precious prose, but it is bearable.

The Sartrean metaphysics is a contemporary expression of a very old insight, which one may be tempted to see not only in the classic myths and stories, but even in the admiration for the other animals, hunters and hunted, expressed in the portraits of them in the ice-age caves of France and Spain. A maturer expression of it is to recognize the indeterminacy of human character as the nega-

308

tive expression of a new capacity, with its own intrinsic determinateness, its own standards and presuppositions. In discussing the concept of freedom I proposed to describe this determinateness as a capacity for importing new order into ourselves, our conduct, and our environment. This capacity seems to require a conception of learning as detached from the primary organic drives and the primary reinforcement-inhibition mechanisms of more primitive learning. Such learning occurs in phases that alternate with phases of overt activity. Each phase requires, literally, the partial suspension of the other. It is a rhythm we are well aware of, from observation and from self-observation. We mark the transitions, as when obstacles "make us think" or thoughts "give us pause." It creates its own problems, as when men of action fall into logical traps or philosophers fall into wells. There is interaction between the phases. Each may inhibit, but may also guide, the other. And each has its own continuity, is suspended and reinstated.

Model-building

The continuity of thought, of self-conscious inquiry, John Dewey analyzed extensively in his *Logic*.† The learnings of one phase of inquiry not only are informative of subsequent action, but are stored up to be reapplied, retested, and extended in later phases of inquiry. However else they may be stored, they are embodied within the informational code of language, socially communicated, recorded, and readied for new application.

Dewey emphasized, and it is right to emphasize, the continuity of thought as covert, "vicarious" activity with the kind of overt activity that is subordinated to thought and that he called "experimental." It would indeed be good to have a word for self-conscious activity wider in connotation than "thought," with its intellectualistic associations. Self-consciousness is organized around the problematic, and seeks certitude, definition; it is an engagement in constructing some order of reality or model of reality. In lieu of "thought" we shall again speak of order- or model-building. In some cases the model might be a literal one like a new tool or a painting. In others it might be almost wholly vicarious, a creation of unexpressed imagination. Or it might be a form of words, a poem, a description or narration, a prescription or command. If in some cases it is warranted as true‡ in a literal sense, in others it is right or good, but none of these terms

---

† John Dewey, *Logic: the Theory of Inquiry* (New York, 1938).

‡ Dewey avoided the specific concept of truth and substituted for it that of "warranted assertibility." But to assert and to assert as true are equivalent acts, so that nothing is really gained by the avoidance.

can be used over the whole range—in current English, at any rate—except analogically.

In place of thought, then, "model-building." And in place of truth, rightness, or other specific terms for what is sought, a neutral term, "finality." We label what the model-builder seeks to build by a term suggesting his readiness to accept the model that meets his specification.

It would be good, in this connection, to think of model-building as a kind of externalization, by the analogy of the special case that produces a set of drawings or a tool or a book. If there is no overt, publicly visible model, there is still the readiness for communication. But what is involved in all cases, even those without public manifestation, is some quasi-external system with sufficient degrees of freedom to be usable as raw material to be modeled. We do not have to play the notes; we can "hear" them. We do not have to shape the clay; we can visualize it shaped. We do not have to say the words, for they reverberate nevertheless. It is not difficult to hypothesize physiological mechanisms of this sort. From a certain point of view it does not matter whether they are intra- or extra-organic. The sense of the term "externalize" is not spatial but functional: it implies a sort of coupling that permits the storage and recovery of information. It is the sort of coupling that man has to the plastic components of his environment. But he can have the same sort of coupling to what are, physiologically, components of his own organism.

Man's physical coupling with his environment is not that of an intrinsic source of energy, but is weaker, more purely thermodynamic. He controls his environment by subtle changes in its order, so that the streams of natural process flow in new channels. But the control runs both ways. Competence is derived from acceptance of the *de facto* order of things. The potter who shapes the clay has long been the image of a god-like power, but this is not the perception the potter has of himself. He must be sensitive to the properties of the mix, and to its responses to firing in shape and color and texture. The potter is as much transformed by his art as the clay is.

So, if we speak of domestication, and extend the range of the concept to the materials and energies of the inorganic as well as applying it to the plants and animals, we also have to extend it to man himself. To domesticate means to reclaim from the wild state, to bring under control. But every such reclamation brings with it a new order. Domesticating the other animals leads to a pastoral culture, and controlling rivers brings about the culture of cities. The substantive ends that have led men to such innovations have been transformed by them. Are there other ends, beyond the impelling but dependent ones, that stand above the evolution of culture and preside over it? Religions and philosophical idealisms have held that there are. If there are such ends, what are they, how do we know them, and what is the nature of their authority? Are they the accumulated distillations of experience, or are they given somehow by direct intuition or revelation? These are not scientific questions, but the contemporary scientific synthesis affects the terms in which they are asked and in which they can, if at all, be answered.

I have spoken against the fixity of concrete ends in human affairs. Ends, as concretely operative, are, no less than means, affected by the evolution of culture. Man domesticates himself perforce. But at every stage—indeed, at every moment of choice—there is a distinction between the domesticated and the domesticator. The variability that shows itself historically as aptness for culture shows itself consciously in the ability to construct models of future conduct; when these are adequate by some standards, they are or can be translated into action and habit. This implies the impermanence of older habit, a certain wildness, which does not disappear, even in the midst of domesticity.

Choice and the Fundamental Theorem of Ethics

At the end of the previous chapter the discussion of freedom was left incomplete. The word was associated with a kind of informational process in which the patterns of human action—ends—are modified, reconstituted. But this process was left in an anonymous condition as a process going on in the interaction of organism and environment or in the field of self-conscious activity. Freedom as a capacity or disposition of something, of an agent in the moral sense, did not seem necessary in the account.

In the present chapter I propose a further step: that we refine the description of choice sufficiently to discover an old and familiar polarity in it. It is the polarity celebrated in the idealistic traditions as self and other, microcosm and macrocosm, the soul and the world. This distinction is latent in the phenomenology of choice. It corresponds to a distinction between fairly distinct phases of self-conscious activity. There are different ways of drawing the line, one of which emerges out of a problem of moral philosophy. It concerns the distinction between "judgments of fact" and "judgments of value" and involves a proposition that I shall call the fundamental theorem of ethics. First, however, some preliminaries are necessary, concerning the traditional distinction between the faculty of intellect and the faculty of will.

In discussing the concept of freedom in the previous chapter, I reached the view that man's capacity for choice is a way of learning and not a sheer unpredictability. There is an old image for choice: the traveler standing at a fork in the road. Like the laboratory rat, he hesitates, oscillates, examines signs and portents. For the rat we have only the fact that there is a time limitation, and after a while he is going leftward or going rightward (or, as in our inductive maze, backward). For the man we have the phenomenology of choice as well. He weighs, deliberates; he seeks advice. He stages internal arguments "before the bar of reason." But the fork is there, and the outcome of deliberation is not just belief, but action. In the end he too takes the leftward, rightward, or backward road.

In an old-fashioned language it is not just that the intellect functions but that the will acts. Freedom is not merely the freedom of the intellect to understand, but the freedom of the will to act. How are these two things related? Does the intellect determine the will, or does the will determine the intellect? In medieval Christian theology some argued that things that are good are good because God wills them, others that God wills them because they are good. In psychological terms there is an isomorphous problem: whether we seek the things that are good, or whether the things that we seek are good. The traditional labels for the disputants are "intellectualist" and "voluntarist." From our point of view there is an important content in these old bottles. The problem of freedom has turned, in modern times, into an issue between the postulate of freedom and the postulate of determinism, which I disposed of in the previous chapter. The older and more important problem is the problem of adjudicating intellectualism and voluntarism.

I have already begun to analyze this problem, at the end of my discussion of freedom and determinism. The free will that is thought to be incompatible with determinism is one that is defined, implicitly, by voluntaristic preconceptions. It is an arbitrary elective capacity, a capacity for uncaused action, an amplification of psychogenic noise. But this is not what men eulogize as moral freedom; when we try to understand the sense of eulogy, we begin to uncover the intellectualistic preconceptions. Free choice is informed choice.

What, then, of the voluntaristic interpretation of choice? Are we committed to denying it altogether, as Hegel did with his pronouncement that "freedom is the knowledge of necessity"? This is a place for diffidence, for the philosophers have been over the ground many times, and the easy errors of analysis have been made repeatedly. We start from the fact that moral concepts, and moral judgments, have two sides to them. From one side terms like "good" and "right," when used in moral discourse, are used predicatively, and judgments as to what is good or right resemble descriptive statements as to what is so. They are, as I suggested above, species of finality, results with which inquiry will rest. As giving approbation of a designated object or state of affairs, such judgments invite agreement or disagreement; there is a subjective universality about them, an implied invariance from one occasion or one person to another. They refer to potential things or states of affairs, and do so propositionally by subordinate clauses. Such judgments have an optative significance. An *it-were-better-that* or an *ought* is attached to the dependent clause.†

This type of grammatical construction parallels the one we discerned, in Chapter 7, in the language of probability. The parallel is interesting, inasmuch as in both cases there are conflicting objectivistic and subjectivistic interpretations, of probability in the one case and of moral value in the other. In my interpretation of probability the assertion of probability is a description of the physical conditions with respect to which a collocation space is defined. With reference to a specific collocation in that space, probability functions not as a property of the collocation but as a modality, a degree of propriety or priority, in predictions of that collocation. Value judgments exhibit a similar duality: they are grounded in discrimination of fact, outcome of investigation, learning, discovery; but they have a bearing on choice, on action, in a way that distinguishes them from other judgments.

The bearing on choice and action is that moral judgments are expressive, emotive, hortatory; they imply desire or aversion, approval or disapproval. These attitudes are not incidental; they are of the essence of what is conveyed by moral judgments. To the extent that one emphasizes this, one is led toward voluntarism. Men *call* good what they desire or approve of. Pushed far enough, separated logically from the learning that informs desire, that evaluates, voluntarism becomes subjectivism.

Judgments of moral value play a linking role, then, as do judgments of probability in another context. I do not wish to run this analogy too far. In order to continue the comparison of factual and evaluative judgment, I return to common ground, that of model-building in general. First of all, there is a possible misconception. Our affinity is for the philosophical tradition that treats knowledge as representational, as picture-building. If one misconstrues and extends this emphasis, however, one gets into some classic epistemological dilemmas, of which I have already spoken in connection with problems of perception.

† A very careful analysis of the grammatical constructions of value statement is E. W. Hall, *What is Value?* (New York, 1952). See the discussion in E. M. Adams, *Ethical Naturalism and the Modern World View* (Chapel Hill, N.C., 1960), pp. 107–19.

To say that the knowledge of nature is a representation, a kind of modeling, implies an isomorphism between the picture and the thing pictured, and it implies a possibility of comparing the picture directly with the thing pictured. But, if we can make the comparison, we do not really need the picture, and, if we cannot get this kind of direct evidence, the metaphor is profoundly suspect. In the tradition of philosophical idealism the metaphor is thrown away. What we create is not a picture of an extra-mental reality but directly *is* reality; the mind constructs reality. For the idealist there is no deep problem about the relation of knowing and choosing. Both are ways of constructing an order of reality and thus fulfilling the potentialities of something called Self.

My use of "model" and "model-building" is not intended to support a representational theory of knowledge in the old sense. What we construct is not a picture to look at. The model is not what we know as reality but an instrumentality of, or a part of, our knowing. Even an extra-organic model, such as a map or an orrery, which may occupy our attention as an object in its own right, may also become incorporated into our cognitive activity. It is then no longer attended to as an object but becomes part of our understanding of what we intend by it. This is almost inveterately true of the physical words and sentences we utter and hear. But it is also true, in greater or lesser degree, of a great section of our more familiar environment, which we appropriate for symbolic use. The better and less questioned the model, the less we are aware of it *per se*. The perfect model is, so to say, transparent. We do not see it but see through it. But we know that the glass is there by its imperfections, and, when these are aberrant enough, our perception of reality is disoriented. What we see now we see as model, and as problematic. There is a reality "beyond," a "something I know not what," of which a new model must be constructed. Using the traditional jargon, we are epistemological dualists when we have problems, and epistemological monists when we solve them.†　Idealists have tried to say that we construct reality, but it is less mystifying to say that we construct a perception, or a knowledge, of reality.

In the case of choice, however, we do construct an order of reality that is not antecedently there. When we achieve a description of what is to be done, it is not a description of an independently existing state of affairs. To describe intended future actions and consequences involves propositional reference to possibilities, not demonstrative reference to actualities. The model informs the potential reality, not the reality the model. Wherein, then, consists the reality, the finality, of a model of choice, of future conduct? First of all it has

---

† Part of Dewey's avoidance of "truth" was connected with the critique of epistemological dualism.

to be feasible. Our own immediate action is never more than a partial cause of what follows. The choice must be constructed in terms of a knowledge of boundary conditions. This limits what we can expect as a result of our immediate actions, but it does not eliminate any immediate action. If we control a set of variables X, and other variables Y are relevant but beyond our control, we are limited to a family of alternatives determined, independently of us, by Y. The criterion of feasibility finds limits but does not eliminate.

This inability to limit choice is important. It is what is meant by the statement that no amount of factual knowledge, in and of itself, is, or warrants, a value judgment.† This is the fundamental theorem of ethics. It remains true when the description of the choice is filled in to the point of including ideally *all* consequences, even enjoyments and sufferings. To investigate fully the conditions and consequences of a proposed choice—to know in that sense *what* the choice amounts to—is limitative only in a subjective sense. It aims to eliminate those futures in which the consequences of action will have been unforeseen. This *is* a kind of limitation, not upon the varieties of behavior but upon the varieties of subjective relation to that behavior. To choose at all is to choose to act with knowledge.

Knowledge of matters of fact not only does not limit action but even expands the array of alternatives available to us. Unknowing action limits us to the usual, to the probable consequences of standard kinds of behavior. Through knowledge of conditions and consequences we are able to design our behavior with increasing subtlety. Informed behavior informs also the consequences of it. Being richer in the variety of the alternatives that it may embrace, informed action has greater capacity than the uninformed to satisfy other criteria than those I have been talking about, which, in the end, will constrain our choice.

So far, then, the fundamental theorem. Knowledge of environing conditions and causal relations defines what *can* be done, but not what *is* to be done. Ethical theories that seem to get round this ineffectiveness do so only by an implicit prejudgment. Among the predictables connected with a particular design of action are the pleasures and pains, enjoyments and sufferings, satisfactions and dissatisfactions that accrue. A classic form of theory regards such prediction as *the* guide to action. For each of a set of alternative courses of action we are able to ascertain its rank in an ordering of values and possibly even assign it, in some way, a numerical value. This is the economist's utility

---

† This proposition is often taken to imply moral subjectivism. It was taken by G. E. Moore to eliminate all naturalistic theories of ethics; see his *Principia Ethica* (Cambridge, England, 1903).

function, which I deal with again in the following chapter. Inquiry defines
new alternatives or alters the description of old ones, and ranks change. When
inquiry terminates, the highest-ranking alternative wins, and action supervenes.
Wins? Or ought to win? If this is a psychological generalization, a law of
human nature, it seems ethically irrelevant. If we can never *not* choose the
highest-ranking alternative, the exhortation to choose it is silly.

There is something else in the picture and a suppressed premise in the argument. We must *now* desire what will be maximally satisfactory. Or else we
need not, and sometimes do not, but persuade ourselves that we ought to.
No doubt there is some coupling between what we predict on factual evidence
and what we now desire. But is it perfect, or is there some decoupling also?
A suspicion arises. Is it possible to distinguish clearly between predicted en-
joyment or satisfaction—predicted in terms of factual knowledge of the causal
conditions of such satisfaction—and *present* emotional reaction to the contemplated future? The prediction may be biased by present attitudes, so that what
is foreseen with a glow of anticipation turns to dust and ashes, or a dreaded
future turns out to be tolerable and even satisfying. The anticipatory reaction
to an imagined future is a primitive mechanism of prediction, liable to failure
in any but the simplest situations. As a mechanism it needs subtilization and
education through training, precept, and vicarious experience.

But the connection is not so simple. Pleasures and satisfactions are not isolated psychological states, but are more or less dependent upon antecedent en-
grossment. A person is said to be satisfied, but so is an interest or need or
requirement. The person must be, as we say, interested. Insofar as the value
achieved is a function of the involvements of the achiever, a ranking of relative values-to-be-achieved will not determine choice but will, on the contrary,
be determined by it. To the extent that inquiry alters our interests and choice
alters our habits, our value rankings are altered also. Theories of ethics that
assert that choice ought to be governed by prediction of resulting value break
down just in the measure in which the human character is itself a product of
choice.

But the ethics of resulting value is not pointless. Someone said, "Man is
the animal that can get used to anything." But this is a bit of meretricious
cleverness. If it were so, misery and despair and neurosis would not plague
mankind as they have plagued him and still plague him. Needs represent
fixed points, invariants, in the transformations of human evolution. Until they
are met far more uniformly and consistently than our history has so far evi-

denced, the utilitarian kind of ethics will continue to have an overwhelming practical point.

But the fixed points do not determine the transformations. The definition of needs is not a definition of how they shall be provided for. Here another phase of choice becomes apparent. In this phase inquiry is not directed to future alternatives, but to present desires. It concerns itself with the possible alterations of interest and disposition, of character, which must be settled in order that there be an adequate ranking of future alternatives. The two sorts of process are interleaved, but they center on different poles. In the previous pages I have been talking about the objective pole, which comes down to a process of delineating what the choices before us realistically are, including not only immediate steps to be taken but remoter consequences as well, required diversion of resources from other activities, etc. Now we turn attention to the subjective pole, to the self or agent who will be committed to this or that course of action, whose motivation will sustain it, and whose achievements will be valued above those to which alternative courses of action would have committed him.

This emphasis is suggested by an alternative way of describing choice. If alternative paths of conduct are represented by paths in a phase space, the value accrued may be thought of as a cumulative sum of increments along any given path—a line integral. Now in general some such integrals, when taken from an initial point P to an arbitrary point P', depend only on the coordinates of P and P', and these are called state functions. They are invariant with respect to a choice of path between P and P'. Other integrals are not invariant, but are functions of the whole path. When a thermodynamic system, for example, is described in this fashion, the entropy change between P and P' is a state function, but the external work done is not.

The hedonistic or utilitarian habit of ethical theorizing depends upon the implicit assumption that values accrued along two paths—diverging from P and reconverging at P'—need not, in general, be state functions, but that utilitarian standards of comparison *are* state functions. If two identical twins chose the paths A and B to P', they would have different experiences along the way and different values accrued at P', but they could agree on the relative values of the two choices. Even though in retrospect their valuations were different from those made in prospect, the relative values accrued would be, in some sense, matters of objective fact.

But suppose that this is not so: what happens along the way is connected with an alteration of character, so that the twins, in a significant sense, are no longer identical when they meet again. Here a paradox is brewing, not unlike the relativistic twin paradox that I discussed in Chapter 8, in which elapsed time is not a state function. Even after the fullest communication the ex-twins will not agree on the relative goodness of their lives from P to P'. If each prefers the other's—as is reported sometimes to be true of marriage partners— a search for new paths is strongly suggested. If each, in retrospect, finds his own career more worthy, the case is, in a sense, happier—but not for the actual person who, standing undecided at P, projects these twin selves in his constructive imagination and is baffled by the resulting incommensurability. Which self shall he become, and which shall remain unborn? He can encompass both in imagination, but he cannot become both in reality. There might be a third path that would dominate both of the incommensurables, but that would destroy the hypothesis.

Let us imagine that we define some measure of the difference, the character distance, between the reconvergent twins. This distance is a measure of the inadequacy of ethical theories based on the notion of weighing the consequences. The measure is not uniform for all choices, and, as indicated before, it may well be small for many choices of great practical importance in the world. But there is something wrong here in principle. Many choices, particularly those affected by specifically moral considerations, do exhibit this sort of incommensurability.†

Ethical theories of the type under discussion are usually called teleological. Pleasure, happiness, well-being—individual or social, terrestrial or celestial— may be the goal. However defined, it is a supreme goal; one cannot help seeking it, and it alone confers value on other, subordinate goals. Teleological theories of ethics are open to other kinds of objection, but here we wish to accept such a theory as a starting point and show its inadequacy in the next approximation.

What are the alternatives? A traditional alternative is the ethics of duty. Not future consequence but present obligation is the source of finality in choice. Duties may be rationalized in teleological theories as means to happiness or welfare. But this misses the point. A commanded action is not entertained as something that contributes to welfare, but as commanded, as required. What has bad consequences is not the disobedient *act,* but the fact that it is disobedient. In a violation of conscience or a breach of commitment there

---

† See David Hawkins, *Ethics and Ethical Experience,* University of Colorado Studies, Series in Philosophy, No. 1 (1958), pp. 57–71.

is an immediate illfare, which stands out most clearly just when one may suspect that the act that breaches *might* in itself contribute to welfare. In spite of obvious contrasts, the sense of duty resembles sheer animal impulse or sheer irrational sympathy in the way it operates without reference to future value consequences.

Thus we come back to the subjective pole of inquiry. Our present affective state, the interplay of our present feelings and reactions to the projections of act and consequence, provide us with a basis of self-description. We build up an image, a model, of ourselves, and every affective response we exhibit in the course of deliberation provides a test. Some of the response is familiar and predictable, but some is surprising and even unnerving. The description falls in terms of habit and disposition, but it is, in principle, just as incomplete, just as subject to revision, as the description of things in our natural environment. Here, perhaps, is the origin of the idea of self as substance, as soul. In choice one perceives oneself as a reservoir of potentialities only incompletely expressed.

But this does not mean that inquiry around the subjective pole is soul-searching. The metaphor is bad because the focus is not upon achieving a better description of what one already is, already desires, or is committed to, but rather upon what sort of self, with what sort of new interests and commitments, can be fashioned out of this—frequently rather unpromising—raw material. The sources of such investigation are partly, but not all, introspective. It exploits an empathy, a criticism of the lives of others, and a scrutinizing of respected authorities. Thus choice involves a simultaneous definition of the pathway of action and of the person who *will* be committed to that pathway as his own.†

And what, now, of the fundamental theorem of ethics? If my account is fair, every discrimination at every step of the process of choice is factual, but the final result *is* a choice. Does this not amount to a counterexample against the theorem? It seems so only if the process of choice is misconstrued. What culminates the constructive activity is not a commitment to belief or statement but a commitment to action.‡ The statements made as value judgments are merely statements, in the first instance, of the finality of the given decision. The moral predicates "right," "good," "proper," "justified," etc. belong to a

---

† The classic statement—in idealist clothing—is that of F. H. Bradley, *Ethical Studies*, 2nd edition (Oxford, 1927), especially Essays II, III, and IV.

‡ This point is made emphatically by Stuart Hampshire in "Fallacies in Moral Philosophy," *Mind*, N.S., LVIII, No. 232 (October 1949), 466–69.

class that asserts, with varying emphasis on different aspects of the choice, this finality. Is such a judgment a judgment of fact? My answer is that it is not a judgment of physical fact, of psychological fact, or of social fact, although discriminations of all these kinds are involved in the choice. What the judgment implies is that the pathway chosen is well informed by all the kinds of considerations that have been recognized as relevant to it. When a laboratory experimenter checks his apparatus and instruments before doing an experiment, he makes a similar reflective comment. One could say that the fact asserted by such a judgment is a *logical* fact if this were understood as an assertion, not of abstract logical relation, but of valid performance on a specific occasion. It implies that a review of procedure will not reveal oversights or errors.

The literature of ethical theory is surprisingly empty of reference to the methodology of choice. Some maxims go along with common-sense moral culture, or have entered it from the traditions of philosophy, such as the doctrine of the mean or the imperatives of self-realization. Kant's famous categorical imperative purports to be a sufficient principle: act so that the maxim of your action may be willed as a universal law. The meaning of "universal" here is not unambiguous. The crucial meaning is what I have called subjective universality. Since one treats one's own purpose as an end-in-itself, the requirement of universality implies that others also should be treated as ends-in-themselves, and never as means only. A more methodological orientation is suggested by Kant's categories of freedom.† These are taken by analogy with Kant's categories of understanding, but the parallel is artificial, and Kant speaks of them almost with embarrassment. These categories represent aspects of any proposed choice with respect to which it requires examination. The choice is to be related to intentions, precepts, laws, other persons and the effect upon their condition, etc. A conscientious choice will presumably be possible only after one has described it under all these categories.

Subsequent experience provides a test of the claim made by moral judgments. The interests and commitments that the choice has defined are adopted as those of the agent; he has to live with them as his own. His retrospective evaluation of the choice, made in the light of fuller factual information and from a perspective altered by experience, confirms or calls in question the judgments formerly made. From accumulated experience of this kind generalized moral judgments are abstracted and acquire social currency. All actual choices are made in the light of such generalizations, accrued from past social

---

† In the *Critique of Practical Reason*, Part I, Book I, Chap. II.

and individual history. I have ignored this in my account, but here, as in science, there are no primary inductions, derived from particular experience alone and without guidance of antecedent belief. Moral judgments that emerge from choice can only be versions, more or less altered and redefined, of moral judgments taken to the choice in the first place. This is relevant to the fundamental theorem: even though all discriminations involved in choice are discriminations of physical, social, and psychological fact, they do not of themselves give rise to moral judgments. The moral relevance of such discriminations is provided by the moral beliefs held antecedently. The logical relation is not

$$F \longrightarrow M$$

but

$$MF \longrightarrow M'$$

In all of this there is a development of what I shall call the *ethical interest*. The appearance of conflict and uncertainty about the patterns of our lives is forced upon us by many circumstances. Any such conflict produces a minor or major vital crisis. Unless some creative resolution is achieved, we suffer. The ethical interest, coupled to the moral culture of a society, is related to these crises of decision as its origin and point of return. It is an interest that cultivates, in one or another way, the resources that prove effective in decision-making, much as science, more externally oriented, cultivates the resources that prove effective in controlling our environment. Like science, the ethical interest may flourish in detachment, in the absence of those occasions when its resources are used in the guidance of action. Like science, also, it may suggest alterations of behavior even when there are no problems; it may create problems where none arise spontaneously; and it may facilitate transitions otherwise impossible. It is widely believed, among us, that no flowering of the ethical interest comparable to that of science is likely or even meaningful. Yet, historically, the greater part of our moral culture is the product of past periods of such flowering. The illusion that morality—usually taken as a fixed code, or system of attitudes and habits—is a kind of unchanging accompaniment of human life, with no evolutionary origin or none not safely remote in time, is strong among us. In this respect we resemble those who, in the past, have asserted the finality and essential completeness of their current knowledge of nature.

The openness of science is toward the reorganization of belief and the extension of experience, "to command more of the hidden potential in nature." †

---

† Jacob Bronowski, *Science and Human Values* (New York, 1958), p. 14.

The openness of the ethical interest is similar, but it is organized more nearly round human subjectivity than round nature at the pole of objectivity. Its goal—only in part the analysis and reformulation of moral norms and rules—includes all the arts that enhance our sensitivity to the conditions of choice. It thus reveals more of the hidden potential of human life.

The discussion so far has been cast largely in the pattern of individual decision-making. The central theme has been the individual capacity for self-information. Seen externally, that capacity is expressed in perturbations, mutations, of behavior, which may prove exemplary and, if so, result in an alteration of social patterns. But the same general description holds for patterns of concerted social choice and of the debate that mediates that choice. We shall examine some of the complexities of the latter in the following chapter, as these affect the conceptual framework of the social sciences.

The Gardens

According to the myth of Eden, man has left one garden to which he cannot return, and is condemned, by the act, to a role of outcast from which he cannot, unaided, save himself. Phylogenetically, the outcast became fully human only as he left the garden, miserable and naked. Taken ontogenetically, this self-consciousness is the awareness of innocence in the loss of it, a pathos that paints the lost estate in colors that it never, in fact, had. The lost estate is the immediacy of animal existence, biologically governed. Or it is the immediacy of childhood, governed by a human authority not yet fully internalized and not yet challenged by him whom it governs.

For a more anthropological version of the myth we can look to, and idealize, the societies that appear to have developed a fairly stable ecology and a culture in which the tempo of evolution has been slow enough to escape the attention of its members. Out of this slow development has emerged a moral culture that equips its members with a considerable discrimination over the range of situations requiring deliberation and choice. The idealization is that every situation has been met with an almost infinite variety of responses, and a kind of all-embracing wisdom has been precipitated therefrom. As though by natural selection, there are habitual answers to all questions.

Why should such a system of behavior be called "moral"? Terms like "custom" and "habit" lack the emotional connotations of "moral" or "immoral," and in the ideally static society we are considering these neutral terms describe the all-embracing framework of life. The emotional flavor of approval or disapproval implies some assertiveness of persons against the rule of habit, a capacity for waywardness, for temptation.

The sources of this waywardness are, in a certain sense, necessarily irrational. They are, in the nature of the case, impulses unsupported by habit, representing interests or viewpoints excluded from the current rationalization of conduct. The *moralization* of custom and habit is derived from their *re*assertion, and thus their conscious definition, in the face of the impulses that would, if translated into action, merely disrupt or disorganize the prevailing economy of existence. In Hegel's famous dialectic of thesis, antithesis, and synthesis, the impulsive and irrational is what instigates the development of the antithesis to a given thesis. Excluded interests and beliefs assert themselves first against the prevailing orthodoxy, as negation of the thesis.

In its most primitive expression, therefore, the moral response is one that tries to exclude the offending impulse. It is negative in turn, the negation of the negation. But let us look at the sources of the disruptive impulses that evoke the moral response.† An obvious source is the whole system of man's animal impulses, the primitive teleology of biological needs. Since every society necessarily, in behalf of a more indirect and less disruptive expression, evolves some system of constraints upon the direct expression of these needs, and since the teleology involved is primitive and unreconstructed, it asserts itself either in open conflict or in the various disguises that Sigmund Freud was the first to analyze systematically.

A second category of impulse, comparable in importance to the sexual and aggressive, is connected with the authoritarian dimension of personality, having its earliest development in the instruction of infant and child referred to before. In this category I include not merely the voice of conscience but all other impulses to obey or follow. Conscience is described as the expression of early authority, internalized as part of the maturation of the individual. But all voices of authority, whether inner or outer, have for him who hears them a distinctive meaning, conveyed by the imperative mood or by the mysterious word "ought." The impulse to obey or comply, whatever its psychological origins and whatever elicits it, is no more accessible to conscious control, as an impulse, than any other.

---

† The list is that of Henry W. Stuart, from a syllabus for a course in ethics at Stanford University in 1932. The viewpoint of this chapter is, in major part, learned from Stuart. See his "Valuation as a Logical Process," in *Studies in Logical Theory*, Decennial Publications, University of Chicago, Vol. XI (1902), pp. 227–340; "A Reversal of Perspective in Ethical Theory," *Philosophical Review*, 29 (July 1920), 340–54; "Knowledge and Self-consciousness," *Philosophical Review*, 46 (August 1937), 609–43.

A third category, not always easy to distinguish from the second, is that of sympathetic impulse. To give needed assistance, to comply with a request, to empathize with the perceptions of another—these are as genuinely impulsive as any human responses. A culture that sanctions harshness and brutality against an internal class or an external enemy needs reinforcement against the corrosion of sympathy. It has to reinforce these impulses in some cases and inhibit them in others. To be parasitic and marauding by way of life is to face these contradictions in their sharpest form, but every social stratification creates them in principle.

We have much to learn about the sources of impulses, generally, and about the kinds of circumstance that release or inhibit them. Among the other animals they are sometimes connected with very simple and stereotyped "releasers"; a patch of black with red in the center, for example, will evoke the eating response among young crows. Human beings are hardly more sophisticated in some of these matters than their animal cousins, and yet our ability to analyze them, without great detachment, is often slight.

Undoubtedly the expressions of impulse are vastly complicated by acculturation and self-consciousness, and so may even the evocation of them be. The biological impulses represent a primitive and crude adaptation, transmitted through early learning or even genetically, to the conditions of survival. But, as in human development they lose the immediate control of action, they gain another function—as sources of information relevant to choice. They are no longer to be followed automatically, but are to be taken account of, to be explored and tested as to their meaning.

It is out of this exploration that the definition of what is desired and what is approved of, and thus of the self, finally emerges.

The subjective phase of choice usually involves the polarity of standard ways of acting, more or less sanctioned by the claims of morality, against self-assertive counter-suggestions that do not initially have that sanction. It is not my purpose here to develop the details of ethical methodology. It represents the conflict and also the argument, mediated by more or less impartial criteria, between initially incompatible interests and ways of living.

If we assume a wider suffusion and an increased competence of the ethical interest, does a Second Garden become possible? Our age is faced with too many crucial issues to be hospitable to utopias in the old literary manner. The probable future is hidden by major uncertainties, but so are the details of any ideal future. We can post some necessary conditions, of human needs and terrestrial circumstances. But we can also define a style for the Second

Garden, the style of an evolution in which variation and selection are functions of deliberation and choice and no longer, in their major outlines, of the law of the jungle. What is this style? Perhaps the Christian Kingdom contains some significant suggestions. Among all the versions of a promised hereafter, it alone is rather fully—for many of us rather embarrassingly—social, at the farthest pole from the flight of the mystics. The Kingdom of Heaven is dominated by personal influences and transactions. Persons mind one another's business, consider the lilies of the field, take no thought for the morrow; and a rich man can hardly enter.

But the style of the Second Garden has to be defined, in the first instance, by reference to that of the First. What gives verisimilitude to the myth of Eden is its play upon the phenomenology of choice. The recognition of the moral dimension of personal experience is generated by conflict in which the immediacy of moral attitudes is replaced by self-consciousness concerning them. This opening phase is dominated by a certain emotionally charged recognition, which Hegel and others have called guilt. Normally, "guilt" means culpability after the deed. But a deed premeditated provokes a similar response. It is both the acknowledgment of an interest that is normally excluded or forbidden and the reassertion of the standard that forbids that interest.

As "guilt" in this rather generic sense marks the opening phase of choice, so the finality of choice satisfactorily concluded brings into play another emotional component. This is not simply the logical satisfactoriness of a model that has been constructed but the irrevocableness of it on the eve of action. Lost innocence and immediacy have not been wholly regained. Especially if action has to be taken within a limited time, there is a sense of peril, of the alienness of what one has elected, and once again a pathos for the carefree days. In every moral choice man has, as it were, to relive the history of the race and of his own shaky independence from the protecting barriers of childhood.

If choices were, ideally, reversible, if, as in some areas of science, the cost of error were small, we could afford to take large risks of error in return for some calculation of ultimate progress. In a wide enough perspective this view may still be asserted, but it smacks of consolation. An aircraft is designed, among other things, for safety. But very often an inadequacy in design is isolated only after one or a few tragedies. The state of the moral art is surely the outcome of a history dotted with tragedies. This is, indeed, part of the force of tragedy as a dramatic form.

All actual choices are, to some degree, irreversible; and those that irreversibly affect individual or social life in ways recognized as major will be taken as final with a minimum of serenity. But *some* course must be adopted, and the phenomenological meaning of moral responsibility is to be found in this fact. One looks backward over the process itself to see if various factors cannot be estimated differently, and one looks forward to life altered by the choice as exemplary for future choices and, possibly, for other persons. The sense of guilt and the sense of responsibility are the twin emotions that mark the development of human freedom.

In this account of choice there lies, perhaps, an answer to the question whether man has the capacity to domesticate himself and, if so, what the meaning of this odd capacity is. Man's wildness, his tendency to break over the barriers of habit reinforced by institutions, is not the capacity for an arbitrary and capricious action. It may take such a form in the extreme case where the forces of custom and tradition are thoughtlessly overridden, but this is not its ultimate meaning. From the point of view of the ethical interest, capricious self-assertion is simply failure, the failure to explore and test the inner sources and resources of that assertion.

The image of man equipped to control his outer environment but helpless to control his own infantile motivation is a horrifying one. But this horror only becomes demoralizing when it becomes metaphysical and is taken as a reflection of the nature of things, beyond repair. The mood of nihilism is coupled to the belief that human decision-making is ultimately not only subjective—which, in part, it must be—but therefore arbitrary and irrational, "beyond good and evil." The phrase is Nietzsche's, who more than any other philosopher struggled with the nature of human choice. His version of the myth of Eden, offered against the prevailing theological interpretations, was more violent: "God is dead." But this points both ways, toward the nihilism that fascinated Nietzsche while he detested it, and toward the ideal of moral progress, aimed at the achievement of generalized moral competence—in his romantic terminology, the "will to power."

According to the view of choice presented in this chapter, the conception of choice as ultimately arbitrary is an error, a misreading of what choice is. The loss of innocence, the primary guilt of self-conscious questioning and doubting, is only the opening phase of a rational procedure of inquiry whose outcome is as little arbitrary as the other types of model-building in which human beings engage. In the chapter on the laws of nature I suggested that nature is, in principle, inexhaustible to human inquiry. In science we organize our experience of nature and extend it, but we do not exhaust the potentialities of things. A similar postulate of the ethical interest is that human nature is inexhaustible on the subjective side. This inexhaustibility arises not simply from the great complexity of the secret springs of human motivation and interest, not simply from the enrichment of biological man by the cultural soil in which he develops, but also from his capacity to enlarge himself through learning and choice. The idea of moral progress is as intelligible as that of scientific progress when it is placed in such a setting.

It is this ideal, then, that defines the style of the Second Garden, the domestication and reordering of man's home, the earth. It implies a vast extension of the power of control over the biosphere. It includes the domestication of the animate and the inanimate environment, and of man himself. It doubtless includes also, through knowledge of genetics, a breaking down of the barriers between the stages of evolution, between the evolution of DNA and the evolution of culture. A refusal to use such powers is possible, and no doubt, by stages, wise; but it provides no escape from responsibility.

The two postulates of infinity imply, in a Second Garden as in our present existence, the unavoidability and the permanency of novelty. In such a world both the scientific and the ethical interest are geared, as at least science is in our world, to a kind of evolution in which novelty is not pathogenic but is welcomed because there are disciplines able to accept it and because it is the condition of progress.

The philosophers have dealt harshly with the concept of moral progress—as they have with all other generalized ends—because it has been presented as a *criterion* of choice, as a guide to the perplexed. But the very nature of choice, when properly understood, precludes this. It precludes the conception of choice as dominated by one single unquestionable goal, to which all else is means. Such concepts as harmony, happiness, duty, the realization of self—even moral progress—are only various aspects of the finality of choice. As high-order abstractions they are not informationally rich enough to determine conduct. The analogy in science would be to speak of coherency, predictability, parsimony, fruitfulness, etc., as though from a knowledge of these abstractions we could forthwith deduce all possible knowledge.

The necessary and decisive detail in the resolution of scientific questions comes only from previously established positive knowledge and from sense experience. In choice the situation is not different. Moral judgments are possible only in a context of antecedent moral generalizations; finality is possible in a particular case only because that case lies in a context of antecedent finalities, precipitated as habits of judgment and verbalized as moral precepts and standards.

We have taken the concept of moral progress as a *criterion* of progress by first describing a direction of progress in which social evolution is presumably tending and then purporting to show that some alternatives of choice tend more nearly in that direction than others. The fallacy is similar, in logical principle, to the popular ethics of "adjustment." Once goals are formulated in such a way that they *can* be carried out, they are necessarily adjusted to the environment; but conformity has no magic that of itself determines goals. The real meaning of the philosophy of adjustment is to avoid constructing new models of conduct by the simple expedient of continuing with those already at hand.

When progress or moral evolution is treated as if it were an all-embracing goal, the fallacy is only a little subtler. It is useful and important to see present trends of individual or social development, but *any* feasible choice will modify such trends in greater or lesser degree and, inevitably, be consistent with them. Progress is not something antecedently defined, which then determines the details of good conduct; rather, the details of good conduct are first determined, and then, if new discrimination and insight result, these lay the basis for moral progress. The utility of general extrapolations into the future, from an ethical point of view, is that they suggest what may prove to be involved in the choices that lie ahead. They are contributory but not decisive.

What is really essential in the idea of moral progress is that it represents as good, as always and in principle satisfying, the prosperity of the ethical interest. To extend the range and power of human adjudicative capacities is not, of itself, to seek any single substantive goal. The ethical interest is a second-order interest, an interest that would have no object in the absence of the other and primary factors of human motivation. As an interest it depends upon material conditions of social organization, of education, and of communication. It is a cognitive and intellectual interest, coupled with literature, with the fine arts, and with the writing of history. It is coupled with the scientific interest, conspicuously and rather directly with medicine, psychology, and the social sciences. But it is also coupled with astronomy, biology, and physics, indeed with any investigation that informs, directly or ultimately, the constituent phases of choice. Morality is the expression and codification of its findings.

Thus, although the ethical interest is a second-order interest, it is an interest that, once established and recognized, permeates all the other things that human beings find engrossing. It may fare well or badly. Like science, it is oriented toward novelty and toward learning. It is the authority, and the only authority, that can define the content of moral progress, in which its own prosperity is the principal element. For to say that a world in which this interest dwindled or disappeared might be morally good would be to deny explicitly what is implicitly affirmed in the very capacity to make the judgment. And to say that a world in which this interest flourished might be morally bad would be to say that it flourished without any achievement.

Responsibility

The concept of moral responsibility has been introduced in this chapter in connection with the phenomenology of choice, but we have not looked at it out of that context. Freedom and responsibility are obvious correlatives. In standard arguments about free will and determinism, for example, a belief in the universality of determinism is held, sometimes, to make responsibility meaningless. The correlation of responsibility and freedom is that of a retrospective and a prospective view of choice. If I have chosen freely, I am responsible for the choice and its consequences. A part of my choice is that I *will* make myself responsible, and a constraining consideration is that I not avoid responsibilities that I have acquired from previous choice.

To work the old argument in terms of responsibility rather than freedom has this force: if freedom is an illusion, it is, at any rate, an illusion operative in the act of choice. To say that I *was* free is not, however, such a "necessary" illusion. Conversely, to insist that I am responsible for the choice is to say that my freedom of choice was not a necessary illusion but a reality.

A good deal of the discussion of freedom in the previous chapter and this one has been an attempt to emphasize the constructive character of choice, of choice as a kind of artisanship. The correlative interpretation of responsibility is to see it as a proprietary relation, a kind of ownership. It was my choice because I made it, I constructed it.

The sense of impending responsibility, of the unavoidability of choice and the irrevocability of what is chosen, lays the basis for a subsequent recollection and review of the choice as a deliberate constructive process. Phenomenologically, one more or less relives the process as though it were to be carried out all over again. The reliving may occur at various levels of emotional intensity. It is particularly intense in self-recrimination. Belief in universal determinism is sometimes recommended as a philosophical medicine: one could not have acted differently. But this psychological approach misses the point completely. Any work of art or craftsmanship can be examined for its psychological causation, but it can also be examined for its structure and its relevancies. To go over a mathematical proof one has invented is to search, not for causes, but for errors or redundancies. If an error is found, there may be a secondary interest in causes. A cause of error, when understood, can be counteracted, perhaps, by methodological precautions. To exclaim that one ought not to have made the error is not a causal statement at all but a methodological one.

This subordination of causal description to methodological prescription is revealing. Correct procedure is not treated causally, but error is ("causes of disease"). This is the connection between "normal" and "normative." If error were not exceptional, procedure could not even be defined. Better procedure reduces the probability of error through avoidance or correction, through better channeling of the flow of information.

Moral errors are not different from others in kind, although they may provoke a deeper anguish. But why any emotion at all rather than a cool and detached registry of fact? I should say that anguish is the perception of error and that its intensity is a register of importance. There is a pathology of self-recrimination, and it may be one of the important psychogenic pathologies. But self-recrimination, in any intensity of anguish, is not, *per se,* pathological. It expresses the continuation of a methodological and, here specifically, of the ethical interest.

Validly to impute responsibility is not to contradict determinism but is simply irrelevant to questions of cause; it is in another universe of discourse. Responsibility may be imputed correctly even for an act that was hastily or irresponsibly chosen. It is not that one chose to be careless or irresponsible, but that one had, accessible, the knowledge and capacity to make the choice more carefully and responsibly. The imputation is again a critical or methodological judgment, not a causal explanation.

Exculpation is the same kind of judgment—namely, that one did not have at hand the means of avoiding an error. Inculpation increases emotional tension; exculpation reduces it. The emotion itself, like all the emotions of tension, appears to function pre-emptively. The choice made, and now reviewed, is attributed to one's self. The self so characterized is not simply past, but is a continuing and still present reality, which has revealed itself, its disposition and habit, through the blameworthy act. It is seen as imperiled by such disposition and habit, and the perception commands a very high priority, comparable to that of physical fear in its directive intensity.

We could say, in a pragmatic spirit, that praise and blame for past acts are meaningful through their potential influence in the reformation of future choice. This is undoubtedly true and important; but it is, again, irrelevant. If the means of avoiding error were, in fact, available and not used, the self thereby stands described as in need of reinforcement or repair. The judgment is a factual and fallible judgment, essentially diagnostic in character. The pragmatic aspect of the judgment is prognostic. Prognosis provides a test of diagnosis because it is dependent on diagnosis. As physical fear gives priority to bodily self-protection against external danger, so the moral emotion gives priority to the self-protection of those human capacities that are involved in what Aristotle called "the practical life of man's rational part." Reason, in this old sense, is a sort of enclave, a system of intellectual capacities somewhat detached and isolated from external disorganizing influences, but not surely or permanently so. Emotions involved in cognition and choice are, I should hypothesize, adaptations of a more primitive vital mechanism to the services of phylogenetically more recent capacities.

The transition from the First Garden to the Second—the harmony that is projected for the future in the recognition of present disharmony and conflict—involves at its core—self-conscious experience—a valid perception of human responsibility. This perception is reinforced through husbandry, self-domestication, the cultural evolution and elaboration of the ethical interest. So reinforced, it is perceived in a larger framework, and the imagery of the two gardens takes on the color and substance of literal truth. The strange career of *Homo sapiens* can be terminated, even self-terminated. But it is organized around the exercise of a capacity in which responsibility for a Second Garden is implicit. This is not an ultimate goal in any ordinary sense, and it is perhaps not steadily a goal at all. It is simply the only possible outcome of man's distinctive capacities, self-evolved to higher levels of competence. It is a morally unavoidable responsibility. It becomes a goal in the face of social choices that already loom in our generation. It becomes a goal for the simple reason that we can now make choices that might lead permanently away from it.

13

ECONOMIC THEORY
AND SOCIAL CHOICE

In my selective treatment of issues in psychology I emphasized the topics that are closest to biological and cultural evolution. These are connected, in turn, with the analysis of decision-making and of the ethical interest. My account of the latter described a new evolutionary mechanism. In the plain story of human history this account is obviously inadequate and one-sided. Men act as they act through complex procedures of choice; but their competence to fashion their individual, not to say their social, existence in a prescient manner has been, and still is, severely limited. What men individually intend they collectively fail, often enough, to achieve. Cultural variation and selection operate; but, far from being brought under logical control, they operate, for the most part, as they operated in the jungle, with a sight that is mostly hindsight. In this sense the previous chapter was utopian; it emphasized a component of social development that, though essential, is rudimentary—a new species of variation-selection that is distinctive of cultural evolution but far from predominant in a quantitative sense.

In the present chapter I shall consider some of the characteristic concepts and conditioning hypotheses involved in the description of societies. My principle of selection here, as in the immediately previous chapters, is continuity with the general theme of the three stages of evolution. At the center of this discussion is the problem of describing the self-perpetuation of material culture and, thus, the science of economics. The presentation of ideas here is rather unorthodox, and the order of topics, in a sense, recapitulates much of the order of the whole book. I deal first with certain kinds of lawfulness; I next discover that this lawfulness, although resembling the grand conservation laws of physics, is essentially statistical and informational in character. Laws of social behavior have upon them the mark of evolutionary development. Finally, I come to the discussion of economic choice, with which most treatments of economics begin, and to the problems of social choice.

Value as Substance

An important topic of this chapter, which has been treated only along the way in previous chapters, is the concept of interaction, of coupling. In systems described by well-defined dynamical laws interactions are, in a sense, already covered by the statement of the laws and only complicate—in most cases seriously complicate—the application. The gravitational interaction of two bodies is simple to describe, but that of three or more is, except in special cases, extremely complicated to work out in temporal extension. A different sort of problem is exemplified, in magneto-hydrodynamics, by an interaction that takes place, not between two spatially distinct systems, but between the electrodynamic property and the hydrodynamic property of a fluid, each of which has previously been studied only in circumstances that minimized or eliminated the significance of the other.

The general and obvious fact is that we cannot investigate everything at once, and that strategic simplifications are part of the art of learning. This is shown in the separation of economic theory from the complexities of psychology, of non-economic group behavior, of the details of technology on the one hand or of politics on the other. In each case the economist first takes account of these things mainly by rather rudimentary assumptions concerning them. His only justification is that the errors so entailed are not gross errors. This amounts to the belief that the couplings in question are unimportant in the first approximation or that he can take them into account without getting into the obscurities of another discipline.

The subject matter of economics is itself a product of cultural evolution, and the science ought to be conceived as a part of anthropology. This does violence to the niceties of academic decorum. The study of technologically undeveloped societies is what anthropologists mainly concern themselves with, while the anthropology of civilized—urbanized—communities splits into divisions of labor under headings of historiography, sociology, politics, and economics.

In some obvious ways this division of labor follows the proliferation of society itself in the urban stage of evolution, and only in urbanized society do the economic interconnections become complex and long-range enough to warrant a special science. The characteristic interests that have prompted the development of economic theory are a product of mercantile and capitalistic society, and the subject matter does not by much antedate the discipline. Indeed, the two are coupled historically in a way that raises new questions about the nature of science. As the maturing of biology leads away from the model of science as mainly a search for temporally deterministic, dynamical law, so the maturing of economics leads away from the model of observation and description appropriate to astronomy or meteorology, in which the coupling of subject matter with human activity is negligible. Knowledge of the structure and behavior of society becomes, *qua* social informant, part of its own subject matter, and this suggests new intellectual responsibilities as well as moral ones. It has been fashionable in some circles to believe that social science is respectable in proportion as it cultivates the art of trying to predict future social states from present ones through equations of social dynamics and mass-distance-intensity relations analogous to laws of force. We do not wish to belittle such programs in all respects, for they have an obvious peripheral value. Human behavior in the mass does have many essentially mechanical characteristics, which we are stupid to ignore. But to isolate these for study is to isolate them within a human milieu, and the boundary conditions are radically different from those that prevail in inorganic nature. There are beautiful problems of communication flow and traffic flow, for example, which can be seen to fall within the range of "social physics." They challenge the virtuosity of the applied mathematician and even provoke new branches of mathematics. Engineering designs derived unimaginatively from such studies may be radically inappropriate, however, simply because persons may respond to them in a quite unmechanical fashion. The (Los) Angelization of American transportation patterns is an unintended consequence, in part, of highway and traffic engineering. The highway is planned for existing patterns, but the adoption of the plan leads to a recasting of the public routines it is intended to facilitate. Public transportation is downgraded, land speculation and suburban development follow, and the final result of many such steps is a mode of life achieved by inadvertence. The boundary conditions of the mechanical system are not themselves describable in mechanical terms but lead, directly or indirectly, into the arena of political decision or default.

In spite of these strictures, the attempt to describe society in mechanistic or quasi-mechanistic terms has been of great importance. The founder of modern political philosophy formulated his description of society in such terms. Hobbes' State of Nature, which I discussed earlier, is a sort of kinetic model of society, and the Social Contract defines the limits of mechanistic description. Through the contract men create the boundary conditions that transform their existence from the state of war to the state of peace.

The most substantial achievements of this way of thought lie in economics, and in the present section I deliberately emphasize the mechanistic aspect, the interacting flows of goods and services.

We must therefore consider production and circulation of goods and services —of commodities—but need not do so at the outset with any technological detail. Production is what goes on in certain "black boxes." We describe it completely by saying what inputs are consumed in producing a given output. These descriptions are *equations of production*. Commodities flow between boxes, and, unless waste and storage are explicitly allowed for, the output of one black box is equal to the sum of its inputs to all boxes. This fact is expressed by the *equations of distribution*. The joint solution of the equations of production and distribution is the complete description, at this level of abstraction, of an economic system.

A simple qualification is to introduce unproductive consumption—boxes that have input but no output and therefore no equations of production affecting the economy. This does not include what is ordinarily called consumption, the greater part of which goes into the box or set of boxes labeled "labor," whose output is the productive capacities of persons. Unproductive consumption may be wasteful, ornamental, or socially necessary; either it has no physical output or its output flows outside the economy.

At this point it is possible to introduce one of the classical concepts associated with the term "value." Although, of course, the word is used because of its association with human valuation, its *definition* in this context is prior to any consideration of the institutional side of economics. The role it plays is to provide a link between the physical and the institutional. Every commodity is measured in units of its own class, and the equations of distribution, for this reason, are dimensionally different from one another. But the equations of production represent the transformation of commodities into other commodities, and this fact permits the definition of a universal unit of measurement.

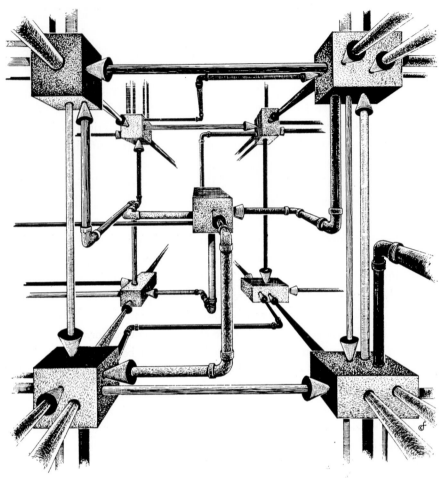

Fig. 30. A Construction of Interacting Flows

With less or greater explicitness the classical economists, from François Quesnay through Karl Marx,† used such a procedure for achieving commensurability.

Pick the output of one box, *A*. The unit in which this output is measured will become the universal unit. When an amount of some other commodity is measured in the *A* units, this measure is called the value of that amount. The procedure is as follows: the *value* of the output of box *B* is defined as the physical measure of the input from *A* to *B*, plus the *values* of all other inputs

† For a recent summary of Quesnay's contribution to the foundations of economics, see Leslie Fishman, "A Reconsideration of the Tableau Economique," *Current Economic Comment,* 20, 1 (February 1959), pp. 41–50. For a brief history of economic theory in which the opposing trends of mechanistic and teleological emphasis are clearly described, see Eduard Heimann, *History of Economic Doctrines* (New York, 1954).

so used, from *C*, from *D*, etc. This sounds circular but is not; for, if these value-defining equations are written for all boxes and solved simultaneously, everything comes out in units of *A*. In effect, the value of an output from *B* is measured by the total amount of *A*, over past time, accounted for in the output thus evaluated.

In the unique case of box *A* we have two measures of output that are both in the same units. One is the direct physical measure of that output; the other is its value defined as for every box. If the value of *A*'s output exceeds its physical measure, the system is declining and, in the steady state, unable to reproduce itself. If the system has unproductive consumption but is stationary, the value of *A*'s output must be less than its physical measure by an amount equal to the value being unproductively consumed. And, finally, if the difference is not all accounted for by unproductive consumption, it must be accounted for in the expansion of the system.

This outline is not formally complete, but the qualifications are not crucial.† It is clear that the transformation of value, defined in such a way, is formally analogous to the law of conservation of mass or, better, of energy. Social scientists concerned about always being "behind" the physical sciences in level of development might wish to contemplate a claim of priority here. Quesnay's eighteenth-century analysis was no imitation of physics. A precise conception of energy-conservation was achieved only in the nineteenth century.

A counter-analogy is worth considering, however. Box *A* is analogous to the *source* of energy. But it dissipates, in production, more or less of its product than it concurrently produces. This suggests that value is not really like energy *per se* but rather more like the free energy of information. Indeed, this is not merely an analogy. Production is the information of material things in various ways; its achievement, as in all vital processes, requires a constant input of free energy. As a mode of information, value cannot come into existence *ex nihilo,* but it can disappear *ad nihil.* The conservation of value that makes it formally analogous to energy is not a law of nature but the idealization of a social achievement, of the fact that a society is able to reproduce its material culture.

---

† Simple mechanical models, defined by linear differential equations, have been described repeatedly since the time of Marx's *Capital*, Vol. III. These are usually known as general-equilibrium models, although the term "equilibrium" is somewhat misleading. For a technical but straightforward account of the mechanistic aspects see David Hawkins, "Stability in Macroeconomic Systems," and a note thereto by the author and Herbert Simon, *Econometrica*, 16, 4 (October 1948), and 17, 3–4 (July–October 1949). Extensive empirical and theoretical studies with this kind of model have been carried on in recent decades, having been initiated in the United States by Wasily Leontiev. See his *Studies in the Structure of the American Economy* (Cambridge, Mass., 1953).

For the classical writers, indeed, the value law was a law of nature, but in a different sense. They regarded it as a normative principle, and my presentation distorts their intent in this respect. We have regarded the value commodity as a matter for arbitrary choice (as one might measure energy in ergs or calories), but they did not. For Quesnay the value commodity was the product of agriculture; for Adam Smith and, with increasing formal definiteness, for David Ricardo and Marx, this commodity was labor: box A consumed wage goods and produced labor power, which was, in turn, consumed in all the other boxes. For the purposes of achieving commensurability the choice of a unit does not matter. If it does matter, it matters in the context of human institutions. Technocrats have urged the adoption of energy units, with power-producers the guardians of value. I might be accused of suggesting units of information. But this would miss the point: the *mode* of information that could be equated with value is specifically defined in the self-reproduction of an economy. The flowers that bloom in the spring are vastly informed, but this information does not count toward value unless the flowers in question do not merely grow but are grown; and then all that counts, of their vast complexity, is that small portion supplied *from the economy* in assisting nature.

At the next stage of analysis we impose on the bare structure of the economy an institutional clothing. We know that the equations of production and distribution are, in fact, inadequate to the description of an economic system. Many variables affecting the system are not determined by those equations. The justification for having ignored this fact is that the variability of the system, in response to changes in these extraneous variables, is bounded. In dealing with the complication now about to be introduced, we shall find it useful to distinguish the value variables from others. Suppose, for this purpose, that the black boxes of production not only have the inputs and outputs connecting them with one another and representing commodity flows, but also are internally variable in the way in which, and the rates at which, they transform input into output. These variations may be described as causally connected (1) with independent physical variables of the environment, such as the weather or changes in the concentration of available ores or in the depth of available oil deposits, and (2) with human decision-makers. This latter mode of connection may be visualized as meters and control knobs on the outside of the boxes.

A mathematical innovation will help to prevent undue complexity in our thinking about this new model. The state of the economy is defined by any given specification of the non-value variables: for any given state of the weather, of mineral deposits etc., and of human decisions, the equations of production and distribution are fixed, and thereby so are the flows of value. If all the variables describing the operation and interaction of the boxes are represented within an n-dimensional phase space, then for every point in this space there is, uniquely defined, a possible economic system. Changes in these variables then bring about a corresponding change in the economy or, more properly, a change from one economy to another. But at any given moment the possible changes, at least in some dimensions, are limited by continuity—both by the existing state of the economy and by the state of technology, the mode of social organization, etc.

In a changing economy, it is clear, values per unit commodity are also changing. If we define an economy only up to some subset of possible economies, values are correspondingly indeterminate; if we take any actual economy, even a changing one, the values at any one time will be perfectly determinate.

Having sketched a generalization of the simplest classical model, I now introduce certain institutional features. In order to do this well, however, I must avoid the error of exaggerating the degree to which an economy will respond to the specific variables of economic decision-making. The needed discipline is to assume first that the economy is totally unresponsive to these variables and to modify this unrealistic assumption later. The assumption that human decisions affect the economy involves relating them to it by means of the knobs and meters of the black boxes of production. But, instead of saying that the economy is determined by decisions, I am going to say that the decisions are determined by the economy. Institutional aspects are going to be introduced, in the first approximation, as inconsequential, as epiphenomena.

The basic institutional concept is that of *property*. The boxes themselves and the commodities they consume and produce are owned by persons, by corporations, or by governments. But ownership may go more widely than this and extend to other things as well: to regions of the earth's surface, to legally defined rights of other kinds such as copyrights and contracts, etc. Because the boxes of production and the value flowing through them are owned, exchange occurs. This is not the physical exchange of commodities, but an exchange of title.

In the simplest economy all technology and rates of production are constant and, by hypothesis, adjusted so that everything produced is consumed. If the economy consists of only two boxes (which may be aggregates of smaller boxes), and if what they supply to each other is simply traded, the flows of value in both directions will be equal; if this is not so, one side will be growing and the other declining. In many-cornered exchange, however, this is true, not between pairs of producers, but only between each producer and the aggregate of the others. In a hard-money economy we remove this difficulty by diverting the product of one of the boxes out of the physical economy into the sphere of ownership and exchange, where it functions as a medium. The exchange between every pair of producers—partly in commodities and partly in money—is now equal: the value of commodities bought is now equal to the value of the hard money exchanged for them. If this were not true, some persons would be gaining in ownership and others losing, and, since the physical economy is, by hypothesis, in stationary equilibrium, this could only mean that the proportions of total value owned by different owners were changing, or that money was being merely hoarded, or that some value was being diverted to unproductive consumption. If we eliminate these possibilities, price ratios are equal to value ratios. To the extent to which such qualifications must be taken into account, price ratios may differ from value ratios, but the difference is significant, and one may discuss its effects on the stability of the economy or on the welfare of society. The introduction of various kinds of soft money is one of the things to be discussed in this connection. We can, in this case, no longer define the value of money as the value cost of its production, but we can still equate price ratios with value ratios or examine the significance of their inequality.

Seeing the connection between market value and value defined in terms of the physical economy was one of the great achievements of the classical writers. Even when all necessary qualifications are made, value ratios will probably explain most price ratios within a certain degree of approximation—in some cases, perhaps, within ten percent, in others only within a factor of five.

The choice of the commodity to be used as a standard of value, though technically arbitrary, may be made in such a way as to put some relations of the economy in bolder relief. With some definiteness, as I said above, Smith, Ricardo, and Marx all chose *labor* as the standard. Smith and Ricardo chose labor for the sake of the contrast between the kind of activity that benefits society by increasing wealth and the kind that is only unproductive. Smith wanted to criticize the mercantile interests that sought to amass money profits without expanding production; Ricardo wanted to criticize the landed interests that diverted the flow of value to unproductive consumption with the same effect. The trading companies and the landed gentry were to be contrasted with the capitalists and their workers, whose activity is productive. In both cases the criticism is based on the deviation between flows of value and flows of money.

In the background of all this is a more fundamental theoretical proposition, formulated explicitly by John Locke, that is often overlooked: the labor theory of *property*. Society reproduces itself by labor, and labor involves the appropriation of the common property to private use. It is not use *per se,* but the necessity of appropriation through labor, that generates private property. The property theory is more important in Marx than the quantitative value theory, for on it he founds the proposition that industrial production, being necessarily collaborative, entails, for stability, a legal system in which productive resources are public property.

In the theory of capitalism, however, Marx used the labor theory not as a norm from which the capitalists deviated, but as *their* norm, from which their behavior did not essentially deviate. For in the exchange between the rest of the economy and the households of wage labor, market values are proportional to labor values. This means that labor collectively is, in fact, paid at its value. Wages and the prices of wage goods are so adjusted that incoming value equals outgoing value: the wage-workers amass no profit. Since labor households are the sole producers of value and the system is capable of expansion, the labor cost of labor power must be less than its physical contribution to the economy. The basic fact of capitalism is, then, the appropriation of this surplus value by the capitalists. This is how Marx *épatait les bourgeois.* From this point of view the standard of value is no longer arbitrary. For, if the standard were steel and steel producers exchanged *at value* (steel-unit value) with the rest of the economy, the result would be that steel producers made no profit and new steel plants were always started by other owners out of the profits of their more lucrative activities. But labor households are the only part of the ideal capitalist economy that does not share in the ownership of its expanding productive capacity.

Within the capitalist sector of the economy commodities do not, in general, exchange at value; they could do so only if all capitalist profits were proportional to output of value. The mobility of ownership tends, instead, to equate, not profit per unit of output, but profit per unit of capital; among the capitalists prices are proportional to values only in the special case of owners who face the same capital/output requirements.†

Value as Individual Preference

Partly from opposition to the classical value theory—with its dire implications for merchants, or landlords, or capitalists—and partly for good reasons,

---

† There has been endless controversy over this matter, but it is of little contemporary importance. Marx at first may have hoped that values would explain average prices in detail; later he saw some of the necessary qualifications.

the nineteenth century developed another tradition: an attempt to recast the whole of value theory. The aspect of real cost—whether defined in labor units or otherwise—was pushed into the background. The other side of the classics, the emphasis upon the bargaining of the marketplace, was put forward instead. If one buries the equations of production and distribution below the visible surface and looks instead at the meters and knobs of the black boxes, one can make a different sort of picture from the one I have been elaborating. The meters will be read for diagnosis and prognosis; and at the point of ownership transfer, in the marketplace, there will be the process of bargaining. The outcome of the bargaining will determine rates of flow, and the knobs of the black boxes will be adjusted accordingly. The economist at this point takes account of human purposes. He does not try to explain them but takes them as given: they define the boundary conditions of the system. He seeks a simple uniform way of defining these conditions. He does not need to know everything about human purposes, but only the reflex effect on the economy. For this he makes use of the concept of utility-maximization.

Any participant in the economy will respond to information received by acting in such a way as to maximize his utility, whatever that may be. This utility is a function of two classes of variables, those the participant controls and those he does not—say categories X and Y, respectively. The function $U(X, Y)$ assigns to each possible set of values of the X and Y variables a number U that measures the utility to him of the state of affairs defined by X under given conditions Y. This measure is invariant, at least up to a monotone transformation. It is now assumed that the participant will select that value, or one of those values, that maximize U under the given conditions defined by Y. Thus the X become dependent variables, dependent on the Y variables. The utility function and the behavior it implies may vary from case to case. As it stands, in fact, the assumption of utility-maximization is not controvertible, since any behavior could conceivably maximize some conceivable utility function. One participant may desire to maximize money income, another the profit per unit of capital, and a third the opportunity to pick daisies. But rather weak assumptions about the shape and character of utility functions are all that the theorist requires except for special types of economic analysis.

In the classical theory of the market such maximizing rules were shown to be stabilizers of the economy. They were at the core of Smith's "invisible hand" argument—the possibility of an economy regulated by the free operation of the market, without supervision or supervention from above. Transient surpluses and deficits in the flows of the system will bring profit-motivated changes in offer and demand; these changes will oppose the deviation from equilibrium and restore the system to its prior condition. Since prices are determined in the market by offer and demand, the counterflow of money among owners in the system is a flow of information about the state of the system, telling each what he needs to know for his own welfare and that of society.

Such is the answer of utility theory to the question "What determines prices?" They are the result of utility-determined bargaining. To have value—to command a price in the market—a commodity need only be desired enough so that someone will divert money to meet the offer of someone else, whose utility will likewise be increased by the sale of it at that price. Prices so determined have nothing to do, necessarily, with the substantive value of the classics. The favorite example is that of "six shiny pebbles" that happen to be the only ones of their kind although they cost nothing to produce. In these terms, moreover, land may also have a value over and above its improvements, as may the flowers that bloom in the spring if someone happens to own them.

The utility theory of prices thus had a wider scope than the classical theory. In the eyes of its proponents it replaced the older theory, but this was an illusion. For in an economy with fixed technology it turns out that the two theories predict the same exchange rates if we assume the same conditions—namely, competition and capital mobility. Since this idealized economy *can* function only in one equilibrium pattern, and since disequilibrium always means surplus storage of some commodities and deficits of others, it is only necessary to make weak restrictions of utility functions in order to achieve this result. The same kind of argument applies to the price mechanism as to physical flows: in the stationary approximation goods will exchange at price ratios that fluctuate around the corresponding value ratios if adequate capital mobility can be assumed.

The fact that very weak restrictions on the shape of utility functions are sufficient to determine prices shows that the important determinants of price lie, not in the subjective preferences of individuals, but in the socio-economic context, in which those preferences will be shaped and to which, in any case, behavior must be adapted. The utility theory comes off a little better if we allow variability of the equations of production. For now, in the utility model, the constraints of the productive system will not wholly determine the economy; within the bounds that system imposes, the complex of utility functions will have at least some scope, to determine both technology and prices. One set of the boxes of production, in particular, has attracted the attention of utility theorists—namely, the set that consumes consumer goods and whose sole output, in the first approximation, is labor. While a certain basic education and nurture are necessary to the production of this or that kind of labor power, there is more variability both to the content of subsistence and to the character of utility function than appears, let us say, in the manufacture of beer bottles. Most persons of humanistic sensibility find it repugnant, in fact, to think of human beings in terms of input-output relations at all, and it is only the power of economic abstractions that forces them to do so. It is more comfortable to our persuasions to break the chain of circulation at this point and to think of consumers as registering a kind of ultimate or final demand, for the sake of which the rest of the economy functions at all, and which is only accidentally connected with the demand for labor power. From this point of view the consumer is king. In his market biddings he determines, directly or indirectly, what and how much of it will be produced.

The doctrine of consumer sovereignty thus accomplishes, by forgetting a set of equations, what the progress of technology is still far short of achieving—a degree of automation that renders consumer income independent of the state of the labor market. This is not at all to question the formal possibility of describing an economy in this way provided the bounds of its significance are recognized. In utility theory generally one is dealing with a second approximation to the first approximation obtainable from the study of the physical economy. When it is presented abstractly enough, its secondary character is lost sight of; like the dangling participle in grammar, it does not clearly modify anything.

As the consumer is sovereign, the producer is subject. He merely does what he is told, what is telegraphed back to him from the consumer market. Like the consumer, he has real choices, but the utility function we impute to him subordinates everything to one purpose, profit-maximization. This motive, in turn, leads to a constant concern for efficiency; and so, in equilibrium, everyone produces as efficiently as possible.

The doctrine of consumer sovereignty is valid up to the limits set by the play in the bearings of the consumer economy, by the consumer's actual range of choice—his "budget plane." Everything else in the economy is treated as a kind of automatism. The decisions of the owners of productive resources are treated by rudimentary assumptions that give perfectly deterministic couplings. The doctrine illustrates my earlier comments about strategic simplification in the account of multiply interacting systems. In my first model all loci of choice are treated deterministically, and the result is a closed system of social circulation. In the model of consumer sovereignty this circle is "torn" where wage-earner becomes consumer; the coupling is ignored as problematic, and consumption decisions are treated as autonomous.

The best corrective of the tendency to overestimate this openness is to treat the consumer as automaton and tear the system somewhere else. An obvious place to do this violence is with the producers. The choices of the producer are bounded by the necessity to maintain his position in the economy. If he is a private producer rather than a government monopoly, he maintains his position by achieving a non-negative rate of profit (profit equals growth), which, under the assumption of capital mobility, equals that of the system as a whole. The consumer is represented simply as an automatic factory that consumes wage goods and produces labor power. By investment decisions the producer channels more or less of the current and immediately future output of the economy into replacement of stockpiles and equipment, into new productive equipment, technological and market research, etc. When rates of profit are unequal, as they commonly are, in fact, over a rather wide range, some centers of ownership expand, not only by producing new capital equipment, but also by the flow of ownership as it takes over erstwhile competitive producers or, in vertical integration, suppliers and users. The economy booms in sectors where new technology, new industries, and government subsidies create high profit rates. Oligopolistic patterns of ownership become standard; barriers to competitive capital flow arise; and consumers become subjects of applied "behavioral sciences," of engineers who work to alter the equations of production in the "household sector" through manipulation of consent. Such is producer sovereignty.

One may tear the closed model of circular flow at other points. Government, grown greatly in size and power in industrial society, enters the economy at the basic level of the black boxes. It becomes a direct producer and consumer and through various political powers permeates the higher levels of ownership, control, and communication. It absorbs part of the manpower and equipment of the economy for long-range capital developments, for regulatory functions, and for the maintenance of military power. Many of these functions are nonproductive at the black-box level.

In a world strongly affected by the historically still recent age of geographical isolation between political units, the variety of economic patterns is great, and the unevenness of their evolution is conspicuous. The socialistic systems alter the character and motivation of producers and the legal patterns of ownership. Investment decisions are more intensely coordinated and centralized, and the sovereignty of producers and consumers is more or less effectively curtailed. Circular flow among nations is still weak and can be torn with more or less plausibility at any one of them, producing an open model in which each faces the rest of the world, whose economic responses to its decisions it will try to predict and exploit. This weakness of coupling produces a traditionally but no longer easily available alternative mode of interaction, war.

Value as Social Choice

The classical value theory and the utility theory have many complications and qualifications that I have not touched. It is not necessarily true, for example, that even quite idealized economies are stable under the rule of the market; there are technological, systemic variables that make for stability or instability in virtual independence of the operation of the market. The evolution of monopolies and oligopolies and various forms of cooperation and coercion have brought some of these systemic variables under control, but the centers of such control are still numerous and practically uncoordinated. The degrees of freedom in the system are reduced, but fluctuations are not. Instability, however, has a positive as well as a negative side. Fluctuations are not merely fluctuations around an ideal norm or trend but may represent incipient and divergent alternative trends. In the space of possible economies the temporal direction of change is not fixed but is more and more sensitively responsive to chance or to decision.

For serious treatment of these problems, in their actual and potential importance, the concepts and conditioning hypotheses of utility theory are woefully inadequate. Whereas the classical value theory was, in form, a conservation law for closed economies, it served, in fact, as a guide to decisions. In its terms one can argue the need for waste-avoiding and wealth-expanding activities. Because the economies described by it were, in fact, fairly open in the governmental sector, the theory, which treated them as closed, could have practical impact—hence the term "political economy." But the classical theory was in no sense a theory of value conditioned by choice. Utility theory, considered as the theory of decision-making, was therefore a step in advance. But it is inherently incapable of describing the full character of choice as a human capacity or the multiple interactions that are significant in any discussion of social choice. We now return to a subject that has dominated the last two chapters, but in a setting determined by the specific character of modern economic existence.

In recent years the basic ideas of utility theory have been subjected to a good deal of re-examination, and certain conclusions are now fairly apparent. One is that the concept of the joint maximization of utilities among several decision-makers leads, in a wide class of cases, to indeterminate results, and it is upon this that I shall concentrate attention.

In the classical utility-theory formulation, several persons engage in independent decisions under circumstances such that the decision of each affects the utility of the others. Each attempts to control his own variables in a way that depends on the variables controlled by the others. If he treats these latter as simply given, as independent variables, there arises a special kind of equilibrium in which each maximizes utility by changing the values of his variables *independently* of the others. But this is a quite arbitrary restriction, and if it is removed the whole problem appears in a quite different light. If we do not specify who controls which variables, the notion of utility-maximization becomes formally meaningless, for it now requires that one maximize several different functions of the same variables, and this cannot, in general, be done. The more general formulation is the one required, however, if we allow the different participants in such a situation to communicate with one another and to try to anticipate and possibly influence one another's decisions.

The logic of this situation deserves careful examination. It may be represented in a series of hypothetical stages in the coupling between the activities of persons. In the first stage, *A* takes account of *B*'s behavior as he would take account of any particular fact of nature, as an independent variable that affects his welfare. In this way *A*'s behavior becomes dependent on *B*'s. But this is a fact that *B* may discover; he then treats *A*'s behavior, *not* as an independent fact of nature, but as dependent, as something he can manipulate. An example of this stage is the leader-follower pattern. A follower *A* treats a leader *B* as a fact of nature, as something to which he must adjust himself. The leader knows this, however, and in making his own decisions counts on the reaction of the follower.

In the next stage *A* may discover the dependence of *B*'s decision on *A*'s own former mode of reaction and the behavior it leads to, may exploit them and thereby render them false. Clearly there is no end to the degree of sophistication in this relationship. Depending on the problem one sets, increasing subtlety of interaction may converge to a stable limiting form of behavior or—more generally—simply lead to indeterminacy.

In the case of an indeterminate solution of this game, *A* and *B* may see the problem, not as one of making specific decisions, but as one of picking specific strategies of decision, specific ways of reacting to each other's decisions. Generally speaking, these may range on a spectrum. At one extreme the strategy may be cooperation; at the other extreme it may be cut-throat competition. Suppose that commensurable utilities, such as money, are involved: under co-operation each tries to maximize the *sum* of utilities; under cut-throat competition each tries to maximize the *difference* between his utility and the other's. The obvious fact of this situation is that, no matter what strategy the competitors jointly adopt, either of them is always capable, by finding out the strategy of the other, of using this fact to improve his own profit.

What happens is clear: on the foundation of a rather simple physical interaction arises a structure of further interactions that can become very complex. This structure is stable at any point only if each participant makes a decision or adopts a strategy and then cuts himself off from the temptation to further refinements. This is, in fact, what happens, for such a pyramiding system of sophistications is a house of cards. The informational cost of achieving and maintaining it rises very steeply, and the more complex it becomes the more its significance is destroyed by small chance fluctuations. The system becomes, at some point, just a noise-amplifier. As with two persons trying to pass in a hallway, it is better for duopolists not to watch each other too closely.

What I have been doing, with a simple model and the precise ideas of utility-maximization, is to recapitulate the logic of Hobbes' state of nature. If men are rational, equal, and independent, their interactions produce indeterminacy. What I have not derived is Hobbes' further conclusion: in the face of uncertainty men are forced to the transition from independence to enmity, and the universal pursuit of happiness ends in universal insecurity.

But Hobbes had another way out, the social contract. The social contract represents the supervention of a rule of conduct that is not a natural consequence of the pursuit of happiness, not a market equilibrium, for the *independent* actions of men never lead them to it, and by independent action men will not remain in it. In Hobbes' picture of civil society this higher equilibrium can be entered only by agreement and enforced only by sovereignty. Otherwise it has precisely the instability of the duopoly game when this is generalized (to the case of N persons).

There is, however, another way of expressing Hobbes' insight, one that removes it from the immediate arena of politics. Utility is defined with respect to certain variables that are regarded as logically *given* prior to the interactions I have been discussing. In the course of these interactions, and as a consequence of them, a new situation appears, in which the maximization of utility as the sole determinant of conduct leads to uncertainty. This is not the uncertainty of statistical probabilities, but more radical. *Contrived* uncertainties may have this character of statistical regularity—for example, in bluffing at poker; but just because they are contrived even the probabilities in such situations can be made uncertain.

The appearance of this special kind of uncertainty does not do away with utility as a principle of private decision, but it does, under circumstances of sufficiently strong social interaction, render that principle impotent. It may be objected that this is only a theoretical conclusion from a hypothetical situation, and that in practice the utility principle describes well enough how people behave, interactions of the sort dealt with here being characteristically rather weak except in artificial situations such as guessing games. One might point to the important example of international relations as a counter-example, however, or to the variety of rather delicate, semi-competitive, semi-cooperative balances that exist within the framework of American industry. But this is not the point. The point is that we ought to examine the fundamental apparatus of any scientific theory with the greatest possible care to see where it may break down.

In the case at hand the interesting fact is that the utility principle breaks down just at the point where we recognize another kind of value than the one that utility theory begins with. This new kind of value is not—like individual utility—prior to the interaction between individual decision-makers, but emerges in the course of it and is logically posterior to it. Its appearance involves no necessary setting aside of private utility, but it fills the logical gap, the indeterminacy, to which, we have seen, the utility principle leads. It does not directly alter the individual utility functions, but it does alter the social arrangements under which private decision-makers, with their private utility functions, interact. Social value affects variables that do not belong to the class controlled by single individuals, that belong to a new class of variables, which can be controlled collaboratively or not at all.

In lieu of Hobbes' social contract, which has to be enforced by a sovereign, we have, for an alternative analysis of social value, the classical model of Jean-Jacques Rousseau, in which the citizen-sovereign gives consent to laws affecting persons *in general,* while as citizen-subject he is free to go his own way, subject to the same laws to which, as sovereign, he has consented. In economic theory, however, this notion of an agreed-upon social pattern must be taken down from the pinnacle of the social contract and made the basis of any social decision-making affecting the choice of an economy, whether this be on a universal scale or in the formation of oligopolies, cartels, or any other pattern of interdependence, whether formed by contract, conspiracy, or custom.

The Hobbesian argument, that social value arises out of the indeterminacy of utility-determined individual behavior, would be combated, by those brought up in the liberal tradition, with the argument that the concept of utility has been too narrowly conceived. Let us consider what happens if, in our duopoly game, A and B are interested not only in profit but also in minimizing uncertainty. The result will be indeterminate, since it is meaningless to try to maximize two things, profit *and* certainty. So there must be some combination, some function of the two, that is to be maximized. But now the previous result will be repeated, resulting in the creation of new uncertainties; the only case in which this will not happen is the special and uninteresting one in which the absolute maxima of both utilities happen to coincide. The attempt to subsume social value under private utility, although superficially plausible, is logically a vicious circle.

Up to this point we have considered the indeterminacies of social decision-making in the context of material interactions among the participants. But we find the same indeterminacies if we consider what has come to be called welfare economics. Welfare economics seeks to play the game in advance and to announce, to the potential participants, what the best solution will be. "Best" here means most efficient and is alleged not to be a moral criterion at all.

As before, we conceive of possible economies as points E in a representative space of many dimensions. Each utility function is defined in this space, so that for every economy E in the space there is a corresponding utility vector, one component for each participant. We do not assume any possibility of comparing utilities interpersonally. An economy P is said to *dominate* an economy Q when each utility component is greater at P than at Q. This domination induces a partial ordering among the economies but leaves a set of *undominated* economies. Some welfare economists have worked with models in which only one economy is undominated (and hence the best). But this is clearly unrealistic, and, in general, the set of undominated economies will be as wide as the area of actual socio-economic controversy. One can reduce the area of disagreement by adding various principles of distribution, but these go beyond the viewpoint of private utility. Here again, therefore, we find indeterminacy.†

Let us, however, assuming that there are various possible ways of ordering undominated economies, represent these orderings by some variable p. For each value of p there is a complete ordering, and this ordering is consistent with the partial ordering established by the vectors of private utility. A set of

† Kenneth J. Arrow, *Social Choice and Individual Value* (New York, 1951), makes the arbitrariness of welfare as aggregate utility abundantly clear.

functions, each of which (considered as a logical whole) is a value of some variable, is called a *functional*. Thus we define a social-utility functional $U(E;p)$, which has the following properties: (1) $U(E;p)$ is uniformly consistent with the partial ordering defined by private-utility functions; (2) for a *given* value of p there is one and only one optimal economy; (3) for formal completeness we add that for each undominated economy there is some value of p according to which that economy is optimal.

Each value of p will have to be defined in great detail to give a complete ordering, but subsets of these values will give partial orderings that are more nearly complete than that based on dominations alone. A general principle of equity will eliminate widely varying income distributions from the undominated set; a principle of capital expansion will eliminate pure consumer economies; etc.

By the formal device of the social-utility functional we can exhibit the virtues and defects of welfare economics. But we cannot stop here unless we imagine that the value of p is determined somehow from above. If alternative economic arrangements are debated by the participants in an economy, and if each participant has a private-utility function that is fixed prior to debate, we get either a system in which debate is futile or a system in which, as in Rousseau's, each individual has a split personality, one half of which is solely concerned with private utility and the other half of which is a disinterested legislator.

The other alternative is to say that even individuals have only partially ordered preferences—utility functionals rather than functions. They have some well-defined and apparently fixed partial preferences, but with respect to many concrete alternatives they simply have not made up their minds. Now the traditional analysis of utility admits this but treats the complete ordering as a kind of harmless fiction. After all, individuals will make up their minds, and it does no harm to assume that they have already decided what they will decide. If their preferences change, we can represent the change by making the utility function a function of time.

But time is an independent variable, and this will not do, for I want to say that utility functions are changed, not through the predictable operation of dynamical processes, but through the informational processes of society—partly through manipulation and deception, no doubt, but also through acquaintance with new areas of experience, through argument, and, in general, through the human capacity to build new models of conduct. I want to say this, not because I overestimate the power of the ethical interest, but because it is a theoretical error to ignore the operation of the capacity that is man's most distinctive trait. In the language of the previous discussion of choice, in Chapter 12, the utility function is *supposed* to be a state function but is not. It depends in some measure on the pathway adopted; it is a functional.

If private utility is only a partial ordering, however, we must also supplement the concept of rational behavior that goes with the utility concept. Insofar as one has genuinely fixed preferences, it is rational to maximize utility. If one has indeterminate preferences, alternatives initially incommensurable, one cannot be rational in that sense. This does not imply irrationality; it implies, rather, that in such a context rationality is something different from maximization. What choice implies in such a context I have already discussed in Chapter 12. We do not weigh alternatives unless we have a scale for weighing them. If we lack such a scale, the rational act is to construct one. If we have a scale but trust it no longer, the rational act is to rebuild it.

These metaphors add nothing to the description of the subjective phase of choice presented in Chapter 12. But they suggest how to link that description with the utilitarian viewpoint. Once a utility function is defined, choice is a matter of selecting or constructing the course of conduct that maximizes utility. But the choice of a utility function is not a maximizing process in the same sense.

A social-utility functional that is the aggregate of individual-utility functionals is less determinate, but more interesting, than an aggregate of utility functions. For it suggests the possibility that the individual may define his utility in a manner that is partly responsive to suggestion, example, authority, or sympathy. This suggests, in turn, the possibility of a kind of social agreement that utility theory rules out. For utility theory social agreement is always, in principle, a compromise grudgingly conceded. The invariant orderings of an individual-utility functional have the same significance: they express the fact that the individual is a fixed biological and social being, who simply cannot bring himself to accept, with consistency and finality, a completely arbitrary ordering. But the variable orderings express his social nature, his responsiveness to the human world about him. On the one hand it describes his acceptance of culturally determined norms and standards; on the other hand it leaves room for his responsiveness to suggestion and authority and for his capacity for self-assertion against custom and tradition.

On such a showing the relation between individual value and social choice is complex, involving an interaction between individual and social purpose, the claims of each affecting and bringing about some redefinition of the other.

Rousseau's separation of citizen-subject and citizen-sovereign remains as a useful distinction, but its absoluteness disappears.

In the classical metaphysical political theory the state is the locus of the definition of ends, and the relation of state and government is that of ends and means. That theory was discredited because it claimed that it represented an *existing* consensus that could be appealed to as a way of settling specific conflicts of classes or factions. For the general will, as for happiness or self-realization in individual ethics, one makes a claim that simply cannot be substantiated except in areas where there is no dispute and where, therefore, it is of no use. Like the moral ideals, it lacks sufficient informational complexity to determine concrete social ends. The metaphysical state represents the hoped-for resolution of political debates but not a source from which that resolution can be derived. It established the principle of government by consent, but it did not establish consensus.

Conclusion

I now wish to draw together and summarize my account of economics. This account is incomplete in various respects, but enough of the substance has been given to show the variety of expedients that the scientific description of society must involve.

First, the idea of dynamical lawfulness has its place, and that place is circumscribed but essential. Dynamical models are simplifications but not always oversimplifications. They give a first approximation, and without them the higher approximations dangle even though they may be cast in a quite non-dynamical form. Social laws of motion do not convey the whole truth; perhaps they convey the least subtle and intriguing part of the truth. To scorn or ignore the *mechanics* of social existence may be culpable on other grounds, but it is, as well, to fail in the high art of scientific approximation. When Quesnay first saw the circular flow of goods as the lifeblood of society and went on to link the ills of pre-revolutionary French society with institutional impairments of that flow, he touched social reality in a way in which few contemporary minds had touched it and that even fewer were willing to embrace. We, in a more sophisticated age, are likely to dismiss this kind of description as inessential because inadequate. These inadequate descriptions have important corollaries that will still stand, however, when descriptions are made adequate and that are neither obvious nor trivial. To take one example, the recent and very influential economic analyses of income and investment by J. M. Keynes must be significantly modified when stated in the context of a closed description of circular flows, and they are sometimes paraphrased in a form that is quite inconsistent with the continuity of commodity flows, with what I have called the conservation law of material values. The history of science exhibits many penetrating new insights that were gained because men saw the full implications of what were found, in the end, to be quite inadequate theories. This is, in fact, the most important pathway of discovery, but it has not always gained adherence in the social sciences.

Yet, as I have said, none of this means that the dynamical abstractions are basic to economics in another sense. Phenomena that are quite adequately describable in such terms are so describable only within a framework of institutions taken for granted. In Newtonian mechanics the claim to completeness (which I discussed in Chapter 5) means that an isolated system is isolated within some more inclusive system, which, when itself isolated, could be described by the same laws. This claim, if applied to the description of human affairs, is the sheerest pretense. Institutional boundary conditions have to be described as evolved through biological and cultural evolution, as products of contrivance and choice, to be followed through many historical stages. The counterpart in physics is not dynamical lawfulness but thermodynamical tendency. The value conserved is not that of a simple, unanalyzable substance but that of species of information evolved through human art. Its conservation always flows through noisy channels, and the transformations of value in production, seen more closely, are essentially statistical processes. The noisy background is of many kinds, but one important kind is the complexity and variability of individual behavior. Men's actions are planned, not random. But the composite action of many men, planning independently of one another's plans, is random, not planned. Within an institutional context and apart from the reduction of degrees of freedom—degeneracy—that communication and concerted planning may bring about, a social noise is part of the human condition. This noise may be benign or perilous. For Hobbes it was perilous under the state of nature, and benign in civil society. For Adam Smith it was the presupposition of the invisible hand, regulating the flow of commodities without dictation by government. For Marx it was the explanation of the anarchy of production, driving the capitalist system through the sequence of cyclical crises to self-destruction.

At this level teleological concepts appear, but they appear only schematically. What counts is not the content of individual purposes but the abstract character of utility-maximization. In the abstract model of classical competition theory the individual's relation to the economy is that of a little servomechanism that locally adjusts production to demand and supply.

Purpose, in the full sense, becomes relevant when the participants in an economy see, and take account of, their own possible actions as consequential for the economy. In the participant's epistemological position, the causal description of things is interrupted at the point of his own incompleted choices; from an outside point of view, such choices are the loci of possible entry of new information into the system. Except in a very local context the decisions of small participants lack consequences in this sense: they add only a small increment to the social noise. But big participants—including governments, large corporations or cartels, trade unions, pressure groups, etc.—may be more consequential. On the one hand they may alter the direction of social development appreciably, and on the other hand the uncoordinated decisions of sizable numbers of such organizations may cause larger social fluctuations, a higher level of noise. A more subtle information of social process is that of public communication and debate, the process that, as I have argued, must require a modification of the utilitarian presuppositions.

Utility concepts maintain an important role even when utility-maximization *per se* becomes an inadequate theoretical tool; partial orderings represent what is more or less stably fixed in the systems of individual preferences; their social aggregation does not determine social choice, but it determines boundaries within which consensus can at any given time be achieved. The achievement of new consensus, even then, is not automatic, and the state of nature is the ever-present alternative. As this kind of achievement becomes habitual, the scientific description of society must, in part, be cast in the language of the ethical interest, of the information of social choice through achieved consensus.

It is because of this function and this intent that the social sciences have ethical orientation. Those who have most firmly denied this have, at the same time, most naively exhibited it. To describe persons as responders to stimuli is an important part of the effort to understand them. To describe them only in this dynamical fashion is to forget the human boundary conditions, to raise a methodology to the level of poor metaphysics. To eliminate the description of the purposes that define such conditions is not to be rid of those purposes but to leave them unexamined. To eliminate them—not just for the moment, that is, but by metaphysical fiat—is to invite the interest of the exploiter and manipulator and thus to justify the complaint and suspicion of those who identify something called "science" with mechanistic description *per se*. I defend the mechanistic as a way—and an indispensable one—to the study of man. But it is not the only one.

What is true of the human animal is true of society as well. To allege, as the economist-sociologist Vilfredo Pareto once did in a lengthy treatise, that the true science of society is a system of equations for social motion (which he wrote down in a quite empty form) is to create *outside* this society another, which Pareto acknowledged as elite, not subject to scientific scrutiny—the "scientific" rulers. We can impute obvious political motives to the Paretan scheme, attacking bad theory by *ad hominem* arguments. But some men of democratic sentiments have felt constrained to go the same way because they believed that this way alone was scientific. The mechanistic description of society, if taken as fundamental theory, is bound to exclude from its purview the scientist himself. In other areas of investigation he may, and even must, retreat to the anonymity of the schematic observer. In the social sciences this is not possible except for specific problems and within specific limitations. Investigators from Mars or Venus may construct a whole system of (human) social science on mechanistic foundations. They need not do so. They may consistently do so only if, at the same time, they separate themselves from the kind of informative influence upon human beings that would make them participants in our society, as they are, presumably, in their own. Their equations may well be less blank than those of Pareto; but, if they are good epistemologists, they will realize that their descriptions are incomplete.

The more competent a society becomes, the more important to its self-description are the organizing concepts that minister to choice. Such a society will have its problems of stockpiles and inventories, of queues of traffic and communicaiton. But, in the measure of that competence, social science will not aim at behavioristic, Paretan prediction of the social path through time. About this dynamic and statistical aspect there will be a learned ignorance: what is open to competent choice is not open to prediction, except by those for whom the choice is already made. To live responsibly as competent administrators of the Garden involves a partial, but necessary, ignorance of the future. The encompassing categories of the social sciences are not those by which we try to link the future to the present in unconditional dynamical ordering. Nor are they merely those of evolution without foresight, the blind selectivity of the law of the jungle. The capacity for choice, though a product of that selectivity, supersedes it and may yet reduce the law of the jungle to a minor position in the affairs of our kind.

In my discussion of the metaphysical problem of the future I stated that there might be circumstances under which propositions about the future were essentially ambiguous, as in the science-fiction stories of "branching" time. This ambiguity appears in our discourse, in fact, when we try to refer to future states of affairs that are the objects of a certain kind of propositional reference: when they are referred to as causal consequences of choices that have not yet been made or even fully explored. Social competence increases the range and efficacy of choice and, thus, of ambiguity. This ambiguity implies no barriers to the growth of the social sciences but is, on the contrary, a measure of their progress. What we cannot predict is, in principle, nothing more nor less than what we have not, as yet, elected.

BIBLIOGRAPHICAL COMMENT

The boundary between general philosophy, the philosophy of science, and some kinds of scientific writing is, and should remain, poorly defined. In these notes, however, I must restrict myself to two main categories of writing: one, defined contextually, has been *called* philosophy of science; the other comprises relevant scientific writings.

I In this section I list current works from American and British sources, including translations, with brief comments on some of them. They match my own choice of subject matter in varying degrees. The list is, of course, very incomplete, but the textbooks and compilations listed all contain bibliographies.

Source Books

Feigl, Herbert, & Brodbeck, May (editors), *Readings in the Philosophy of Science* (New York, 1953).

Danto, Arthur, & Morgenbesser, Sidney (editors), *Philosophy of Science* (Cleveland and New York, 1960). In my opinion the most useful collection.

Madden, Edward H. (editor), *The Structure of Scientific Thought* (Boston, 1960).

Wiener, Philip (editor), *Readings in the Philosophy of Science* (New York, 1953).

Journals

Many journals publish papers in the philosophy of science, but two, in English, are specialized: *Philosophy of Science* and *British Journal for the Philosophy of Science*.

Textbooks

Braithwaite, R. B., *Scientific Explanation* (Cambridge, England, 1954). This parallels other technical discussions of law, causality, and probability, but puts the technicalities into a good explanatory context.

Cohen, Morris R., *Reason and Nature* (Glencoe, Ill., 1953). This older book (first published in 1931) is pre- and also anti-positivistic; it has a good bibliography.

Frank, Philipp, *Philosophy of Science* (New York, 1957). Eminently clear, although limited in scientific range.

Nagel, Ernest, *The Structure of Science* (New York, 1961). I find this judicious, cogent, close-textured, and, for these reasons, valuable.

Pap, Arthur, *An Introduction to the Philosophy of Science* (New York, 1962). A clear and fair statement of the issues it analyzes, with a very useful bibliography.

Reichenbach, Hans, *Experience and Prediction* (New York, 1943). Preoccupied with his own analysis of probability (as is another author!), but raises many excellent philosophical questions.

Toulmin, Stephen, *Philosophy of Science* (London, 1963). Primarily a discussion, informal and lively, of models and theories.

Weyl, Hermann, *Philosophy and Natural Science* (Princeton, 1949). Compendious, disjointed, but full of the excitement of theory in science.

Compilations

Churchman, C. West (editor), *Measurement, Definition, and Theories* (New York, 1959).

Colodney, R. G. (editor), *Frontiers of Science and Philosophy* (Pittsburgh, 1962–63), Vols. I–II.

Feigl, Herbert, & others (editors), *Minnesota Studies in the Philosophy of Science* (Minneapolis, 1956–62), Vols. I–III.

Feigl, Herbert, & Maxwell, G. (editors), *Current Issues in the Philosophy of Science* (New York, 1961).

Frank, Philipp (editor), *The Validation of Scientific Theories* (New York, 1961).

Körner, Stephan (editor), *Observation and Interpretation* (New York, 1957).

Nagel, Ernest, & Suppes, Patrick, & Tarski, Alfred (editors), *Logic, Methodology, and Philosophy of Science* (Stanford, 1962).

II On a separate footing from most of the work listed above is that of certain outstanding philosophers of the twentieth century:

Russell

Russell, Bertrand, *Our Knowledge of the External World* (London, 1926). Provoked a generation of inquiry about the relation of knowledge and sense experience.

Russell, Bertrand, *Human Knowledge: Its Scope and Limits* (New York, 1948). Less influential than the work listed above, but relevant to many topics in the philosophy of science.

Russell, Bertrand, *Introduction to Mathematical Philosophy* (London, 1938). Russell's special contributions to logic and the foundations of mathematics.

Schilpp, Paul A. (editor), *The Philosophy of Bertrand Russell*, 3rd edition (New York, 1951).

Whitehead

Schilpp, Paul A. (editor), *The Philosophy of Alfred North Whitehead* (New York, 1951). Essays on Whitehead's philosophy.

Whitehead, Alfred North, *Science and the Modern World* (New York, 1948). A rather popular work, blending a broad sweep of historical vision of science with his peculiarly secret metaphysical language.

Dewey

Dewey, John, *Experience and Nature* (Chicago, 1929). Dewey's philosophy of nature.

Schilpp, Paul A. (editor), *The Philosophy of John Dewey* (New York, 1951). Many other writings, referred to here, are pertinent.

III Here I list writings that are relevant to special areas and topics in science and the philosophy of science.

Mathematics

Black, Max, *The Nature of Mathematics* (New York, 1933).

Blumenthal, Leonard M., *A Modern View of Geometry* (San Francisco, 1961). A good mathematical survey.

Courant, Richard, & Robbins, Herbert, *What is Mathematics?* (New York, 1941). The question is that of the insightful mathematician rather than that of the philosopher. One of the best of numerous surveys.

Geach, Peter T., & Black, Max (translators), *Translations from the Philosophical Writings of Frege* (Oxford, 1952). Logical foundations.

Hilbert, David, & Ackermann, Walter, *Principles of Mathematical Logic* (New York, 1950). The classic of formalist interpretation.

Körner, Stephan, *The Philosophy of Mathematics: An Introduction* (New York, 1962). A good elementary exposition of philosophical viewpoints.

Newman, James R. (editor), *The World of Mathematics*, 4 vols. (New York, 1956). An extraordinary compendium of essays and selections in and about mathematics.

Poincaré, Henri, *Science and Hypothesis* (New York, 1962); *Science and Method* (New York, 1952); *The Value of Science* (New York, 1952). Classics all.

Ramsey, F. P., *The Foundations of Mathematics* (New York, 1950).

Reichenbach, Hans, *The Philosophy of Space and Time* (New York, 1957).

Reichenbach, Hans, *The Rise of Scientific Philosophy* (Berkeley, 1951). Contains a clear elementary discussion of physical geometry.

Suppes, Patrick, *Introduction to Logic* (New York, 1957).

Tarski, Alfred, *Introduction to Logic and to the Methodology of the Deductive Sciences* (New York, 1941).

Physics

Blum, Harold F., *Time's Arrow and Evolution* (Princeton, 1951). Useful mainly for biology, but contains a nice introductory exposition of thermodynamical ideas.
Bohm, David, *Causality and Chance in Modern Physics* (New York, 1957).
Bohr, Niels, *Atomic Theory and the Description of Nature* (Cambridge, England, 1934; New York, 1958); *Atomic Physics and Human Knowledge* (New York, 1958). The essays in these two collections are thought by some to be obscure. The style is sometimes circumambient, rather than obscure, but there are big issues at stake.
Born, Max, *The Restless Universe* (New York, 1952).
Born, Max, *The Natural Philosophy of Cause and Chance* (Oxford, 1944).
Brillouin, Léon, *Science and Information Theory* (New York, 1956).
Einstein, Albert, *The Meaning of Relativity* (Princeton, 1945).
Einstein, Albert, *Relativity, the Special and the General Theory,* translated by R. W. Lawson (New York, 1955).
Einstein, Albert, & Infeld, Leopold, *The Evolution of Physics* (New York, 1948).
Mach, Ernst, *The Science of Mechanics* (Chicago, 1902). A classical critique and clarification, sometimes narrow.
Nash, Leonard, *Elements of Chemical Thermodynamics* (Reading, Mass., 1962).
Peierls, Rudolf, *The Laws of Nature* (New York, 1956). Clear and systematic.
Pierce, John R., *Symbols, Signals and Noise: The Nature and Process of Communication* (New York, 1961).
Weisskopf, Victor, *Knowledge and Wonder* (New York, 1963). A clear and original synthesis of the physicist's account of things, for high-school students, physicists, and philosophers.
Wiener, Norbert, *Cybernetics* (New York, 1961).

Law, Verification, Probability

Bronowski, Jacob, *Science and Human Values* (New York, 1958).
Brown, Harcourt (editor), *Science and the Creative Spirit* (Toronto, 1958). Essays on creativity in science and on its relations with other endeavors.
Carnap, Rudolf, *Logical Foundations of Probability* (Chicago, 1950).
Duhem, Pierre, *The Aim and Structure of Physical Theory,* translated by Philip Wiener (Princeton, 1954).
Feller, William, *An Introduction to Probability and its Applications* (New York, 1950).
Gnedenko, B. V., & Kinchin, A. Ya, *An Elementary Introduction to the Theory of Probability* (San Francisco, 1961).

Hadamard, Jacques, *The Psychology of Invention in the Mathematical Field* (New York, 1954).

Hanson, Norwood R., *Patterns of Discovery* (New York, 1958).

Hawkins, David, "Existential and Epistemic Probability," *Philosophy of Science,* vol. 10, 4 (October 1943). This stems from Peirce.

Keynes, John Maynard, *A Treatise on Probability* (London, 1921).

Laplace, Pierre Simon de, *A Philosophical Essay on Probability* (New York, 1951).

Mises, Richard von, *Probability, Statistics, and Truth* (New York, 1939).

Peirce, Charles S., "The Probability of Induction," in *Philosophical Writings of Peirce* (New York, 1955).

Poincaré, Henri, *Science and Hypothesis* (New York, 1962), Chap. XI: "The Calculus of Probabilities."

Polya, György, *How to Solve It* (Princeton, 1945).

Polya, György, *Mathematics and Plausible Reasoning,* 2 vols. (Princeton, 1954).

Popper, Karl, *The Logic of Scientific Discovery* (New York, 1959).

Weaver, Warren, *Lady Luck* (New York, 1952).

Evolution and Man

Ashby, W. Ross, *Design for a Brain* (New York, 1960).

Asimov, Isaac, *The Genetic Code* (New York, 1963). No bibliography.†

Boring, Edwin G., *History of Experimental Psychology* (New York, 1957).

Brunswik, Egon, *The Conceptual Framework of Psychology* (Chicago, 1952).

Childe, V. Gordon, *Man Makes Himself* (New York, 1951).

Dobzhansky, Theodosius, *Mankind Evolving* (New Haven, 1962).

Engels, Friedrich, *The Origin of the Family, Private Property, and the State* (New York, 1942).

Freud, Sigmund, *Civilization and its Discontents,* translated and edited by James Strachey (New York, 1962).

Hawkins, David, "Design for a Mind," *Daedalus,* Summer 1962.

Hilgard, Ernest R., *Introduction to Psychology* (New York, 1962).

Labarre, Weston, *The Human Animal* (Chicago, 1954).

Marcuse, Herbert, *Eros and Civilization* (Boston, 1955).

Needham, Joseph, *Time, the Refreshing River* (London, 1943).

Rapaport, David (editor and translator), *The Organization and Pathology of Thought: Selected Sources* (New York, 1951).

Schrödinger, Erwin, *What is Life?* (New York, 1944).

Simpson, George G., *The Meaning of Evolution* (New Haven, 1962).

Skinner, Burrhus F., *Science and Human Behavior* (New York, 1953).

Tax, Sol (editor), *Evolution After Darwin,* 3 vols. (Chicago, 1960).

---

† The best source is the last ten years of the *Scientific American,* which has popular accounts and bibliography. This periodical has given extensive space to what a harsh and skeptical critic has called "the DNA story."

Ethics

Arrow, Kenneth J., *Social Choice and Individual Value* (New York, 1951).

Bergson, Abram, "Socialist Economics," in *Survey of Contemporary Economics* (Homewood, Ill., 1960), Vol. I.

Boulding, Kenneth, "Welfare Economics," in *Survey of Contemporary Economics* (Homewood, Ill., 1960), Vol. II.

Dewey, John, *Theory of Valuation* (Chicago, 1939).

Edel, Abraham, *Science and the Structure of Ethics* (Chicago, 1961).

Evans, Griffith C., *A Mathematical Introduction to Economics* (New York, 1930).

Heimann, Eduard, *History of Economic Doctrines* (New York, 1954).

Melden, A. I. (editor), *Ethical Theories: A Book of Readings* (New York, 1950).

Morris, Bertram, *Philosophical Aspects of Culture* (Yellow Springs, Ohio, 1961).

Neumann, John von, & Morgenstern, Oskar, *Theory of Games and Economic Behavior* (Princeton, 1944). Read at least the prose.

Rogin, Leo, *The Meaning and Validity of Economic Theory* (New York, 1956).

Roll, Erich, *A History of Economic Thought* (Englewood Cliffs, N.J., 1956).

Samuelson, Paul A., *Economics: An Introductory Analysis* (New York, 1958).

Samuelson, Paul A., *Foundations of Economic Analysis* (Cambridge, Mass., 1958).

Sellars, W., & Hospers, J. (editors), *Readings in Ethical Theory* (New York, 1952).

Stark, Werner, *Ideal Foundations of Economic Thought* (London, 1943).

INDEX

$7.50

The Language of Nature

BY DAVID HAWKINS

This disquisition on the philosophy of science presents an original analysis of a wide range of scientific topics and leads the reader through a search for unifying ideas among them. In addition to the classic problems of philosophy, such as causality, chance, and purpose, it deals with subjects that are unorthodox for a book in this field: information theory, the relation of thermodynamics to problems in biology and psychology, economic theory, and ethics. Recent trends in the sciences are exploited.

The author has taught courses in physical science and the philosophy of science for many years. His book, written in an informal style, is addressed as much to scientists as to philosophers.

"Its sweep is impressive; its erudition is matched by its urbanity; it is ambitious and serious, and yet avoids the pretentious, the platitudinous...his analogies and his wit light up the analysis . . . a substantial contribution to the literature of the philosophy of science."—A pre-publication reviewer.